THE AMERICAN AUTOMOBILE

The American

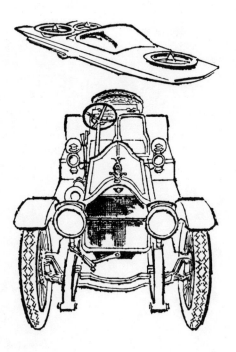

THE CHICAGO HISTORY
OF AMERICAN CIVILIZATION
Daniel J. Boorstin, EDITOR

Automobile

A BRIEF HISTORY *by John B. Rae*

 THE UNIVERSITY OF CHICAGO PRESS
CHICAGO & LONDON

Library of Congress Catalog Card Number: 65-24981

The University of Chicago Press, Chicago & London
The University of Toronto Press, Toronto 5, Canada

To Florence, Helen, and Jim, who all helped

Editor's Preface

The automobile has been the great vehicle of American civilization in the twentieth century. Seldom has a people found in technology so appropriate, so versatile, and so pervasive an expression. Originating in Europe, the automobile acquired novel forms in the United States. Here within a half-century, although it still remained in most of Europe a toy for the few, it had become a new social force touching everybody—an expression of and an instrument for speedy movement around and across the continent and up the social scale.

When before has a civilization found so powerful a catalyst? The automobile was peculiarly well suited to reinforce the characteristic tendencies of American civilization. A providential instrument for a people with much space and little time, the automobile has diffused and leveled and stirred and homogenized a continent-civilization. It has spread the freedom to travel among all classes and at the same time has helped remove the very differences between parts of the country, between kinds of landscapes which were once an incentive to travel. The automobile has brought farmers to the city and the city to the farm; it has siphoned city-dwellers to the suburbs and has made suburbs more city-like. More than any other device, it has been responsible for transforming large tracts of America and the dwelling places of most Americans into an environment neither urban nor rural, not properly to be called landscape. Dominated by superhighways and motels and drive-ins and parking areas, much of America can now be called motorscape.

If we are an automobile-riding, we are also an automobile-ridden people. Despite the daily offerings that Americans insert in parking meters, and the grand new parking temples rising in the centers of our cities, we seem unable to appease the motor goddess. She remains wayward and voracious, every year more independent in her demands, more unpredictable in her needs, until all we can confidently forecast is that her power is not likely to decrease. The yearly births of automobiles have for some time now been exceeding those of the human population.

The story of the automobile—so recent that we have hardly begun to think of it as history—touches nearly every aspect of the American economy and of American culture in this century. As Mr. Rae reminds us, the whole American economy has been crucially involved with the automobile. It is the story of booms and depressions, of the rise of industrial unionism, and of the national effort in two world wars. We cannot understand what we mean in America by competition or by monopoly, by advertising, by industrial leadership, or by know-how, unless we have understood the role of the automobile. It touches the most intimate regions of our life—courting practices and the family and a man's feelings about his place in the social scale—and the most public. It touches the history of American taste. And, not least important in the perspective of history, the automobile industry, through its decisive role in the Second World War, has helped develop the know-how and the machinery by which we move into the age of the airplane, without yet having left the age of the automobile.

The automobile, then, has long ceased to be only an instrument of technology and has become a characteristic American institution. But its history has been neglected in favor of more conventional and more traditional subjects. In this book, Mr. Rae helps us discover the automobile as a touchstone of our civilization. He admirably serves the purpose of the "Chicago History of American

Civilization," which aims to make each aspect of our culture a window to all our history.

The series contains two kinds of books: a chronological group, which provides a coherent narrative of American history from its beginning to the present day, and a topical group, which deals with the history of varied and significant aspects of American life. This book is one of the topical group, which includes, among others, John F. Stover's *American Railroads*.

DANIEL J. BOORSTIN

Contents

Illustrations

MAPS

PLATES

Tables

CHAPTER I

The Birth of the Automobile

The automobile is European by birth, American by adoption. The internal-combustion engine, upon which most automobile development has been based, is unmistakably of European origin, and both the idea and the technique of applying it to a highway vehicle were worked out first in Europe. On the other hand, the transformation of the automobile from a luxury for the few to a convenience for the many was definitely an American achievement, and from it flowed economic and social consequences of almost incalculable magnitude. The American automobile industry has grown into the largest manufacturing operation in the world, its annual performance is the most important single indicator of the condition of the American economy, and American life is organized predominantly on the basis of the universal availability of motor transportation. All this would have been an impressive accomplishment over a period of centuries: as it was, it took place in two generations.

EARLY EXPERIMENTS

The dream of a self-propelled vehicle goes far back into history. Roger Bacon wrote in the thirteenth century that "cars can be made so that without animals they will move with unbelievable rapidity," and he evidently thought that the scythe-bearing chariots of antiquity had some kind of mechanical propulsion. Three

hundred years later Leonardo da Vinci revived the idea, specifically for a military vehicle analogous to the modern tank. For both
Bacon and Leonardo these had to be speculations, since in neither
age was a feasible power plant available.

The first real step toward making the dream a reality was taken
by an eighteenth century French artillery officer, Nicholas Joseph
Cugnot. In 1769 he built and ran a three-wheeled carriage mounting a steam engine of his own design, with the idea that it might be
used for pulling guns. It was a clumsy contraption that left the road
the first time it had to take a curve at its top speed of three miles an
hour, and it offered no improvement whatever over the horse; but
it was indisputably the first self-propelled highway vehicle.

Following Cugnot there was a long lapse while the steam engine
was undergoing refinement so that it could meet the eternal demand
made of any locomotive engine: more power for less weight. In the
early years of the nineteenth century Richard Trevithick, a British
mining engineer, and the versatile American genius Oliver Evans
made crude but workable steam vehicles. Evans's machine, which
he called the *Orukter Amphibolos,* was actually a dredge for use in
the harbor of Philadelphia. He put it on wheels to get it through the
streets of the city (1805)—and incidentally to demonstrate the
practicability of the "steam waggon"—but he still failed to persuade the Pennsylvania legislature to let him use steam power on the
state's highways.

In Great Britain, although Trevithick abandoned his experiments, others carried on. The first half of the nineteenth century
witnessed several impressive English experiments with steam omnibuses. Some of these vehicles operated for lengthy periods on
regular routes with excellent records of punctuality and safety.
Their success, indeed, brought about their downfall, because railway and stagecoach companies joined forces against them. They
were harassed by discriminatory tolls and fees, and their operation
became impossible with the passage of the "red flag" law in 1865,
which limited self-propelled vehicles on public highways to a
maximum of four miles an hour and required that each be preceded

by a man on foot carrying a red flag. This law remained in force until 1896. It was a short-sighted piece of legislation whose only perceptible consequences were to cut off a promising development in highway transportation and retard the growth of the British automobile industry.

As it turned out, the future of the automobile was not to be with steam anyway. Because the steam engine was expensive and inefficient for supplying small amounts of power, inventive effort by the middle of the nineteenth century was being directed to the possibilities of the internal-combustion engine. The first practical machine of this type was a two-cycle engine patented in Paris in 1860 by a Belgian mechanic named Etienne Lenoir. It was a crude and noisy contraption, but it worked and it was a commercial success. A contemporary of Lenoir's, Beau de Rochas, filed a French patent description in 1862 explaining accurately the principle of the four-cycle engine, but there is no evidence that he ever built one. The four-cycle engine as an operational mechanism was introduced by a German, Nicholas Otto, in 1878. Meanwhile, George B. Brayton, an American engineer, designed a two-cycle engine of his own in 1872 and exhibited it at the Philadelphia Centennial Exposition in 1876. Brayton's engine compressed the fuel in a separate chamber outside the cylinder, whereas Lenoir's had no compression but depended solely on the expansion of the gases when the fuel was ignited.

These early efforts were clumsy affairs, intended mainly to provide power for small industrial plants. Coal gas was the principal fuel, with petroleum products coming gradually into use as that industry expanded. The possibility of using the internal-combustion engine for locomotion was appreciated from the start. Lenoir built a vehicle using his engine and ran it in Paris in the 1860's, but since this was an isolated experiment without continuing results, Lenoir has never been considered to be the originator of the automobile. This honor has also been claimed for the Viennese inventor Siegfried Markus, who began experimenting with motor carriages at about the same time. The evidence indicates, however, that Markus did not have an operable vehicle until the 1880's, and his experiments likewise failed to get into the mainstream of automotive history. He was handicapped by the disapproval of his neighbors and the Viennese police. He tried to make his test runs at night, but although darkness could conceal his vehicle from sight, he was totally unable to keep it out of hearing, and ultimately he had to discontinue his work.

In the United States the Brayton engine was tested on a street railway in Providence, Rhode Island, in 1873 with unsatisfactory results. But the model displayed at the Centennial Exposition attracted the attention of George B. Selden (1846–1932), a patent attorney and inventor of Rochester, New York. Selden believed that the Brayton engine could be adapted for use in a highway vehicle, and in 1879 he filed an application for a United States patent on a "road engine" combining a motor using a liquid hydrocarbon fuel, a mechanism for disengaging the engine from the driving wheels, and a steering devic. He did not at this time build a vehicle conforming to his specifications. None of these men—Lenoir, Markus, Selden—had any continuing influence on the evolution of the gasoline automobile, although Selden's patent would later create a major crisis in the American automobile industry. Nevertheless by 1880 the idea of a motor carriage driven by an internal-combustion engine was intriguing inventive minds.

The following decade saw still another source of power emerge—the electric motor. Technically the "horseless carriage" had become feasible, even though its ultimate form was still to be determined. A technical innovation, however, can run into a dead end if it arrives at the wrong time or in an unfavorable environment. More than a power plant was needed if the motor vehicle was to be accepted as a mode of transportation.

THE BICYCLE PRELUDE

A highway vehicle manifestly has to have an adequate highway system if it is to be of any use. Yet even in the industrial Western world good roads were limited in extent in the nineteenth century, not from any lack of ability to build them but simply because it was felt there was no need for extensive highway construction. Travel by road was of minor importance, because the railway was smoother, faster, and more economical than any existing method of highway transportation. Where a respectable highway system already existed, as in France, it was maintained; on the other hand, the United States as late as 1900 had only about two hundred miles of hard-surface roads outside the large cities.

Public interest in improving roads was first stimulated by the popularization of the bicycle. This became noticeable in the 1870's and rose to a high point after the introduction of the "safety" bicycle by J. K. Starley in Coventry, England, in 1885. Starley's invention was the modern low-wheeled bicycle with gearing and chain drive. It superseded the high-wheeled velocipede of the mid-nineteenth century whose use was limited to riders of considerable physical prowess. Because the driving wheel of the velocipede was turned directly by the pedals, it had to be of large diameter to give enough speed to keep the machine upright. The safety bicycle was of universal appeal; it could be ridden by women and children just as well as by men, and in the eighties and nineties it put people by the thousand on the roads of the Western world. This flood of bicyclists soon became conscious of the inadequacies of their highway systems and raised a clamor for something to be done. In the United States, for example, an organization known as the League of American Wheelmen was able to get action from state and local authorities to improve the condition of the roads. In 1893, in fact, the year the Duryea car made its appearance, pressure from the bicyclists induced Congress to appropriate $10,000 for a Bureau of Road Inquiry in the Department of Agriculture to study and provide information on improved methods of highway construction. This was the forerunner of the Bureau of Public Roads and of the federal highway program.

The influence of bicycling in reviving highway travel and preparing people's minds for the motor vehicle is lucidly expressed

by Hiram Percy Maxim (1869–1936), one of the outstanding
American automotive pioneers, in his charming autobiography,
Horseless Carriage Days:

It has been the habit to give the gasoline engine all the credit for
bringing the automobile—in my opinion this is the wrong explanation.
We have had the steam engine for over a century. We could have built
steam vehicles in 1880, or indeed in 1870. But we did not. We waited
until 1895.

The reason why we did not build road vehicles before this, in my
opinion, was because the bicycle had not yet come in numbers and had
not directed men's minds to the possibilities of long-distance travel over
the ordinary highway. We thought the railroad was good enough. The
bicycle created a new demand which it was beyond the ability of the
railroad to supply. Then it came about that the bicycle could not
satisfy the demand which it had created. A mechanically-propelled vehicle was wanted instead of a foot-propelled one, and we know now
that the automobile was the answer.

Maxim's appraisal can be accepted as generally valid, although in its
entirety it is more accurate for America than for Europe, where the
automobile did not supersede the bicycle so completely as it did in
the United States.

There were other influences besides the stimulation of highway
travel. From the bicycle manufacturers the early automobile industry inherited steel-tube framing that combined strength with light-
ness, the chain drive, ball and roller bearings, and differential
gearing (developed for the multiwheeled variations produced at the
peak of the bicycle craze). The vital role of the bicycle in preparing the way for the automobile is strikingly illustrated in the long
roster of men and companies who moved from one industry to the
other; prominent on the list are Morris in England, Opel in
Germany, and Duryea, Pope, Winton, and Willys in the United
States.

Beyond question, the most important contribution of the bicycle
to the automobile was the pneumatic tire, invented by John B.
Dunlop in Ireland in 1888 specifically for use on bicycles. (Rein-
vented, to be strictly accurate. It first appeared in the 1840's but

was promptly forgotten because it could not be used to advantage on either the vehicles or the roads of that period.) The combination of the pneumatic tire and the hard-surface road was indispensable to the success of the motor vehicle. Without both, highway travel could never have competed with rail transport in comfort or speed.

EUROPEAN BEGINNINGS

The lineal ancestors of today's gasoline-powered automobile were the vehicles constructed in Germany in 1885 by Karl Benz and Gottlieb Daimler. Both men approached automobile manufacture after gaining experience as manufacturers of stationary internal-combustion engines; Daimler had been an engineer with Nicholas Otto's firm, Otto and Langen. Whether Daimler or Benz is entitled to priority is still an unsettled question. Daimler began with a motorcycle, Benz with a tricycle. Both used a one-cylinder engine. Daimler's was a high-speed motor and thus more distinctly the forerunner of the modern automobile engine, but Benz was using spark ignition where Daimler had the less efficient hot tube. The dispute between their partisans has no validity for us. The essential point is that from their work stemmed a continuing, uninterrupted development of the motor vehicle.

Within ten years after Daimler and Benz had successfully demonstrated their inventions, Armand Peugeot and the firm of Panhard and Levassor were making cars with Daimler engines in France, a syndicate was formed to do the same thing in Britain and was agitating for repeal of the red flag law, and in the United Sttes the piano manufacturer William Steinway was vainly trying to interest the American public in this German gadget. The most rapid progress was made initially in France where a good highway system encouraged motoring. There as early as 1891 Emile Constant Levassor designed the prototype of the modern automobile. The earlier "horseless carriage" was just that: a buggy (or sometimes a bicycle frame) with a motor attached wherever it happened to be convenient (under the driver's seat was a common location). Levassor's car was planned around the fact of mechanical propulsion. The engine was in front, where its weight helped to hold the vehicle on the road, leaving the rest of the chassis to support a body for the accommodation of passengers.

The decade of the 1890's saw an automobile industry in western Europe engaged in regular commercial production, with France in the lead, Germany second, and Britain energetically trying to overcome its self-imposed handicap. A variety of gasoline, electric, and steam vehicles were on the market, and road races and trials were attracting attention. Levassor won a Paris-Rouen race in 1894 and a year later performed the astounding feat of driving a Panhard the 1,200 kilometers from Paris to Bordeaux in forty-eight hours, maintaining an average speed of fifteen miles an hour. These cars were all individually constructed, and facilities for repair and maintenance were practically nonexistent. An automobile was therefore expensive to buy and operate. For the most part it was a plaything for wealthy sportsmen, although by the turn of the century the touring car and the limousine were beginning to gain acceptance at the upper levels of society as substitutes for the family carriage, and ladies were using electric automobiles for city travel.

THE AMERICAN INVENTORS

It is an oddity of automotive history that Americans should have had to reinvent the automobile for themselves, with the result that until the beginning of the twentieth century American development was about ten years behind European. The reasons are a historical mystery. There was ample mechanical skill available in the United States, and there was some knowledge of the early European experiments. It may be that American talent was slow to get interested in motor vehicles because of the discouraging prospect for highway travel in a land of vast distances and poor roads.

At any rate, if some earlier but unproductive experiments are disregarded, the automobile era in the United States dates from September 21, 1893, when a motor carriage with a one-cylinder gasoline engine chugged noisily along the streets of Springfield, Massachusetts. It was the creation of two brothers, Charles E. (1861–1939) and J. Frank Duryea (b. 1869), bicycle mechanics who had read a description of Benz's car in the *Scientific American* in 1889 and had gone to work to build one of their own. By coincidence powered flight was also achieved by two brothers who made a living by manufacturing and repairing bicycles. There is evidence here of the technological significance of the bicycle, but there the parallel ends. The Wrights had more a conclusive first than the Duryeas, and they did not plunge into an irreconcilable quarrel, as did the Duryeas, over which one was entitled to credit for the achievement.

A second, two-cylinder Duryea car with Frank driving won the highly publicized *Chicago Times-Herald* race on November 28, 1895, plowing through icy streets to complete the fifty-five-mile course at an average speed of five miles an hour (seven and one-half when time for repairs was deducted). Of the six entries only one other, a Benz, finished. This performance may be compared with the Paris-Bordeaux race of the same year. In 1896 the Duryeas gained further prestige by taking part in an automobile parade from London to Brighton, held to celebrate Britain's repeal of the red flag law. Shortly thereafter, however, the brothers parted and their subsequent roles in the history of the automobile were minor.

By this time others were coming into the competition. Elwood Haynes (1857–1925), a trained engineer, began working on a mechanical vehicle in 1891 because he was tired of the horse and buggy travel required by his job as superintendent of the Indiana Natural Gas and Oil Company. He enlisted the aid of two machinists, Edgar and Elmer Apperson of Kokomo, Indiana, and with them produced a one-cylinder car that made its first run on July 4, 1894. Haynes and the Appersons remained in partnership for the next ten years, eventually putting a car named the Haynes-Apper-

son on the market. Then they separated, and both Haynes and
Apperson cars were made in Kokomo until the 1920's. The partners
seem to have quarreled, among other things, over credit for the
1894 car. At any rate the Appersons later asserted that they, not
Haynes, were its real designers, but they were unable to get this
claim accepted. Haynes, for his part, tried with equal lack of
success to argue that he was entitled to priority over the Duryeas,
apparently on the dubious ground that he started working on his
car first. He has a more convincing claim to have been the first
American motorist to get a traffic ticket, having been ordered off
the streets of Chicago by a bicycle-riding policeman in 1895.

Next came Hiram Percy Maxim, son of the inventor of the
Maxim gun and a graduate of the Massachusetts Institute of Technology. Following the family bent, young Maxim went from
college to the American Projectile Company in Lynn, Massachusetts. According to his own account, the idea of building a powered
vehicle came to him late one night as he was pedaling a bicycle
from Salem to Lynn, with his head somewhat up in the clouds after
calling on an attractive young lady. His experience offers a striking
revelation of the state of American automotive technology. He
knew enough about the principle of the internal-combustion engine
to be aware that it might provide the mechanism he wanted, but he
had never actually seen one until after he started to work on his
vehicle. Then he went to see an Otto engine working a pump. Even
then he did not know whether gasoline could be used as a fuel, and
he was completely unaware both of what had already been done in
Europe and of the contemporary experiments of the Duryeas and
Haynes.

So Maxim bought a secondhand Columbia tricycle for $30 and
then took himself to a remote corner of the Projectile Company's
lot with a half pint of gasoline and some empty cartridge cases to
find out what happened when gasoline was ignited in a cylinder. He
was lucky and got his information without damage to himself, but it
took another three years of trial and error before he was able in
1895 to put an engine on his tricycle so that the combination

functioned after a fashion. Maxim's work has a special significance because he attracted the attention of the Pope Manufacturing Company of Hartford, Connecticut, the country's largest producer of bicycles (Pope products carried the trade name Columbia, and so Maxim already had an association with the company). Maxim accepted an offer to go to Hartford as chief engineer for a motor carriage department established by Pope, and this was the first effort at large-scale commercial production of motor vehicles in the United States. Somewhat to his disappointment Maxim found himself concentrating on electric carriages because Colonel Albert A. Pope (1843–1909) at first insisted, "You can't get people to sit over an explosion." In two years the company built five hundred electric and forty gasoline carriages.

In the meantime other inventors were crowding into the American scene: 1896 saw the gasoline automobile arrive in Detroit. Charles Brady King drove a car down Woodward Avenue on March 6, and the first automotive venture of Henry Ford (1863–1947), the quadricycle, made its test run on Bagley Avenue. This was on June 4, after its builder had knocked down the wall of his landlord's barn to get his creation out on the street. The landlord arrived to protest and remained to push (the normal method of starting these pioneering experiments). The quadricycle was a relatively lightweight vehicle (500 pounds) and may therefore have foreshadowed in its design Ford's dream of a cheap car. It was sold for $200 to Charles Ainsley of Detroit, who later resold it; and so if Henry Ford was not, as many people have believed, the inventor of the automobile, he may well have contributed the first used car to appear on the American market. Two other famous names emerged on the automotive scene in September of 1896— Ransom Eli Olds (1864–1950) in Lansing, Michigan, and Alexander Winton (1860–1932) in Cleveland, Ohio. With them the gasoline automobile may be considered to have completed the stage of invention in the United States, since both Winton and Olds were able to go on promptly to production.

There was also Edward Joel Pennington (1858–1911), who

exemplified a direction the nascent automobile industry might have taken but fortunately did not. A glib promoter with some mechanical talent (he was the prototype of Get-Rich-Quick Wallingford, the fictional creation of American author George Randolph Chester), Pennington organized a company in Racine, Wisconsin, in 1895, purporting to manufacture motor carriages using the "Kane-Pennington Hot Air Engine." It was an engine that was supposed to cool itself by heat dissipation from the cylinder walls, and Pennington professed to have used it on a vehicle as early as 1890. No supporting evidence for this assertion has been found. His designs were published in technical journals and were plausible enough to give Henry Ford useful ideas during his experimenting days.

Pennington's performance never matched his claims. He was to enter four cars in the *Chicago Times-Herald* race, but they never appeared, allegedly because of mechanical difficulties. The same thing happened when Pennington went to Britain a year later to engage in promotional schemes. He was always going to display the superiority of his vehicles, but they invariably developed some undisclosed defect and were not available for the trial. Meanwhile Pennington joined forces with Harry J. Lawson, a British promoter who had at least acquired the British rights to the Daimler engine. The two men organized a concern in 1899 called the Anglo-American Rapid Vehicle Company with capital of $75 million, an alleged 200 motor-vehicle patents, and a proposal to merge the existing British and American automobile companies. Even if they had succeeded, their combined assets would have been far short of $75 million. When the scheme collapsed Pennington disappeared from the automobile business.

The origins of the gasoline-powered vehicle have necessarily attracted the greatest amount of historical attention because it was the type that came to dominate the automotive world. This outcome was far from obvious in the 1890's, and a good deal of inventive effort was expended on electric and steam cars. The first electric automobile to run on the streets of an American city appears to have been built by William Morrison of Des Moines,

Iowa, in 1891. Commercial production in the United States started with Henry G. Morris and Pedro Salom of Philadelphia, whose Electrobat appeared in 1894 and took part in the *Times-Herald* race a year later.

Because it was silent, clean, and easy to operate, the electric automobile enjoyed an early popularity. Colonel Pope's views on sitting over an explosion were widely shared. Pedro Salom, an electrical engineer, was even more vehement about the virtues of electricity and the evils of gasoline. He pointed out in the *Journal of the Franklin Institute* in 1896 that electric motors had no odor whereas:

All the gasoline motors we have seen belch forth from their exhaust pipe a continuous stream of partially unconsumed hydrocarbons in the form of a thick smoke with a highly noxious odor. Imagine thousands of such vehicles on the streets, each offering up its column of smell!

No one, however, has ever been able to provide an electric automobile with current other than through a battery, or to develop a battery of sufficient endurance to make long runs and high speeds possible.

The long history of experiments with steam power makes it impossible to say that the steam automobile was "invented." What was achieved in the 1890's was to design engines light enough for use in an automobile, as distinct from an omnibus or a steam roller, by using steam pressures of 600 pounds per square inch. A kerosene or gasoline burner was used to heat the boiler. The early steamers required about twenty minutes to work up a sufficient head of steam. The flash boiler, invented by Leon Serpollet in France in 1889 but not generally used until after 1900, removed this handicap by permitting steam to be raised in two minutes.

The first Americans to produce steam automobiles commercially were the twin brothers Francis E. (1849–1918) and Freelan O. Stanley (1849–1940), who went into business in Newton, Massachusetts, in 1897 after a few years of experimenting in their home town of Lewiston, Maine. They were also, for practical purposes, the last. By the time Francis died the market for steam automobiles had declined so much that his brother simply gave up. An engineer named Abner Doble subsequently acquired the Stanley designs and produced an improved steamer in the 1920's; but the Doble car, although technically of high quality, could not be made to sell for less than $8,500, and it was not a commercial success. The White brothers of Cleveland, Ohio, actually made better steam automobiles than the Stanleys. They went into production in 1901 and introduced the flash boiler for American cars. After ten years of successful manufacturing, however, the Whites gave up on steam and turned to gasoline-powered cars.

The steam automobile had and still has its partisans. Compared with the early gasoline cars, the steamer had definite advantages. It had more power, and it did not require a complicated transmission—there were a good many "experts" in those days who were convinced that the ordinary individual would never be able to learn how to shift gears. On the other hand, the makers of steam automobiles never could overcome fear of boiler explosions, although available records show that the fear was unfounded. Even if this ghost had been successfully exorcised, the steam automobile had handicaps which its enthusiasts overlook. A lightweight reciprocating steam engine operating on pressures of 600 pounds per square inch requires constant skilled maintenance, and so it would have been an unsatisfactory mechanism for a car intended for mass consumption. Moreover, keeping the boiler filled was simple enough in the Northeast, where soft water was readily available and where at the turn of the century there were towns and villages comfortably close together, each with its horse trough ready to serve the thirsty engine as readily as the thirsty animal. Conditions were different elsewhere. Any extensive use of steam automobiles in the Southwest, for example, would have necessitated service stations supplied with boiler water brought in from distant points, just as the railroads had to do for their steam locomotives.

These difficulties could have been surmounted if manufacturers had considered it worthwhile to make the attempt. The insuperable handicap for the steam-driven automobile was and is that an internal-combustion engine has greater thermal efficiency than a steam engine, so that the same amount of technical effort would inevitably produce better results with the gasoline car than the steamer. There is no evidence that the steam automobile was the victim of a conspiracy on the part of the manufacturer of gasoline automobiles, as has sometimes been alleged by its partisans. What happened to it was simply a manifestation of the survival of the fittest.

CHAPTER 2

The Horseless Carriage

By the late 1890's the automobile was emerging from the status of an experimental curiosity and was beginning to make a place for itself in American life—a minor place to be sure, but growing with phenomenal rapidity. In 1900 the Census Bureau lumped automobile manufacturing with "miscellaneous." Output for the year was 4,192 units, sold for an average price of just over $1,000 each, this total representing predominantly the work of innumerable small shops. In 1908, which is a landmark in the story of the American automobile as the year in which the Model T was born and General Motors was founded, production had risen to 65,000 and automobile registrations were approaching 400,000.

Production was not the whole story of the early horseless carriage days. In a variety of ways the social impact of the motorcar was beginning to be felt and still more to be foreshadowed. Nevertheless, production was the most pressing question because of a fact that became increasingly manifest: Americans wanted cars, so that the United States offered a practically limitless market for those who could offer the proper combination of quality and price.

THE FOUNDING OF THE AUTOMOBILE INDUSTRY

The total number of firms to engage in manufacturing automobiles in the United States can never be accurately determined. In the

17

early years especially, when regulations regarding motor-vehicle registration were likely to be casual or nonexistent, there were individuals or small concerns who turned out one or two experimental cars and then disappeared from view without leaving any record. The most complete and authoritative list, compiled by the Automobile Manufacturers Association and the Automobile Club of Michigan, shows more than three thousand makes of cars and trucks built by some fifteen hundred identifiable manufacturers in the United States from the time that Duryea car made its appearance to the present. The great majority of these went through their brief life span before the First World War.

In those days automobile manufacturing was as classic an example of free competitive enterprise as could be found. All that was needed to go into business was a modicum of mechanical ability and a place to put the car together. No heavy investment in plant and equipment was necessary because automobile production was almost exclusively an assembly operation, using parts and components bought from outside firms. This feature has remained characteristic of the automobile industry, although the role of the independent supplier has gradually lessened in importance as automobile companies have become larger and more self-contained. There was a time, indeed, when some producers, like the Cole Motor Company of Indianapolis, proudly advertised the superiority of the "assembled" over the "manufactured" car, claiming that the former incorporated the expert specialized talent of all the separate parts manufacturers.

Financial requirements for entering the automobile industry were also slight. Bank credit was seldom available because making horseless carriages was such a speculative enterprise that no respectable banker would touch it. But very little cash was needed to get the operation going. Many of the small firms financed themselves by buying from suppliers on credit and selling to dealers for cash. The marketing structure of the automobile business was also in the preliminary stages of development. Cars were frequently sold direct from the factory or else marketed through regional distributors who were free to create their own local sales agencies in their territories. There were also independent local dealers doing business directly with the manufacturer. The organization of marketing through elaborate networks of dealers came later, when there were producers with a sufficient volume of business to support them.

Nevertheless, the basic relationship that still prevails between manufacturer and distributors in the automobile industry was established at the outset. As a condition of his franchise the distributor or dealer agreed to accept the sight draft which came with the bill of lading on each shipment of new cars. In effect, much of the American automobile industry in its pioneering period was financed through its dealers and their banks. Since most dealers in those days had customers waiting in line and prepared to pay cash for their cars, this arrangement was not as one-sided in favor of the manufacturer as it might seem. Moreover, with hundreds of firms trying to put motor vehicles on the market, a dealer who felt aggrieved could change to a different line with considerably greater ease than was possible later.

This technique of buying on credit and selling for cash enabled the individual with limited finances to get started in automobile manufacturing and stay in it if he could produce and sell promptly enough to keep ahead of his creditors. It was by no means a foolproof method, as the high attrition rate in the automobile industry demonstrates, but it worked well enough and often enough to be an important factor in the growth of the industry. It accounts, for example, for the survival of the Ford Motor Company through the hazards of infancy.

But although getting into automobile production was easy enough, staying in it was another matter entirely. Competition was intense and rigorous, and with a novel commodity like the motor vehicle, deciding what the buying public would accept called for a combination of shrewd judgment and luck. The best prospects for survival among the initial entrants were generally those companies that grew from an established firm and therefore had some resources in plant, managerial and technical skill, and capital. The parent concern was most likely to be a vehicle manufacturer, either bicycles or carriages and wagons, or else to be making mechanical equipment of some kind. Thus Pope was the country's leading bicycle producer and Studebaker the largest manufacturer of horse-drawn vehicles in the world before they turned to automobiles; Ransom E. Olds made stationary gas engines; and the first White steamers were built in the White sewing machine factory. There were endless variations also. David Dunbar Buick (1855–1929) was a manufacturer of plumbing fixtures, and the once famous Pierce-Arrow emerged from a company that had started with bird cages. (The sequence was from wire cages to spokes for bicycle wheels, then to complete bicycles and motorcycles, and so to automobiles.)

The cars themselves were very much in the "horseless carriage" category, buggies with one- or two-cylinder engines. After the turn of the century the influence of European design brought the engine from under the driver's seat to the front of the car and added a *tonneau*, for the accommodation of passengers. The tonneau, or body, was made in carriage factories and showed its heritage even in the names given to body styles—brougham, stanhope, surrey, landaulet. In fact, the carriage tradition persisted so strongly that many automobile bodies came complete with whip sockets, which could well have been useful accessories in a day when any automobile trip might end with the cry, "Get a horse." Steering at first was by tiller rather than by wheel. There are several claimants for the distinction of introducing the steering wheel, but this is an irrelevant issue; the critical step was the invention of the steering knuckle in 1902, the little device that permits the front wheels to turn instead of the entire axle.

At the opening of the twentieth century the prospecive purchaser of a motor vehicle had a bewildering variety of choices available to him. He had to decide among electric, steam, and gasoline cars; if he picked gasoline he had an option between water- and air-cooled engines, and he could even have a two-cycle motor if he wished. There were various types of transmissions; Pope experimented with electric transmission, and one fairly prominent model, the Cartercar, had a friction drive. What was bewildering for the consumer was critical for the producer, since a small-scale manufacturer operating on a financial shoestring could not afford to make a mistake about what to offer. In a surprisingly short time, however, a discernible trend appeared—to the gasoline car with a multicylinder, four-cycle engine, ordinarily water-cooled. For those who combined the business and technical skill to judge this trend and adapt to it, there were glittering rewards; for the others at best a niche in the memories of the antique automobile enthusiasts.

PIONEERING PRODUCERS

These conditions can be observed in the companies that figured prominently in the founding of the American automobile industry. The sampling is of necessity incomplete because the total number of firms involved was so large, and it may be unrepresentative because information about the failures generally does not exist; but all the companies whose stories are related can be shown to have made an identifiable contribution to the development of the industry.

The year 1897 marks the effective start of the automobile industry in the United States, if production of a few vehicles of various types in previous years is discounted. In that year the Pope Manufacturing Company put its Columbia electrics and a few gasoline cars on the market; the Stanleys began to build steamers commercially; and Ransom E. Olds and Alexander Winton formed companies for the manufacture of gasoline automobiles. Only Pope at this time could rank as a major producer. Olds was handicapped by lack of capital and did not get into operation for another two years. Winton, a testy Scot who had been a successful bicycle manufacturer in Cleveland, built six omnibuses, each to carry six passengers, in 1897. They were intended for use on Cleveland's

Shore Drive, but the first trial trip frightened horses and brought so many threats of lawsuits that the promoters hurriedly abandoned the scheme and never even paid Winton. He then turned to passenger cars and was able to go into regular production and sale in 1898.

According to a plausible legend, Winton even helped to start a competitor. Winton No. 12 was bought by James W. Packard (1863–1928) of Warren, Ohio; and when Packard went to Cleveland to complain of defects in the car, Winton reputedly told him to go and make a better one himself if he was dissatisfied. Packard accepted the challenge. As a matter of fact, he had been experimenting on his own for some time, and in 1900 he began to make cars in Warren under the name of the Ohio Automobile Company. Given Packard's engineering talent (he was an engineering graduate of Lehigh University) and a solid base in the Packard Electric Company, this venture had good prospects from the start. Packard, for instance, introduced the H-slot gearshift employed almost universally until the introduction of the automatic transmission.

The company's rise to prominence, however, was fortuitous. In 1901 a group of Detroit capitalists headed by Henry B. Joy (1864–1936), son of the railroad magnate James F. Joy, was becoming interested in automobiles. Joy himself and Truman S. Newberry, who would run successfully against Henry Ford for the United States Senate in 1918, visited the 1901 automobile show in New York. After an unfortunate experience with a steam car, whose boiler gauge burst and showered them with hot water and broken glass, they were attracted to a Packard parked outside the exhibition building. While they were inspecting the car, a fire engine went by, whereupon the owner dashed out of an adjoining building, started his motor with one spin of the crank, and went off in pursuit. Joy and Newberry were greatly impressed and did not learn until later that for demonstration purposes the car was equipped with an imported French carburetor. The upshot was that Joy and his friends acquired control of Packard's company, changed its name to the Packard Motor Car Company, and moved it to Detroit in 1903. Packard himself stayed in Warren and gradually withdrew from active participation in the automobile business.

There is no indication whatsoever that Joy tried to force Packard out of his company, and it is beyond question that the change of location was fortunate. For a budding automobile manufacturer, there was greater promise in Detroit than in Warren, Ohio. The Michigan city was not yet Motoropolis, but it was visibly a major center of automotive activity. Certain features of this activity stand out as of primary importance. First in point of time was the arrival in Detroit of the Olds Motor Works in 1899, Ransom Olds having found a backer in a copper and lumber magnate named Samuel L. Smith who put $199,600 into the company in return for 95 per cent of its stock. Olds contributed the rest of the $200,000 of paid-up capital. They moved from Lansing because they believed that Detroit offered more in the way of skilled labor and accessibility of materials. Actually, the outstanding event of the company's stay in Detroit was that its factory burned down—a most historic conflagration. Only one thing was saved—a little buggy with a one-cylinder engine and a curved dash: Olds had designed this as a possible low-priced car. Since it was all that was left, the company concentrated all its effort on the curved-dash buggy. Engines were ordered from Leland and Faulconer, a firm of machine-tool manufacturers that had also been making motorboat engines, and transmissions from a machine shop owned by two brothers named Dodge, John (1864–1920) and Horace (1868–1920).

The result was spectacular. The little buggy became the "Merry Oldsmobile" of popular song, the first car in the world to be produced in really large quantity over a period of years: 600 were made in 1901, 2,500 in 1902, 4,000 in 1903, and 5,000 in 1904. At that point Olds broke with Smith. By then the company was back in Lansing, attracted by a fifty-two-acre site bought for it by the Lansing Businessmen's Association. Smith decided that the time had come to drop the buggy in favor of heavy touring cars. Olds disagreed and left the company, to be put right back into automobile manufacturing by a group of Lansing associates as the Reo (for R. E. Olds) Motor Car Company.

At first glance it appears that the Olds Motor Works threw away the opportunity that Henry Ford later grasped. Had Olds been allowed to continue, perhaps he would have progressed to full mass production; but it would have had to be with a different design. For all its charm the Merry Oldsmobile was not the car for the mass market. It was too light, too small, and lacking in power for an all-purpose family automobile.

Besides creating a famous car and a popular song, the Olds Motor Works in those years was a school for ambitious young men who would make their own way in the automotive world. One was Jonathan D. Maxwell (1864–1928), who had previously worked for the Appersons on the Haynes car. After three years with Olds, Maxwell left in 1903 to join Benjamin (1869–1945) and Frank (1875–1954) Briscoe in the production of a car named the Maxwell-Briscoe. The Briscoe brothers were sheet-metal manufacturers of Detroit who had turned successfully to making automobile radiators and unsuccessfully to backing David D. Buick. Oddly enough, the Maxwell-Briscoe combination was unable to raise funds in Detroit, but the Briscoes had Morgan connections in their sheet-metal business and were able to raise $100,000 to buy the Tarrytown, New York, factory of the defunct Mobile Company, a short-lived builder of steam automobiles.

A second Olds graduate was Robert C. Hupp (1861–1931). He went from Olds to Ford and then in 1908 raised $25,000 to start building his own car, the Hupmobile. It was a well-designed car and the enterprise prospered, although Hupp himself left in 1911. Still more distinguished were two men from the University of Michigan: Roy D. Chapin (1880–1936), who would rise to be one of the ablest executives in the automobile industry, and Howard E. Coffin (1873–1937), one of the greatest American automotive engineers. They left the Olds Motor Works in 1906 and after trying partnerships with two other automobile manufacturers, E. R. Thomas (1850–1936) and Hugh Chalmers (1873–1932), finally got their own company started in 1909 with the aid of $90,000 from J. L. Hudson, owner of the great Detroit department store. Chapin did the managing and selling and Coffin the engineering; in this instance, however, the Hudson car and the company that built it were named for the sponsor rather than, as was the usual custom, the designer.

While Ransom E. Olds was the leading American manufacturer, Henry Ford was struggling to get established. Although he was the son of a Dearborn farmer, he was not exactly the barefoot boy of popular legend, come to the city to astonish the world by mass production of a cheap car. Since his boyhood Ford had had a flair for machinery and he had spent close to twenty years as mechanic, machinist, and engineer before he built his first car, the "quadricycle" of 1896. Ford later claimed that he had actually built a car in 1892, but there is no evidence for this claim beyond Henry Ford's memory, notoriously unreliable where his own reputation or interests were concerned. The quadricycle has to be accepted as the first and for some time the only Ford car.

In 1896 Ford was chief engineer of the Edison Illuminating Company (now Detroit Edison), a respectable position but not one that enabled him to step directly into automobile manufacturing. It took him until 1899 to find support from a group of Detroit businessmen headed by a lumber dealer named William F. Murphy, organized first as the Detroit Automobile Company and later as the Henry Ford Company. Neither succeeded. Ford drove in automobile races as a means of advertising, but the Murphy syndicate complained that he was so absorbed in building racers that he ignored the desirability of having something to sell. He was dropped in 1902, and Murphy called in Henry M. Leland (1843–1932), the sixty-year-old head of Leland and Faulconer, to straighten things out. Leland, a bearded patriarch and a precisionist with a lifetime of experience in machine tools, got the company into production and reorganized it under a new name—Cadillac. So Ford and Cadillac have a common ancestry.

Ford himself was not long unemployed. In 1903 he founded the

Ford Motor Company with another group of partners. Alexander
Y. Malcomson, a Detroit coal dealer, supplied the $28,000 that
represented the company's liquid capital. The Dodge brothers
became stockholders in return for providing chassis, engines, and
transmissions for the first Ford cars; and Malcomson's bookkeeper,
James S. Couzens (1872–1936), put in $2,500 and joined the Ford
Motor Company as its business manager. So far Ford's experience
resembled closely that of most other automotive pioneers. The
departure from the pattern came when Ford quarreled with Malcomson in 1905, just as Olds had quarreled with Smith, and as
Henry Ford would quarrel with almost every outstanding individual who worked with or for him. The significant fact is that on
this occasion Ford won and emerged in complete control of his
company, free to pursue his own policies. It was an outcome with
momentous consequences for the future of the automobile in
America.

Reference has been made to David D. Buick as an automotive
pioneer. He was a Detroiter who turned from plumbing supplies to
automobiles in 1899, and in three years lost all his money. His
engineering was good enough—the Buick valve-in-head engine was
a notable contribution to automotive design—but he could not get
into production. Then after several backers, including the Briscoes,
had become discouraged, the Buick Motor Car Company in 1904
came under the control of William Crapo Durant (1860–1947), a
carriage manufacturer of Flint, Michigan.

"Billy" Durant came from a wealthy family, but he started
making his own living when he was sixteen, and he had risen to be
head of the Durant-Dort Carriage Company, the largest of a group
of companies that made Flint the "carriage capital" of the country.
He proved to be what the ailing Buick concern needed. He moved
it to Flint, and by 1908 he had made it one of the Big Four of the
automobile industry—the others being Ford, Reo, and Maxwell-
Briscoe. At that time, their eminence rested on the fact that each
had attained an annual production in excess of 8,000.

The rise of Detroit should not obscure the fact that automobile production was still widely dispersed. New England had the Pope and Stanley companies as well as a host of smaller competitors. The five Mack brothers of New York City built their first truck in 1900, and Syracuse, New York, in 1902 became the home of the Franklin, the best-known American car to use an air-cooled engine. There were important producers in Buffalo, Pittsburgh, Cleveland, and St. Louis, and until about 1905 Indianapolis had more automobile manufacturers than Detroit. Two can be singled out for special mention. The Marmon Motor Car Company, started by a firm that had previously made flour-milling machinery, eventually produced the nearest American approximation to the Rolls-Royce; and its founder, Howard C. Marmon (1876–1943), was the first American to be chosen as honorary member of the British Society of Automotive Engineers. The Overland was an Indianapolis product (except for the first model which was built in Terre Haute in 1902) until John North Willys (1873–1933), a bicycle and automobile dealer, took it over during the panic of 1907 when the company was about to collapse under an indebtedness of $80,000. Willys, faced with the prospect of being unable to fill his customers' orders for cars, decided that the remedy was to take charge of the manufacturing operations himself. He satisfied the creditors and then, in search of better production, moved Overland into the Pope Manufacturing Company's plant in Toledo. Pope, as we shall see, had been the victim of bad judgment and Willys got the factory for $285,000.

In South Bend, Indiana, the Studebaker Brothers Manufacturing Company began to experiment with electric automobiles in 1898 but did not fully commit itself to motorcar manufacturing until 1904. In that year Studebaker, besides making some cars in its own plant, arranged to buy motors and chassis from the Garford Manufacturing Company of Elyria, Ohio, added the bodies in South Bend, and marketed the product through its established network of dealers in carriages and wagons. Studebaker therefore varied from the customary pattern in that its principal asset in entering the automobile business was not its technical capabilities but its organization for distributing and selling wheeled vehicles.

Before long the Garford capacity proved inadequate, and in 1908 Studebaker made a similar arrangement with the newly formed Everitt-Metzger-Flanders Company of Detroit, builders of the EMF car.

   This company, an amalgamation of several small Detroit automobile concerns, was the creation of three pioneer figures of the automobile industry, none of whom quite achieved greatness: B. F. Everitt, whose Wayne Automobile Company was one of the nuclei of EMF; William E. Metzger, who became Detroit's first automobile dealer in 1898 and later was sales manager for Cadillac; and Walter E. Flanders (1868–1923), who came to EMF from a brief period of organizing production for the Ford Motor Company. The Studebaker-EMF partnership proved unsatisfactory, with each party accusing the other of failing to live up to its obligations. The result was that in 1910 Studebaker bought out the EMF partners and consolidated its automobile activities under its own name, with factories in South Bend and Detroit. Thus Studebaker in part also contributed to the concentration of major automobile manufacturers in Detroit.

   Finally, Thomas B. Jeffery (1845–1910), who had been Pope's principal competitor as a bicycle manufacturer, began to make cars in 1901 at Kenosha, Wisconsin, with the same trade name he had used for his bicycles: Rambler. Unlike his New England rival, Jeffery had enough sense to stay out of the bicycle business once he had left. His company has gone through several reincarnations, but it has survived.

   This picture of the geographical distribution of the automobile industry shows a marked Middle Western orientation almost from the beginning. For this a variety of reasons can be offered. The claim has been made that Middle Western bankers were more sympathetic to the fledgling automobile industry than the tradition-bound Easterners, but the evidence on this point is unconvincing. The self-financing technique so generally employed has been described; until about 1905 bank credit, Eastern or Middle Western, was available only to companies already well established in another field, such as Pope or Studebaker. The Middle West's chief initial advantage over its principal competitor, New England, was that the hardwood forests of Michigan and Indiana had made the region the center of carriage and wagon manufacturing, from which the transition to motor vehicles was natural. There was little to choose between the two areas in machine-shop facilities and supply of skilled labor; but when in the course of time automobile manufacturing became large-scale enterprise, the odds swung inexorably in favor of the plants that were close to the major centers of industrial production.

THE RESPONSE TO THE HORSELESS CARRIAGE

All this energetic production of motor vehicles was based on a strong public demand for them. From the outset the American people took enthusiastically to the horseless carriage. There were exceptions. There was bitter hostility from horse lovers and opposition from those who are always suspicious of something new. The feeling that the automobile was somehow undesirable expressed itself all the way from petty legal harassment of motorists to Woodrow Wilson's pronouncement in 1906, when he was president of Princeton, that possession of a motorcar was such an ostentatious display of wealth that it would stimulate socialism by inciting envy of the rich.

Wilson was wrong. The motorcar did incite the common man in the United States, but what it incited was a desire to own an automobile, not to change the social system. This response was not fully manifest in 1906, but the indications were clear that the horseless carriage was exerting a powerful attraction on people at all levels of American life.

The first automobile magazines, *Horseless Age* and *Motocycle*, began publication in New York and Chicago respectively in 1895 with enough support for the former to stay in business more than twenty years. The more appropriately named *Motor Age* followed in 1899. The American Automobile Association was organized in

Chicago in 1902 as a federation of local automobile clubs, the form it has retained ever since. Its founding in that year implies that before 1902 there already existed local automobile clubs with sufficient membership and vigor to warrant promoting a national association. The Society of Automobile Engineers, later changed to Society of Automotive Engineers, followed in 1905, demonstrating that in just ten years the horseless carriage had become an important factor in American technology. These events were symptoms of the emergence of the motor vehicle in America to a position beyond that of a curiosity or plaything. A Duryea "motor wagon" was featured in a Barnum and Bailey circus parade on April 2, 1896, but the concept of the automobile as a freak was short-lived.

There was a longer period in which much of the effort of designers and builders was directed toward racing. There was valid reason for this because racing was good advertising and also provided a means of testing designers' ideas. Both Alexander Winton and Henry Ford drove in automobile races, and the Ford Motor Company received much favorable publicity in its beginning years from the exploits of racing driver Barney Oldfield and the Ford 999.

The first track used for automobile racing was Narragansett Park in Cranston, Rhode Island (not the present horse-racing track of the same name). There on September 7, 1896, two electric automobiles and three Duryeas rolled through five one-mile heats with the same entrant (an electric) winning each until the bored spectators began to call, possibly for the first time in America, "Get a horse!" The maximum speed attained was 26.8 miles an hour. Subsequently automobile racing provided better entertainment. In the course of time it provided not much else. Both testing and advertising came to be done in other ways, although as late as 1911 the Indianapolis Speedway was built for the ostensible purpose of providing a test track for American automobiles.

Of greater importance in getting the motor vehicle accepted were demonstrations of ability to cover long distances. In 1897 Alexander Winton drove one of his cars from Cleveland to New

York in 78 hours 43 minutes actual running time. The whole trip, including stops for repairs, took from July 28 to August 7 and covered 800 miles via Rochester, Syracuse, Utica, and Albany. Four years later Roy D. Chapin drove a curved-dash Oldsmobile 820 miles in seven days from Detroit to the automobile show in New York, and the Apperson brothers drove one of their cars the 1,050 miles from Kokomo, Indiana, to New York. In 1903 no fewer than three trips from San Francisco to New York were made, each requiring about two months. The first was undertaken by Dr. H. Nelson Jackson of Burlington, Vermont, and his chauffeur, Sewall K. Crocker, to settle a $50 bet. On his return to his home Jackson was fined for exceeding a six-mile-an-hour speed limit. The climax of this kind of road test was a New York-to-Paris race in 1908, westward across the United States, thence by sea to Vladivostok, and so to Paris. The original intention of going via Alaska and the Bering Strait was abandoned; just getting across the United States was difficult enough. The race began on February 12, 1908, with American, French, Italian, and German cars and drivers participating and was won by an American "Thomas Flyer" which arrived in Paris on July 30, to the accompaniment of the claims and counterclaims over interpretation of the rules that seem to plague most sporting events aimed at promoting international goodwill.

These spectacular feats attracted attention to the potentialities of the motor vehicle but otherwise had little bearing on what use an ordinary individual might make of an automobile. More useful for this purpose were the Glidden Tours, begun in 1904 by Charles Jasper Glidden (1857–1927), who made a fortune in the telephone business and then retired to pursue his interests in automobiles and aviation. The tours were not races; they were intended to demonstrate the reliability of the automobile as a means of travel. Entries were expected to be stock cars operated by their owners, ample time was allowed to cover the designated route, and the Glidden Trophy was awarded to the entrant with the best all-round touring record. However, the Trophy came to carry so much prestige that automobile firms took to entering specially built cars, so that the tours lost their real purpose and were finally discontinued in 1914.

The endurance runs and Glidden Tours both served to reveal the woeful inadequacy of the American highway system. On his Cleveland–New York run Winton described the roads as "outrageous," and in 1901 Chapin, following his predecessor's route through upstate New York, took to the towpath of the Erie Canal for 150 miles because it was better than the highways. Roads were not only poor in quality but inadequately marked. Guide books began to appear in 1901, not as efficient perhaps as the tourist aids now available but somewhat more colorful: "Bear left at the town hall and proceed 0.8 miles to covered bridge. Turn sharp right—." A Good Roads Association was formed, with understandably strong support from the automobile industry, but some time would elapse before tangible results appeared.

There were also less glamorous but equally significant events in the development of the automobile. Trucks came into use in the late 1890's, in small numbers and chiefly for light local deliveries, but nonetheless recognizing the commercial potential of the motor vehicle. In 1899 the Post Office Department began to experiment with trucks for delivering mail, a step that might be construed to give official sanction to this new device.

In those horseless carriage days no one could have foretold just what the future of the automobile would be. Some enthusiasts were carried away. The editor of *Horseless Age*, writing in 1896 of the perils of runaway horses, said "The motor vehicle will not shy or run away. These frightful accidents can be prevented. The motor vehicle will do it." He was no farther amiss than his counterpart of *The Automobile*, who predicted in 1909 that the general use of automobiles would relieve traffic congestion. Yet if the enthusiasts were wrong in specifics, they were right in their vision that the automobile would change American life.

CHAPTER 3

Growing Pains

Between 1900 and 1910 motor-vehicle production in the United States rose from 4,000 to 187,000 and registrations from 8,000 to 469,000. The automobile industry was moving up to become big business, with ancillary enterprises such as sales, service, and repair facilities growing from it and a pronounced influence on related industries such as petroleum and rubber. As this process of growth continued, the organization of the industry naturally changed, including some ambitious efforts at consolidation and combination. Although the initial attempts misfired, they left their mark on the history of the automobile.

THE SELDEN PATENT

At this point we have to go back to George B. Selden and his patent application in 1879. If Selden had operated under slightly more favorable conditions, he would now be regarded, beyond doubt or challenge, as the inventor of the gasoline automobile. He showed excellent engineering insight when he realized that the clumsy Brayton engine, which weighed almost half a ton per horsepower, could be refined for use in a highway vehicle, and he and a Rochester machinist, William Gomm, performed a considerable mechanical feat in designing and building a three-cylinder Brayton-type engine with a ratio of 185 pounds per horsepower. According

33

to William Greenleaf, whose *Monopoly on Wheels* is the most thorough study of Selden's career, the engine in its tests never ran for more than five minutes or on more than one cylinder. It was enough, nevertheless, to justify Selden in applying for a patent, claiming novelty in the combination of a liquid hydrocarbon engine with the other elements of his vehicle—clutch, steering gear, and so on. Normally he would have received his patent in 1881, two years after filing his application, and it would have expired in 1898, just when it might have begun to have commercial value. As the law then stood, however, an inventor could delay issue of his patent without sacrificing his claims to priority by filing amendments to his application, provided he did not let more than two years elapse without acting. Selden, a competent and experienced patent lawyer, contrived by this means to keep his application pending for sixteen years, finally getting United States Patent No. 549,160 on November 5, 1895.

What did he intend? The conventional interpretation is that Selden deliberately held up the issue of his patent until such time as there was prospect of an automobile industry coming into existence to pay tribute to him. Greenleaf characterizes Selden as "a consummate master of systematic and intentional delay." Supporting this thesis is the fact that Selden kept in close touch with automotive development in both Europe and the United States and in amending his patent was careful to broaden its language so as to have it cover the advances that were taking place. Specifically, he changed his wording so as to include compression-type internal-combustion engines, which would presumably extend his patent to include highway vehicles using Otto or Daimler engines.

Yet this explanation of Selden's performance is only partially satisfactory. If he was acting with such Machiavellian calculation, he showed remarkably poor ability in exploiting his patent when he finally got it. His long delay could equally well have been due to a desire to hold up the issue of his patent until he had a marketable vehicle. It was his misfortune that he was ahead of his time and could not get financial support. He almost had a promise of $5,000.

but when he remarked that some day there would be more motor vehicles than horses on the streets of Rochester, the prospective investor was frightened away. He can be justified for changing his patent specifications regarding the engine. He had never claimed that he invented the internal-combustion engine, nor had he stipulated that his vehicle must use the constant-pressure engine that he himself had worked on. He sincerely believed that he was entitled to priority for the *combination* of mechanical features that would create a highway vehicle powered by an internal-combustion engine; from this point of view, the particular kind of engine employed was immaterial so long as it used liquid hydrocarbon fuel. If during the 1880's he had built even the clumsy car that he and his sons later constructed as an exhibit in the patent suit, his claims would have been extremely difficult to refute. History has been unkind to George B. Selden.

As it was, he got his patent and then did nothing with it. Lack of funds is offered as the explanation; another possibility is that until 1900 there was no one really worth suing, but there is an exasperating obscurity about what Selden did or thought. All we can say for certain is that in 1899 he sold his patent, for $10,000 and one-fifth of any royalties collected, to a syndicate composed of William C. Whitney, Thomas F. Ryan, and other prominent Wall Street figures of that day. Their immediate objective was to promote a scheme for operating fleets of electric cabs in the principal American cities. The origin of the plan was a company organized in New York City by Isaac L. Rice, founder of the Electric Storage Battery Company and the Electric Boat Company and originator of the Rice gambit in chess. After some complex financial and corporate maneuvering, Rice's company and the motor carriage department of the Pope Manufacturing Company became the Electric Vehicle Company.

What the promoters of a project based on the electric automobile wanted with a patent for a gasoline automobile was never spelled out. However, they were shrewd businessmen with a fondness for monopoly, and it was an understandable precaution for them to secure a foothold in the gasoline car field at a time when the course of automotive development was unpredictable.

As it turned out, the electric cabs were a monumental failure. About two thousand were built and put into service, but they were clumsy, expensive vehicles to operate, with batteries that weighed a ton and had to be replaced after each trip. Before long the Electric Vehicle Company, dubbed by the press "the Lead Cab Trust," was in serious trouble and had to try to make what it could of whatever assets it had, including the Selden patent.

Legal proceedings charging infringement of the patent were begun in 1900 against the Winton Motor Carriage Company, then the biggest of the gasoline automobile manufacturers, and others. Before any decision was reached, however, the attractions of a negotiated settlement and the needs of the participants led to an agreement in 1903 placing control of the patent in the hands of an Association of Licensed Automobile Manufacturers (ALAM). An executive committee of five, with the Electric Vehicle Company as a permanent member, allocated licenses. The licensees paid a royalty of 1¼ per cent on the list price of each car manufactured, and the royalties were to be divided two-fifths to the Electric Vehicle Company, one-fifth to Selden, and two-fifths to the ALAM, to be used for the benefit of the industry.

For the participating manufacturers this was a very satisfactory arrangement. It is doubtful whether any of them really accepted the validity of Selden's patent, but none of them felt strong enough to face a prolonged and costly lawsuit with equanimity, and they saw in the control of the patent by the ALAM a means of stabilizing their industry, especially by eliminating what they termed the "fly-by-nights"—the people who went into the business, built a few cars, and then for one reason or another disappeared, leaving "orphan" vehicles in the hands of the public. The Electric Vehicle Company accepted the arrangement because it promised revenues instead of a long and uncertain court battle. Selden remained the forgotten man. He is reported to have been obligated to pay part of his share of the royalties to George H. Day, president of the Electric Vehicle Company. The evidence on this point is hazy, but it is reasonably well established that his earnings from his patent were somewhere between $200,000 and $500,000, and probably nearer the lower than the higher figure.

At this juncture the Ford Motor Company came into existence. Henry Ford did not believe in patents, but he inquired among friends in Detroit about the possibility of getting a license from the ALAM and was told that his application would be refused because he had still to demonstrate that he could build cars capable of meeting the association's standards. What newcomers in the automobile industry were supposed to do is puzzling. They could not get a license until they had established themselves as responsible manufacturers; on the other hand, if the Selden patent was valid, no one could legally manufacture motor vehicles without a license. The peak of absurdity was reached in 1908 when George B. Selden himself finally found the means to start making cars in Rochester and, for precisely the same reason that was given to Henry Ford, was denied a license to manufacture under his own patent. As it happened, a year later he was able to become legitimatized by acquiring a defunct company that had a license, but the incident provided an illuminating commentary on the situation created by Selden's claims.

At any rate, Henry Ford and his business manager, James S. Couzens, decided to fight the patent, partly on the strength of a promise of support from John Wanamaker, who at that time included Ford cars in his merchandise. They were not alone. Other prominent producers such as Ransom E. Olds and the Briscoes refused to recognize the Selden patent and formed their own organization, the American Motor Car Manufacturers Association, which at the start had more members than the ALAM. The French firm of Panhard also challenged the patent.

The resulting lawsuit dragged through the courts for eight years. Batteries of experts on both sides delved into the history of the automotive art, and two vehicles were built to Selden's original specifications of 1879 in order to prove that his idea was workable.

It was—just barely. The battle raged in the advertising columns as well as the courtroom. ALAM members warned prospective purchasers, "Don't buy a lawsuit with your car," and Ford and his allies countered by posting a bond with each car sold guaranteeing the buyer against liability. Ford won both the legal and the public relations battles. The district court ruled against him in 1909, causing an abrupt dissolution of the AMCMA, but two years later the Circuit Court of Appeals held that the Selden patent was valid but not infringed, on the grounds that Selden's claim covered only the Brayton-type two-cycle engine.

Although by 1911 Ford had become the largest single American automobile manufacturer and the Electric Vehicle Company had disappeared in bankruptcy during the panic of 1907, in the public eye the Selden patent case pitted Henry Ford as the champion of the "little man" against the monopoly. The ALAM was never an effective monopoly: its members competed among themselves; and if they expected to restrict competition by excluding newcomers from the automobile industry, they were conspicuously unsuccessful. Even if the association had won its case, it would have been little better off since the patent was going to expire in 1912 anyway. There might have been back royalties due from the Ford Motor Company, but Ford could have absorbed these by 1911 without undue difficulty and still been very much the gainer because of the advertising the company had received. The legend of Henry Ford, marked by his emergence as an American folk hero, began with the Selden patent case.

CROSS-LICENSING AND STANDARDIZATION

There were other important consequences of the patent controversy as well. The automobile industry concluded that patent litigation offered no advantages to offset its cost, and in 1915 adopted an agreement for a mutual cross-licensing of patents. All patents, except those embodying a major technical change, were to be made freely available to the participating companies one year after issuance. Supervision of the system was in the hands of the National Automobile Chamber of Commerce, successor to the ALAM (which became defunct at the end of the Selden suit) and predecessor of the Automobile Manufacturers Association. During the first ten years of the agreement only one patent was claimed to be revolutionary and this claim was rejected.

There were some exceptions. The cross-licensing system did not apply to parts manufacturers or to specialized vehicles such as motorcycles and fire engines. Packard stayed out of the agreement because it wished to keep control of some of its engine patents, and the Ford Motor Company refused to participate because Henry Ford disapproved of both associations and patents. Nevertheless the system worked. Ford took out patents merely as protection and permitted free use by others, in return considering himself eligible to help himself to the patent pool. The agreement was renewed at intervals until 1955, when the reduction in the number of automobile firms to five made its continuation needless.

The other major consequence of the Selden patent was the promotion of technical standardization in automobile manufacturing. In the agreement creating the ALAM it was stipulated that two-fifths of the income from royalties was to go to the association for the benefit of the industry. The money was used for precisely this purpose. The ALAM established a technical section in Hartford whose principal achievement was to initiate a program for standardization of parts and materials. With several hundred firms engaged in making motor vehicles, it was manifestly desirable for manufacturers, parts suppliers, and automobile owners alike that parts should be as uniform as possible so that, for example, any sparkplug would fit any engine, and that such elementary components as nuts and bolts should conform to generally accepted specifications.

When the ALAM dissolved, its technical section was taken over by the Society of Automotive Engineers, which had been an advocate of standardization since its founding in 1905. The subsequent development of the SAE program revealed a sharp divergence between the large and the small automobile manufacturers. The latter wanted maximum standardization of everything that went into a car; some of their spokesmen even suggested the adoption of standard designs. The small producers were assemblers. Industrywide standardization of parts would mean economies in production for them, and it was much to their advantage not to be dependent for a given part on a single supplier. Besides lessening the risk that parts might not be available when they were needed, standardization offered firms placing comparatively small orders the benefit of being able to shop among competitors.

The big companies, on the other hand, could achieve the necessary efficiency in production by internal standardization, which gave them greater flexibility in controlling their own operations that conforming to industrywide specifications would have permitted. They were less dependent on supplier firms because they had their own parts-making subsidiaries, and when they bought in the open market they bought as large-scale purchasers who could negotiate with the suppliers for price concessions. Consequently they were less interested than their small competitors in intercompany standardization, although they accepted it in such obvious essentials as screw threads and poppet valves.

The result was that during its early years the SAE standardization program was dominated by the small companies. The driving force was Howard E. Coffin, one of the founders and an early president of the SAE. The large firms by and large were indifferent. Subsequently, however, the possibilities of interindustry standardization began to attract the big companies. As large-scale producers they stood to benefit by steps that would encourage the wide use of motor vehicles, such as standard specifications for tires and petroleum products; and as heavy buyers of commodities like steel, they were interested in the adoption of standard grades, which would make for more efficient and economical purchasing.

Eventually, as might have been expected, the standardization program conformed to the pattern preferred by the big companies.

The early 1920's saw a rapid shrinkage in the number of minor producers, with a consequent reduction in pressure for detailed intraindustry standards. By 1925 the policies of the large firms were clearly dominant. In spite of this internal conflict in the automobile industry, the standardization program was a most significant achievement. SAE concepts of standardization were carried by automotive engineers into the aircraft industry, and the society contributed to the creation of the American Standards Association. The steel, rubber, petroleum, and other industries accepted SAE specifications, sometimes reluctantly. For the development and use of the automobile itself, standardization was of paramount importance. Without it, maintenance and servicing would be considerably more difficult and expensive. Very few motorists have been aware that the program exists; yet anyone who drives his car into a gas station is likely to make use of SAE standards.

THE COMING OF BIG BUSINESS

The promotion of the Electric Vehicle Company was the first serious attempt at large-scale organization in the automobile industry. It was badly conceived, first concentrating on the wrong kind of motor vehicle and then making a clumsy effort at patent monopoly just when public opinion was acutely trust-conscious. It was also premature. The automobile was not yet a large enough factor in the American economy to support an overcapitalized experiment in high finance on the late nineteenth-century pattern. The Electric Vehicle failure was matched by the Pope Manufacturing Company, which started from a far more substantial foundation. After selling their motor carriage department, the Popes turned to organizing a bicycle trust, the American Bicycle Company, but this venture failed and they returned to automobiles, making cars that were well known in their day, the Pope-Hartford and Pope-Toledo. Yet the company had made a basic blunder when it fell for the allure of the Electric Vehicle scheme and gave up its own promising start in motor-vehicle manufacturing. Pope could not survive the 1907 depression, and with its fall the automotive center of gravity shifted conclusively to the Middle West.

In that region big business organization in the automobile industry developed at the hands of men who had a clear, if sometimes overenthusiastic, vision of the future of the motor vehicle in the United States. The Ford Motor Company presents a unique pattern of a monolithic structure built on mass production of a single model, and it will be considered later in connection with the rise of mass production. The other large-scale organizations were combinations, typified by General Motors.

The founder of General Motors was William C. (Billy) Durant, the Flint carriage maker and salesman extraordinary who took over the ailing Buick Motor Car Company in 1904 and made it one of the leading producers. Durant had a boundless faith in the market potential of the automobile, and he saw brilliant prospects for a big company producing a variety of cars. In this way, if one model failed to sell in a given year, the others would pull the company through, whereas for a small manufacturer with only one make, a single bad year was likely to mean ruin. The large combine, as Durant saw it, would also have its own parts manufacturers and thus be free from dependence on supplier firms.

His first effort, made in 1907 in conjunction with Benjamin Briscoe, aimed at uniting the four major producers: Buick, Maxwell-Briscoe, Reo, and Ford. Negotiations seemed well on their way to fruition, with a price of $3 million agreed on for both the Ford and Reo firms, when Henry Ford wrecked the project by requiring payment in cash. When R. E. Olds heard of Ford's demand, he insisted on getting cash too, and $6 million was more than the two promoters could scrape together. The deal was abandoned—certainly a fateful moment in the history of the American automobile—and Durant and Briscoe then went their separate ways.

Durant's next move was to incorporate the General Motors Company in September, 1908. Buick was the base and to it were added Cadillac, Oldsmobile, Oakland (eventually Pontiac), and a miscellaneous assortment of other concerns acquired in an aggressive campaign without much attention being paid to the actual value or earning power of the property. There was apparently a second attempt to buy Ford. By this time Henry Ford had raised his price to $8 million, still in cash and still beyond Durant's resources. Whether Ford would actually have sold his company for any price just when the Model T was being put on the market is open to question. It is difficult to believe that he really was serious about this second negotiation with Durant.

Durant's whirlwind empire-building caught up with him in just two years. By 1910 General Motors was in trouble. Its rapid expansion had exhausted the resources of cash and credit with which Durant had started. Most of the purchases had been financed by issuing securities, and the accumulation of unprofitable subsidiaries at exaggerated prices had saddled the corporation with a burden of debt considerably beyond its earning capacity. General Motors was saved from dissolution only by the intervention of a bankers' syndicate headed by James J. Storrow of Lee, Higginson and Company. This syndicate has been harshly criticized for the severity of the terms it imposed. It advanced $15 million at 6 per cent but took $2½ million of this amount as commission along with $6 million worth of General Motors stock. Durant, needless to say, was removed from control of the company, although he retained a seat on the board of directors.

Yet there is a case for the Storrow syndicate. The General Motors situation was so bad that the bankers initially thought of dissolving the company and salvaging the sound parts, Buick and Cadillac, independently. General Motors was kept alive at this juncture largely by the urging of Henry M. Leland and a pledge of Cadillac's resources. Even then the trust debentures could be sold only by distributing the $6 million in General Motors stock as a bonus to purchasers. The Storrow regime, moreover, effected a healthy reorganization; among other things it brought Charles W. Nash (1864–1948) and Walter P. Chrysler (1875–1940) into the top echelon of management.

Both these men of course would make their mark on the American automobile industry, and both personified the traditional American success story. Nash rose literally from rags to riches. Orphaned in early childhood, he was bound out to an Illinois farmer from whom he ran away at the age of twelve. He spent his adolescence in poverty as a migrant farm laborer, until eventually he found a job as a trimmer in the Durant-Dort carriage factory. He rose to be general manager, and just before the 1910 crisis he moved over to become head of Buick, largely because Buick owed the carriage company several million dollars for automobile bodies and Nash asked Durant for a chance to set things right. He was recommended to Storrow by Durant, with the result that in 1912 the onetime penniless orphan became president of General Motors.

Walter Chrysler did not start quite so far down the economic ladder. He was a Kansas farm boy with a passion for machinery and the good fortune to grow up in Ellis, Kansas, where the Union Pacific had railroad shops. Chrysler rose to be master mechanic on several Middle Western railroads and eventually to be superintendent of the American Locomotive Works in Pittsburgh, where he became acquainted with Storrow. By this time his enthusiasm had switched from locomotives to automobiles, beginning with the purchase of a Locomobile at the Chicago Automobile Show in 1905. He paid $5,000: his entire savings of $700 plus $4,300 that Chrysler borrowed from a banker friend. He reports in his autobiography that his wife had nothing to say when he took his treasure home and told her what he had done, but he thought the kitchen door banged shut a little harder than usual. At any rate, when Storrow asked him to join Buick to provide the technical skill that Nash lacked, he accepted the offer even though it meant a reduction in salary from $12,000 to $6,000 a year. Then, when Nash moved up to be president of General Motors, Chrysler replaced him as president of the Buick Motor Car Company.

So General Motors survived and indeed flourished. What might have happened is illustrated by the experience of Durant's former associate Benjamin Briscoe, who tried at this time to organize a rival corporation, the United States Motor Corporation. Founded in 1910, it was based on one prosperous company, Maxwell-Briscoe, and its other acquisitions were a collection of lame ducks, including the Columbia Motor Car Company, formed from the wreckage of the Electric Vehicle Company. In 1912 United States Motor went bankrupt. Alfred Reeves, who was an official of the company before serving for forty years as manager of the National Automobile Chamber of Commerce and the Automobile Manufacturers Association, explained what happened thus: "Ben just plain ran out of money." There was no syndicate to rescue United States Motor. Instead, Walter Flanders, formerly of Ford and Everitt-Metzger-Flanders (EMF), was called in to salvage what there was of value. He reorganized the company as the Maxwell Motor Car Company, which would in time be the parent of the Chrysler Corporation.

The record of attempts at large-scale organization before the First World War is therefore unimpressive. Yet Durant and Briscoe were right in their basic assumptions. They were not mere speculative promoters; their principal error was an excess of optimism about the speed with which the automobile industry would grow. They also gave inadequate attention to production and technology, as compared with promotion and finance. Durant made some wild guesses about what might be useful for his company, but he can readily be excused on the ground that no one then could be certain of the technical development of the automobile. The fact remains that Durant and Briscoe first envisaged the organizational pattern that the automobile industry would finally adopt. Like so many pioneers, both were destined to see their dreams realized by others.

TECHNICAL PROGRESS

While the automobile industry was wrestling with the organizational problems of growth, its product was also undergoing changes. By the time Durant and Briscoe made their bids for leadership, the day of the horseless carriage was definitely over. By 1910 most American passenger automobiles were powered by four-cylinder engines, although in the higher-priced lines (including one Ford model offered in 1906) there was an increasing trend to sixes. The first passenger car to go into production with a V-8 engine was put on the market in 1907 by Edward R. Hewitt, son of Abram S. Hewitt and grandson of another inventor in the field of transportation, Peter Cooper. The Hewitt car failed to sell. There was nothing wrong with the engine technically; it was just too expensive to find an adequate market. Yet within ten years sufficient progress was made so that a number of manufacturers, led by Cadillac in 1914, were able to offer eight-cylinder engines successfully, and in 1915 Packard went up to twelve.

The touring car continued to be the most popular type, since the cost of the closed car body was too high for general use. There was during this period a beginning of metal body construction on a limited scale. More important was the employment of alloy steels and aluminum in engines and chassis in order to save weight. A minor but significant change in styling that occurred about 1910 was shifting the steering wheel from the right to the left side of the car. This change represented an abandonment of the practice of imitating European usage for the sake of prestige and an adaptation to the conditions of American driving.

None of these steps did more than keep American automotive design up with European. From other developments, however, came indications that Europe's leadership in the automotive field was terminating. Excluding for the present the events connected with the introduction of mass production, several distinctive American contributions to the automobile can be identified about 1910. In 1908 Otto Zachow and William Besserdich produced a four-wheel-drive car in Clintonville, Wisconsin, the long-range precursor of the jeep. Of more immediate impact was the introduction in the same year of Charles Y. Knight's sleeve-valve engine. As the name implies, the engine had valve ports operated by a sleeve outside the cylinder. The Knight engine was more expensive to build and maintain than the poppet-valve motor, but it was smoother and quieter, especially in a day when low-grade gasoline left carbon deposits on cylinder walls and valve seats. The "silent Knight" survived until further progress in engine design and fuels destroyed its advantage over the simpler poppet-valve engine.

The outstanding American technical contribution of this period, apart from production methods, was the electric starter. The desirability of some kind of mechanical starting system for the gasoline automobile was obvious from the beginning. Hand cranking an automobile engine was a backbreaking, frustrating, and risky job, as many readers of this book will undoubtedly remember. Consequently, there was constant experimenting with a starting device, but without success until the combined talents of Henry M. Leland and Charles F. Kettering (1876–1958) were applied to the problem.

Leland came into the picture because a friend and business associate, Byron Carter, had died as the result of a starting accident. Carter, builder of the Cartercar (remembered for its friction drive), went to the assistance of a lady whose car had stalled; he suffered a broken jaw when the crank handle kicked back, and gangrene subsequently caused his death. Leland thereupon determined to keep such tragedies from happening again and turned the energies of the Cadillac engineering department to the starting problem. There it was determined that an electrical system was the answer. The major difficulty was to provide an electric motor small enough to put in a car and at the same time powerful enough to turn the engine over.

Charles F. Kettering, electrical engineering graduate of Ohio State University and free-wheeling genius, offered the solution as the first of his several vital contributions to the development of the motor vehicle. After leaving college he went to work for the National Cash Register Company, where one of his assignments was to design a motor for an electric cash register. He did this by recognizing that this motor need not be built to carry a constant load but only to deliver occasional bursts of power. Kettering left National Cash Register to join Edward A. Deeds in organizing the Dayton Engineering Laboratories Company (Delco) to design and manufacture automobile ignition systems. This operation brought him into contact with Cadillac, and when his aid was invoked on the starting problem, he saw that the motor that was required involved the same principle as his electric cash register. It was possible to install electric starters on Cadillac cars in 1912, although the final step in making the technique complete came a year later when Vincent Bendix (1883–1945) contributed the starter drive that still bears his name.

The electric starter was more than just a convenience or a safety measure. It was a major factor in promoting widespread use of the gasoline automobile, particularly because it made the operation of gasoline cars more attractive to women. In fact, the electric starter may be regarded as the decisive factor in the triumph of the gasoline over the steam automobile. Once the starting problem was solved, the internal-combustion engine appealed more to the ordinary motorist than the steam engine with its high pressures and need for constant skilled care of boiler tubes.

ANCILLARY INDUSTRIES

As more and more motor vehicles poured onto American highways, their effect on the American economy became increasingly pronounced. In the first ten years of the twentieth century, automobile manufacturing climbed from 150th to 21st in value of products among American industries, and in this phenomenal climb it had a marked influence on the growth and direction of other industries. It was becoming a major consumer of steel. In addition, automotive demand was not only becoming the largest single outlet for machine tools but was affecting the character of the product. For example, the need to process alloy steels in automobile manufacture called for elaborate development of grinding machines.

The effects were naturally greatest in the industries that contributed most directly to the motor vehicle, specifically those that provided it with fuel and tires. The petroleum industry was literally revolutionized. Before 1900 only about one-tenth of the

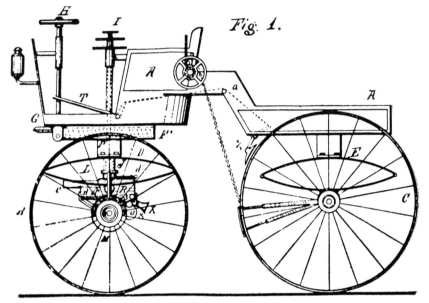

Fig. 1.

THE SELDEN PATENT

"The object of my invention is the production of a safe, simple, and cheap road-locomotive light in weight, easy to control, and possessed of sufficient power to overcome any ordinary inclination. . . ."

EARLY ELECTRIC CAB

Produced by the Electric Vehicle Co. in Hartford, Conn., these electric hansoms were often seen on the streets of big cities in the early years of the twentieth century.

COLUMBIA CARRIER

The Columbia Carrier of 1897, designed by Hiram P. Maxim for the Pope Manufacturing Co., was a gasoline-powered delivery vehicle employing a three-wheeled chassis.

THE DURYEA CAR

This is the original "Motor Wagon" of 1893 after restoration in 1958. It is on display at the Smithsonian Institution.

THE STANLEY STEAMER

This picture shows the Stanley brothers in their first steam car, 1897.

THE MERRY OLDSMOBILE

A TRANSCONTINENTAL RACE

Two curved-dash Oldsmobiles prepare to start from New York City in 1905 for a transcontinental race to celebrate the Lewis and Clark Exposition in Portland, Ore. "Old Scout," which is still in running condition, won, making the trip to Portland in 44 days.

EARLY CRANKSHAFT FACTORY

This picture, taken in 1911, shows crankshafts being ground in the plant of the Norton Company, Worcester, Mass. These automatic grinders could turn out a crankshaft in fifteen minutes, compared with five hours by the earlier method of turning, filing, and polishing.

(Courtesy Studebaker-Packard Corporation)

EARLY STUDEBAKER

This car was produced in 1909–10.

(Courtesy Ford Motor Company)

TIN LIZZIE

(Courtesy General Motors Corporation)

THE FIRST CHEVROLET

In 1912 Louis Chevrolet (standing at left, without hat), after two years of development work on the car, poses beside the first Chevrolet, a massive six-cylinder model. At the wheel is W. C. Durant's son Cliff.

(Courtesy Ford Motor Company)

THE FIRST MOVING ASSEMBLY LINE

A pivotal point in the history of mass production was the setting up of this moving assembly line at the Ford plant in 1914.

Somewhere West of Laramie

SOMEWHERE west of Laramie there's a broncho-busting, steer-roping girl who knows what I'm talking about. She can tell what a sassy pony, that's a cross between greased lightning and the place where it hits, can do with eleven hundred pounds of steel and action when he's going high, wide and handsome.

The truth is—the Playboy was built for her.

Built for the lass whose face is brown with the sun when the day is done of revel and romp and race.

She loves the cross of the wild and the tame.

There's a savor of links about that car—of laughter and lilt and light—a hint of old loves—and saddle and quirt. It's a brawny thing—yet a graceful thing for the sweep o' the Avenue.

Step into the Playboy when the hour grows dull with things gone dead and stale.

Then start for the land of real living with the spirit of the lass who rides, lean and rangy, into the red horizon of a Wyoming twilight.

JORDAN MOTOR CAR COMPANY, Inc., Cleveland, Ohio

(Courtesy Automobile Manufacturers Association)

ROMANCE IN AUTOMOTIVE ADVERTISING

This advertisement, which first appeared in 1926, marked a change of emphasis in automobile advertising from the car itself to the pleasures of automobile travel. The "Playboy" referred to was a Jordan model, not related to the car which appeared briefly in the late 1940's.

petroleum refined was converted into gasoline. Gasoline, in fact, was frequently regarded as an undesirable waste product and thrown away. It was known to have high illuminating qualities, but its volatility made it dangerous. As a fuel for internal-combustion engines, however, gasoline was clearly to be preferred.

The advent of the gasoline automobile was materially aided by a spectacular increase in the supply of crude oil through the opening of new fields, beginning with the Spindletop field in East Texas in 1901. The presence of oil there was dramatically demonstrated on January 10 of that year when the first gusher in the United States shot 160 feet into the air, carrying with it the drilling rig and the derrick. Other new fields followed in quick succession, with the result that by 1914 crude-oil production rose from the 60 million barrels of 1900 to about 250 million. Without the motorcar the petroleum industry would have been in trouble, since the kerosene lamp was retreating before gas and electric illumination; but this great increase in the supply of petroleum occurred fortuitously just as the automobile began to create a seemingly limitless demand for gasoline.

Remarkable as the expansion of the oil industry was, it still had trouble keeping pace with the increasing numbers of motor vehicles. By 1910 there was serious concern that the future development of the automobile would be jeopardized by lack of fuel, and in the next three years it was demonstrated that this was not mere alarmism when the price of gasoline in the United States rose from 9½ to 17 cents a gallon. The heart of the difficulty was that existing techniques of refining yielded less than 20 per cent of gasoline from crude. If this proportion could be significantly raised, the problem would be solved.

Important as this matter was to the automobile industry it was still more so to the petroleum industry, already largely dependent on automotive demand for its markets. The Standard Oil Company addressed itself to the problem as early as 1909. Four years and $1 million later the Standard Oil Company (Indiana) patented and simultaneously put into production the Burton cracking process, named for William M. Burton, who supervised the research and development, although much of the actual work was done by his lieutenant, Robert E. Humphreys. The Burton process doubled the yield of gasoline from a given quantity of crude and took care of the automotive fuel supply until the 1920's, when new and improved techniques were being developed. In all this process of change, one overmastering factor remained constant: the energies of the petroleum industry were focused on satisfying the demands of the automobile.

With rubber the story was similar. The manufacture of rubber goods had reached respectable proportions in the nineteenth century, especially after Charles Goodyear introduced vulcanizing in 1839; but the character of the industry changed completely with the appearance of the automobile. Rubber manufacturing in the United States migrated from the eastern seaboard to Akron, Ohio, and concentrated on turning out automobile tires. The career of one man dramatically illustrates what happened. Paul W. Litchfield, who went to the Goodyear Tire and Rubber Company when it was founded in 1900 and rose to be its head, calculated that in his various official capacities with the company, he had been responsible for ordering the purchase of one-eighth of all the natural rubber produced in the world from the time it was discovered by the white man until Litchfield's retirement.

In view of the marked bicycle strain in its ancestry, it was natural for the automobile in its early days to take over from the bicycle the clincher tire in which the bead locked on the rim. By 1905, however, both Firestone and Goodyear (there was no connection with Charles Goodyear—the name was simply picked for sales appeal) had abandoned the clincher for the straight-sided tire. There were two reasons. One was that the manufacture of clincher tires threatened patent complications; the other, and more compelling, was that as cars became bigger, the physical effort needed to get a clincher tire on or off the wheel was too much for the ordinary motorist. The straight-sided tire was difficult enough, in spite of demountable rims and other ingenious devices intended to facilitate the tire changing and repairing which were integral features of travel by automobile. In those days, a familiar sight on the highways of America was sweating motorists laboriously and profanely removing tires, patching them, pumping them manually to their sixty pounds pressure, and wrestling them on the wheels again.

The need to satisfy the motoring public led the rubber industry into a constant search for better methods of making tires, with results which reflected back on the design and use of motor vehicles. In 1907, for example, an automotive editor argued that passenger cars would have to be limited in size because no pneumatic tires could carry a load of more than 3,000 pounds. Larger vehicles, such as trucks, had to depend on solid rubber tires, which put definite limits on their utility. The development of stronger tire fabrics changed these limitations until in 1915 it was possible to introduce pneumatic tires for trucks.

Along with these major industries were the service operations that grew up around the automobile: the garages, the service stations, the repair shops, the automobile supply houses. In this era before the First World War gasoline pumps were not as plentiful as in later years, and in wide stretches of the West and the South automobile travel still required the traveler to be equipped as for a safari. Nevertheless, over a growing area motorists no longer had to gamble on the next general store carrying gasoline or trust the ingenuity of the village blacksmith if the car broke down. Highway conditions were still unsatisfactory but action was being taken to improve them. The Lincoln Highway Association was founded in 1913 for the purpose of promoting a high-quality, coast-to-coast highway across the United States. The idea originated with Carl Graham Fisher, founder of the Electric Auto-Lite Company of Indianapolis, and it was supported by other distinguished automotive figures, notably Henry B. Joy and Roy D. Chapin. Segments of the route were eventually marked, but the financial magnitude of the operation and difficulties of dealing with state and local authorities led the association to terminate its work when the federal Road

Aid Act of 1916 offered a prospect of attaining an effective national highway system.

This law provided for federal aid to the states to improve their road systems. Technically it was based on Congress's constitutional power "to establish post offices and post roads," but the declared intent of the law was to promote farm-to-market communication. Rural congressmen were not yet ready to cherish the motor vehicle for its own sake, although the impact of the Model T can be discerned in the enactment of this law. If the automobile was to justify its existence, it was expected to do so by demonstrating that it could help the farmer.

CHAPTER 4

The Assembly-line Revolution

One of the great paradoxes of American life is that mass production, the greatest distinctively American contribution to present-day industrial civilization, is a concept widely misunderstood even in the country of its creation. To its critics (generally speaking, those who don't have it) mass production has meant the manufacture in quantity of cheap articles, inferior in quality to the product of handicraft methods and acceptable only because they are lower in price. Too often the apologists for mass production have meekly accepted this definition and tried to defend the technique accordingly. Yet this interpretation of mass production is almost wholly erroneous. The purpose of mass production is to combine increased output with decreased unit cost. It achieves this purpose by using manufacturing methods that have an exactness of co-ordination and synchronization and standards of accuracy and interchangeability far beyond the capacity of the most skilled craftsman. The alleged sacrifice of quality to quantity is a myth.

In his autobiography, *Adventures of a White Collar Man*, Alfred P. Sloan, Jr. (b. 1875) tells how, early in his career as president of the Hyatt Roller Bearing Company, he had to go to Detroit to investigate complaints about the accuracy of bearings purchased from Hyatt by the Cadillac Motor Car Company. Henry M. Leland, the perfectionist, showed Sloan by micrometer measurement that the rejected bearings did not meet the exact specifications

53

demanded of them and waved aside Sloan's excuses with, "Young man, Cadillacs are made to run, not just to sell. You must grind your bearings. Even though you make thousands, the first and last should be precisely alike." Sloan credits this encounter with impressing on him that mass production demanded the utmost in accuracy and precision. But grinding thousands of bearings exactly alike can be done far better by automatic grinding machines than by any manual process; indeed it cannot be done manually at all with the same degree of accuracy or within any reasonable limit of time and cost.

True mass production requires not only mechanization, but a systematic combination of precision, standardization, interchangeability, synchronization, and continuity. Its origins go back at least five hundred years into history. Johann Gutenberg's movable type was one of the earliest identifiable applications of the idea of interchangeable parts. During this same period Venetian war galleys were fitted out by installing components and stores while the hulls were being towed through the Arsenal. At the end of the line the galleys were fully equipped for sea, and as many as ten could be thus processed in a single day. The concept of true mass production, however, first emerged with the coming of industrialism in the eighteenth century. Early in that century a Swedish engineer and manufacturer, Christopher Polhem, attempted with some success to make iron products by mechanized processes that did not require skilled craftsmen, but he could not make his ideas fully effective because he was just ahead of the development of efficient metalworking tools. Toward the end of the eighteenth century a superintendent in the French royal arsenals, whom we know only as Blanc, fully anticipated the work of Eli Whitney and others in making muskets by machine manufacture of interchangeable parts. During the French Revolution, however, pressure from the gunsmiths compelled the government to terminate Blanc's experiments.

Great Britain became familiar with the mechanization of production during the late eighteenth and early nineteenth centuries. It also witnessed one interesting experiment embodying some of the principles of mass production. This was a factory engaged in making pulley blocks for the Royal Navy during the Napoleonic wars. It was established by three colorful individuals: Marc Isambard Brunel, French emigré engineer and father of the still greater Isambard Kingdom Brunel; Samuel Bentham, inspector for the Royal Navy and brother of the eccentric Utilitarian philosopher Jeremy Bentham; and Henry Maudslay, mechanical engineer and one of the outstanding pioneers in the development of machine tools. The factory used forty-four machines designed and built by Maudslay, arranged in a planned sequence so as to eliminate handwork. Ten unskilled workers were employed, and the plant was capable of turning out 130,000 blocks a year. With the end of the Napoleonic wars, however, the mass market for pulley blocks disappeared, and the operation was discontinued.

So the evolution of mass production was left in American hands. The fast-growing United States offered conditions in which it was profitable to employ techniques that achieved quantity production with a minimum of labor, particularly if the high cost of skilled craftsmen could be dispensed with, and there were no strong vested interests to resist innovation. Eli Whitney is generally regarded as the father of machine production of interchangeable parts in the manufacture of firearms, although recent scholarship indicates that he probably knew about Blanc's work and that his methods were certainly known and used in the Springfield and Harpers Ferry arsenals before Whitney succeeded in putting them into operation. The important feature, however, is not who did it first but the fact that in the United States the initial achievements of men like Whitney and Simeon North in the manufacture of firearms were continued by Samuel Colt and others. The same technique was applied to making clocks and watches by Eli Terry and Chauncey Jerome, and it spread to other industries until by 1850 machine fabrication of standardized parts was generally referred to as the "American system of manufacturing."

Continuous-flow operation was given its first practical commercial application by Oliver Evans, who built a grist mill near Philadelphia in 1787 in which the grain was passed mechanically through each stage of the milling process. His technique became accepted practice in American flour-milling. In the latter half of the nineteenth century American meat-packing establishments used conveyors to carry carcasses through the plant in what might be termed a disassembly line, and in 1890 the Westinghouse Company had an endless-chain arrangement for carrying sand into its foundry and bringing the castings out.

By the turn of the century, therefore, the ingredients of mass production already existed in American industry but had not yet been integrated into a coherent system. For that, there was needed a commodity of some mechanical complexity whose manufacture required the assembly of a large number of components and for which there was a prospective mass market if low-cost production were achieved. These conditions were met by the automobile. There was one other prerequisite, quite indispensable: there had to be men with the vision to see what was possible and the ability to do it.

PRELIMINARY STEPS

The dream of the low-priced car followed the introduction of the automobile into the United States in astonishingly short order, and equally astonishingly it appeared nowhere else until after it had become an American reality. What there was in the American scene to stimulate development in this direction can be at least partially identified: a higher standard of living that made widespread purchases of motor vehicles a practical possibility; and a greater propensity among American businessmen than among European to think in terms of a mass market rather than the luxury trade. Business in the United States had become accustomed to a domestic market of continental proportions, with disposable income distributed through more levels of society than was the case in Europe. At any rate, if we date the beginning of the commercial production of automobiles in the United States with Pope and Winton in 1897, fewer than four years elapsed before the first major bid for the low-priced market was made by Ransom E. Olds.

We have already touched on the rise and fall of the curved-dash Oldsmobile. To achieve his peak output of four to five thousand cars a year, Olds organized production according to the most efficient techniques then available. The flow of materials was carefully controlled to eliminate delays, and the cars were assembled by work gangs whose members each had specific functions to perform. Perhaps Olds would have arrived at the assembly line if he had been able to continue with his buggy. Yet he seems to have realized that this lightweight car was a dead end, because he dropped the idea and turned to heavier vehicles when he left the Olds Motor Works and founded Reo.

Nevertheless he had numerous imitators. The first decade of the twentieth century saw a variety of lightweight, low-priced, buggy-type cars offered to the American public. Next to the Oldsmobile, the best known was probably the Brush Runabout. It used wooden construction extensively, had a one-cylinder 10-horsepower engine, and sold for $500. Its designer, Alanson P. Brush, had previously designed the first Cadillac. The company that made the Brush was headed by Frank Briscoe, brother of the organizer of Maxwell-Briscoe. It became part of the United States Motor combine and disappeared when that venture collapsed.

Whether the Brush would have survived longer by itself is dubious. These experiments with light buggies all had the same basic defect: a car designed with cheap construction as the prime consideration came out a cheap car. It simply would not stand up to the stresses of day-to-day use on rough roads. Popular as it was for a while, the Brush was still described, somewhat unjustly, as "wooden body, wooden axles, wooden wheels, wooden run."

The road to the mass-produced car lay through superior rather than inferior manufacturing techniques. That the American automobile industry possessed the requisite standards of precision and

accuracy was dramatically demonstrated in 1908 by the Cadillac
Motor Car Company. Three Cadillacs were dismantled at Brook-
lands, the test track of the British Royal Automobile Club. The
parts were heaped in a pile, ninety of them removed and replaced
from the stocks of the Cadillac agency in London, and the pile
scrambled. Cadillac mechanics reassembled the three cars, which
then made perfect scores in a 500-mile test run. The achievement
made a profound impression on British observers and made Cadillac
the first American car to be awarded the Royal Automobile Club's
Sir Thomas Dewar trophy. The Cadillac was not a mass-produced
car and it was not aimed at the mass market, but the fact that
interchangeability of this order of accuracy could be achieved in
American automobile manufacturing was the most important single
item in making mass production possible.

HENRY FORD AND THE MODEL T

For all the millions of words that have been written about Henry
Ford and the Model T, much of the story of the innovation of
full-fledged mass production by the Ford Motor Company remains
fragmentary. Ford himself still defies interpretation: mechanical
genius (probably) but woefully ignorant in most other matters;
visionary, sometimes shrewdly so and sometimes incredibly naive;
and completely imbued with the attitudes and prejudices of nineteenth-century rural America. It is impossible to say when he first
had the idea of a "car for the great multitude," or more specifically,
as he sometimes said, a car to help the farmer. His own reminis-
cences have to be disregarded. Except where machinery was
concerned, Henry Ford's thought processes were seldom logical,
and he had the human propensity for remembering things the way
he wanted them to be.

The first models offered by the Ford Motor Company after its
establishment in 1903 were definitely not aimed at the low-priced
market. They were competitive in the medium-price range
($1,000–$1,500) with cars like Buick and Maxwell-Briscoe. At the
same time Ford's quarrel with Malcomson, insofar as it involved a

policy issue and not simply Henry Ford's distaste for any rival in the control of his company, appears to have stemmed from Ford's desire to experiment with a low-priced car. It is clear that Ford had definitely set his sights on the mass market and knew what must be done to reach it. In 1903 he told one of his partners, John W. Anderson, "The way to make automobiles is to make one automobile like another automobile, to make them all alike, to make them come from the factory just alike—just like one pin is like another pin when it comes from a pin factory."

Henry Ford succeeded where others failed, principally because, instead of starting out to produce a car as cheaply as possible, he concentrated first on designing a car that would be suitable for the mass market and then turned his attention to the problem of cutting manufacturing costs. There is nothing to suggest that he himself was consciously aware of the significance of this two-step progression; if he grasped it he did so intuitively. Low price was only one of the characteristics required in an automobile intended for use by the general public. It also had to be durable, easy to operate so that it could be driven by any ordinary individual, economical to maintain, and simple to repair—preferably simple enough for the owner to do most of the maintenance and repairs himself. After some experimentation these qualities were achieved in 1907 with the Model T—the "flivver," or "Tin Lizzie,"—the most famous motor vehicle ever built. First offered to the public in 1908, it had a rugged body, mounted high to enable it to negotiate country roads. Its 20-horsepower four-cylinder engine was a marvel of mechanical simplicity, as was its planetary transmission, which had two speeds forward and one in reverse and required only the pressing or releasing of foot-pedals to operate. Some of the strength in its construction was achieved by using alloy steels, an innovation in American practice although European automobile builders had been using them for some time. Ford, in fact, was responsible for introducing the manufacture of vanadium steel to the United States, since the market for it had previously been so small that American steel firms did not consider it worth producing.

The basic concept of the "car for the great multitude" and the qualities it ought to have was definitely Henry Ford's. In the design of the car itself he contributed a good deal but has to share credit with others, conspicuously C. H. (for Childe Harold) Wills (1878–1940), who was the proponent of alloy steels, and Joseph Galamb, who worked out many of the mechanical features of the Model T. Only Ford himself, however, could have taken the next step along the way: namely, the decision in 1909 that the Ford Motor Company should give up all its other models and concentrate exclusively on the production of the Model T.

The car was there; so was the market. The problem was to bring the two together. The company's calculations—undoubtedly those of its brilliant business manager, James S. Couzens, later United States senator from Michigan—were that to tap the mass market, the selling price of the car should not exceed $600. The Model T, however, could not be produced by existing methods to sell for less than $850. An impressive array of talent was directed to finding a solution: Ford himself and Wills; P. E. Martin, in charge of production (Ford executives were never dignified with titles or even clear definition of their responsibilities); the two "Great Danes," Charles E. Sorensen (b. 1881)—cast-iron Charlie—who would perform the remarkable feat of retaining Henry Ford's confidence and goodwill for forty years and William S. Knudsen (1879–1948), future president of General Motors; Clarence Avery, one-time manual training teacher of Edsel Ford (1893–1943) at the Detroit University School, who probably made the initial suggestion of the moving assembly line; and Walter E. Flanders, machine-tool expert and production engineer. Among them they achieved their goal. After prolonged experimentation with the improvement of existing production techniques, they decided early in 1913 to try a conveyor-belt system for assembling magnetos. The results were highly encouraging, and in the same year the idea was tested for chassis assembly by pulling some chassis through the plant with rope and windlass. Even this crude technique cut the time of chassis assembly in half from the twelve hours and twenty-eight minutes which was the best that was achieved by stationary assembly.

When full assembly-line production was attained early in 1914, the time for chassis assembly was reduced to an hour and a half.

This brief account cannot give a clear picture of the detailed experimentation that had to be done to determine the optimum speed for the various assembly lines, the correct height at which work should be placed, the positioning of the workmen, and countless other items that required accurate co-ordination and synchronization. While this work was going on in Detroit, the Ford Motor Company was also introducing a system of branch assembly plants, largely Knudsen's responsibility and an important device for cutting costs, since it was much cheaper to ship frames and parts from Detroit than finished cars. Nor should the contribution of James S. Couzens be overlooked. The ultimate success of the assembly-line experiment depended on selling Ford cars in quantities beyond anything previously achieved in the automobile industry. Couzens not only managed capably the business affairs of the Ford Motor Company, an area in which Henry Ford had neither interest nor ability, but he also put together a body of carefully selected dealers, numbering more than seven thousand in 1913, who went out and peddled the Model T's with evangelical zeal. The results of all these developments are shown in the accompanying table.

TABLE 1

MARKETING OF MODEL T FORDS, 1908–16

Calendar Year	Retail Price (Touring Car)	Total Model T Sales
1908....	$850	5,986
1909....	950	12,292
1910....	780	19,293
1911....	690	40,402
1912....	600	78,611
1913....	550	182,809
1914....	490	260,720
1915....	440	355,276
1916....	360	577,036

The spectacular nature of this achievement naturally gave rise to conflicting claims for credit. These need not concern us. However credit may be allocated, there can be no question of where responsibility must be placed. It was Henry Ford's and his alone. No one else could have made the critical decision to commit his company to a technique of production that involved such great risk. In order to achieve the price level Ford desired, it was necessary to make a large number of units at a low cost per unit, and this process demanded a heavy initial investment in specialized equipment and tools. To justify this investment there had to be a market capable of absorbing all these units. As it turned out there was, but Ford could have been catastrophically wrong. He had a good many contemporaries who expected him to fail. Considering that in 1908, when the Model T first appeared, the total output of motor vehicles in the United States was 65,000, it would have taken a vivid imagination to predict that in less than ten years one company would be able to sell more than half a million cars in a single year.

THE FORD ASCENDANCY

The achievement of full-scale mass production was enough in itself to give Henry Ford his place in history. His assembly-line technique was crude by present-day standards, but to an astonished world it was a miracle of production to have Model T Fords, all identical in engine and chassis, pour off the assembly line at the rate of one every three minutes. By 1920 every other motor vehicle in the world was a Model T Ford, and the Ford Motor Company simply had no competition in its price class.

But that was not all. Simultaneously with the appearance of the complete assembly line came the announcement of a basic wage rate at the Ford Motor Company of five dollars a day, approximately twice the going rate in Detroit at the time. This announcement likewise drew worldwide attention to Ford, besides giving consternation to a good many business leaders. Job seekers converged on Detroit by the thousand; in fact, shortly after the new policy was put in effect, fire hoses had to be used to disperse the mob of applicants around the Highland Park plant. There was some fine print in the contract. Ford employees had to work for six months to become eligible for the five-dollar rate and even after that had to be "worthy" of it.

The precise origin of the five-dollar day is as much a mystery as that of the moving assembly line. Part of the motive behind it was a desire to reduce the high turnover in the company's labor force, and for this purpose James S. Couzens was interested in raising wages. Again, however, the final decision had to be made by Henry Ford. The five-dollar figure—simple and dramatic—came from the flair for publicity that he possessed to an unusual degree. Beyond this, and more important as a contributing factor, was Ford's own philosophy of business. He believed that the gains made by improving techniques of production should be passed on to society as a whole in three ways: to stockholders in the conventional form of dividends, to consumers in the form of lower prices, and to labor in the form of higher wages.

In Ford's mind this was undoubtedly an intuitive concept rather than a logical body of thought—the rationalizing was done for him later by others—but it was still as revolutionary in its implications for the economic structure of capitalism as the assembly line was for its technological development. He was the first man not only to preach but to practice the doctrine that the buying public had a legitimate interest in the operations of a big business organization, and he grasped a vital aspect of the relationship of mass consumption to mass production: namely, that labor is something more than a commodity to be procured at the lowest possible cost. The worker is also a consumer. For this reason a distinguished French observer of American society, R. L. Bruckberger, insists in *The Image of America* that for the twentieth century Ford's revolution is far more important then Lenin's.

Henry Ford being Henry Ford, the implementation of his ideas was colored by his own personal quirks. In 1915 he not only continued to reduce the price of his cars but gave his customers a rebate of $50 on each car purchased. The inflationary pressures of the First World War prevented continuation of this policy. His attitude to his workers was strictly paternalistic. To be worthy of the five-dollar wage rate his workers were expected to live according to his own rather puritanical standards, and to see that they did so, he organized a Sociological Department, headed by an Episcopal clergyman, Samuel N. Marquis. To what extent Ford workers resented having their private lives investigated by this agency is uncertain; it may be that if they felt resentment they were afraid to show it. On the other hand, the Sociological Department was in some respects the spokesman for the workers. It heard their grievances and tried to find remedies. Since the Detroit Manufacturers Association had just succeeded in making Detroit a non-union town, there was no other agency to which workers could turn, and to this extent Ford's Sociological Department represented a forward step in labor relations.

The third of the beneficiaries of mass production, the stockholders, held a low priority in Henry Ford's scale of values. He felt that they contributed nothing to increasing the efficiency of production and so had no real claim on profits after they had recovered their original investment and a reasonable return on it. In 1914 his low opinion of stockholders (other than himself) was accentuated by the fact that the Dodge brothers had very successfully put their own car on the market, financed, as Ford saw it, by Ford Motor Company profits. So Ford simply stopped paying dividends, whereupon the Dodges still further incensed him by suing and eventually in 1919 compelling him to pay $19 million in back dividends. Ford's rejoinder was to buy out all his remaining stockholders at a cost of $100 million. Couzens made the best deal. He too had joined the ranks of the Ford alumni by 1919, but he knew Henry Ford and the condition of the company better than any other man, and so he held out for a thousand dollars a share more than the other stockholders accepted. He sold his holdings for $29 million, a spectacular return on the $2,500 he had put into the Ford Motor Company in 1903. The Dodges came out with $25 million between them on an original investment of $20,000.

THE COMPETITORS

Ford's brilliant success naturally stimulated others to adopt his methods, or at least to try. One of the most ambitious of these attempts even tried to utilize the glamour of the Ford name. Hugh Chalmers, builder of the Chalmers car, raised $100,000 in 1914 to start a company for the purpose of manufacturing a car called the Saxon, which was to compete with the Model T, and the head of this company was an advertising man named Harry Ford. But advertising was no substitute for production, and the Saxon was never able to match the Model T in price. Harry Ford died of influenza in 1918, and after that the venture quietly collapsed.

A greater potential threat came from William C. Durant. Always irrepressible, Billy promptly rebounded from his General Motors debacle. In 1911 he joined forces with Louis Chevrolet (1878–1941), a Swiss-born mechanic and racing driver who had worked for Buick, to produce a popular-priced car. This first Chevrolet challenge to Ford reached its peak in 1915 with the Chevrolet 490, so named because it was supposed to sell for $490, although in fact it could not be produced at that price level. Perhaps if Durant had concentrated his unquestioned talents on the Chevrolet, he might have done for it what William S. Knudsen was to achieve ten years later, but it is doubtful. The popularity of the Model T was rising rapidly in 1915—its sales passed the first million mark in that year—whereas a decade later it was definitely on the decline.

As it was, the initial success of the Chevrolet diverted Durant to the more absorbing prospect of recovering control of General Motors. He began by offering to exchange Chevrolet for General Motors stock, which currently was not paying dividends. He also found allies in the Du Pont family, who saw in General Motors a potentially good investment for their own company's large war-time earnings. The result was that when the bankers' trust expired in 1916, Durant triumphantly returned to power, in the anomalous situation that General Motors was controlled by the Chevrolet

Motor Car Company—surely a striking example of the tail wagging the dog.

When his old boss returned, Charles W. Nash, far too conservative and cautious to work with Durant, left. With Storrow's support he bought the Thomas B. Jeffery Company of Kenosha, Wisconsin (Rambler), and reconstituted it as the Nash Motor Car Company. He was not, however, interested in competing with Ford. Neither, for that matter, was Durant. He did not give up the idea; it was just that with all of General Motors under his management, the promotion of Chevrolet became a secondary consideration.

For the time being therefore Tin Lizzie had the low-priced field (below $600) almost to herself, but this was not the whole story. Between 1914 and 1917 the output of motor vehicles in the United States more than trebled, from 573,000 to almost 1,900,000. Ford's success was a stimulus to the entire automobile industry by popularizing the idea that ownership of a car, instead of being a luxury, was something that any American family might reasonably aspire to. Next to Ford himself, the principal beneficiaries of this expansion were naturally the cars in the medium-price range (up to about $1,500), a category that then included Willys-Overland, Dodge, Maxwell, Buick, Studebaker, Reo, and Chevrolet. To offset their higher cost they could offer the buying public something the Model T could never match and which would become an increasingly important consideration in the motor-vehicle market—status. Even in those days the automobile was enough of a status symbol so that people who could buy something more elegant than a "flivver" did so. In fact, during most of the lifetime of the Model T, for most purchasers it was the family's first car. After cutting their automotive teeth on Henry Ford's creation, people were likely to seek a higher level for subsequent purchases. Some of these companies, moreover, were already beginning to appeal to families with modest incomes by offering time-payment plans.

It would be several years before this activity posed a challenge to Tin Lizzie. At the end of the First World War, Ford had half the market for automobiles in the United States. General Motors, despite having two of the strongest sellers in Buick and Chevrolet, had a fifth of the sales, and the remainder was divided among the mass of other producers. These proportions could be, and soon were, changed and they did not affect the total picture. In 1918 the number of motor-vehicle registrations in the United States passed the five million mark and doubled that figure in the ensuing four years. Fundamentally, this was the direct result of the introduction of the assembly-line technique. A longer-range consequence that would presently emerge was the domination of the industry by a few large firms. The small-scale manufacturer found himself in an impossible quandary; he could neither compete in price with the mass-produced car nor could he afford to adopt the assembly-line technique for a limited output. In the course of time, therefore, the smaller firms found it increasingly difficult to preserve a share of the market for passenger cars.

The effects of the assembly line were worldwide. Ford, with subsidiaries in every important country, made the Model T a familiar sight around the globe, even though the car was heavy and high-powered by European standards. Where motor-vehicle taxes were based on horsepower, the Ford, like most American cars, was at a disadvantage, but its durability and ease of operation still made it a popular car. There was no overseas competition in production techniques. The assembly line did not appear in European automobile manufacturing until some years after the First World War.

The absence of direct competition for Ford at this early stage of mass production was of minor consequence. What mattered was the demonstration that a fairly complicated mechanical contrivance like an automobile could be manufactured in quantity and marketed at a price within the reach of even the low-income groups in American society. Ford's example was certain to be followed, not only for motor vehicles but for other commodities in the category of "durable consumer goods," such as refrigerators, washing machines, and similar household appliances. It was appropriate that the first widely known electric refrigerator, the Frigidaire, should have been a General Motors product. The mass-production technique was also extended to farm machinery. This indeed seemed such a logical field in which automobile manufacturers might apply their skills and methods that most of the larger firms experimented with it, but only Ford had any success, and that was limited to tractor manufacturing.

Principally, however, the assembly line meant an unending stream of motor vehicles pouring into American life, a technological cornucopia from which would come not only cars but new industries, new economic forces, and sweeping changes in the structure of American society. In 1917 the process was still in its preliminary stages; it was not even clear what was going to happen within the automobile industry itself.

CHAPTER 5

War and Readjustment

When the First World War broke out in 1914 the automobile and
the automobile industry had achieved sufficient stature to play
major roles in the conflict. Although this was not a motorized war
on anything like the scale of the Second World War, motor
vehicles were an increasingly important factor in the conduct of
military operations. Armored cars were employed, although the
static warfare of the western front severely limited their usefulness;
to remedy this condition the tank was introduced and demonstrated
what mechanized war could become. Still more important was the
use of ordinary cars and trucks for the movement of troops and
supplies. This potential of the motor vehicle was dramatically
illustrated at the very beginning of the war when the taxicabs of
Paris rushed troops from the city to strike at the flank of Von
Kluck's columns. There was less glamour but more underlying
significance two years later in the unending line of *camions* rolling
along the *Voie Sacrée* to beleaguered Verdun, carrying the supplies
and reinforcements that kept the defense alive.

Of equal or possibly greater importance was the capacity to
produce offered by the automobile industries of the belligerent
countries. In each of them the automobile manufacturers supplied
the armies not only with vehicles but with a multitude of other
items of military equipment. Had this productive capacity not
existed, the needs of the military machines would naturally have

been supplied in some other way. In this case the war would have had a somewhat different character, perhaps not decisively so, although the Germans, with superior rail communications but a critical lack of oil and rubber, would have been better off if the Allies had been unable to use motor transport as freely as they did.

THE AMERICAN AUTOMOBILE INDUSTRY IN THE FIRST WORLD WAR

Until the United States itself entered the war, the automobile industry was largely unaffected by the conflict. It was absorbed in the introduction of the assembly line, the reorganization of General Motors, and the appearance of important new cars like Chevrolet and Dodge. Henry Ford's "Peace Ship" expedition in 1915 was a matter of personal idiosyncrasy, as was his announcement that his company would refuse war contracts. Neither had any relationship to the conduct of the automobile business. Production for the civilian market continued unabated right through 1917. There were exceptions. The White Motor Company built 18,000 trucks for the Allies, doing so well that it decided to give up the manufacture of passenger cars altogether, a decision that proved to be fortunate for the future of the company.

For the "business-as-usual" attitude, responsibility has to be placed chiefly on the government because of its unwillingness to recognize that some bolstering of the nation's defenses was desirable when the rest of the world was at war. Serious industrial mobilization began only after the declaration of war, so that with due allowance for the delays and confusion inevitable in this process, accentuated by the fact that this was a new experience for the United States, it was many months before tangible results emerged. Passenger-car production continued without restriction until well into 1918, when the War Industries Board ordered output for the rest of year reduced to half of what had been built during the corresponding months of 1917. This goal was approached (925,388 passenger cars in 1918 as compared with 1,740,792 for 1917), but the reduction was due more to shortages of materials than to mobilization planning.

Nevertheless the job was done. While the manufacture of pleasure cars was being curtailed, production of trucks doubled. Automobile firms in addition made such items as shells, guns, recoil mechanisms, gun carriages, tractors, and aircraft engines. The Ford Motor Company also built forty-three submarine chasers of a type known as Eagle boats. This achievement, which was overrated because the Eagles were of limited value in service, offered evidence that Henry Ford had withdrawn his objection to war work. Instead he announced that he would refund to the government all profits on war contracts, although he seems to have forgotten about it later.

The war also provided for the United States an impressive demonstration of the value of highway transportation. The road system still left much to be desired, but it was imperative that it be used as much as possible in order to relieve the congestion on the railroads. This task was handled by Roy D. Chapin as head of the Highway Transport Committee of the Council for National Defense. His outstanding achievement was to halt the wasteful employment of rail facilities involved in hauling finished trucks from the Middle Western factories to the Atlantic seaboard. Careful plotting of feasible routes and invoking the co-operation of local authorities to keep them open made it possible for thousands of army trucks to be driven to their ports of embarkation, each carrying a load of freight and thereby further assisting the over-burdened railroads. It was a significant demonstration for the future, showing as it did that highways could be kept in operation the year round and that motor trucks could successfully undertake long hauls.

The least successful of the automobile industry's wartime operations was its foray into aircraft manufacturing. There were extenuating circumstances. Despite the fact that the airplane was an American achievement the country did almost nothing to stimulate aviation before the war, with the result that an aircraft industry practically did not exist. As late as 1915 the country's total output of military aircraft was twenty-six. There was, moreover, among political leaders and the general public, as well as among automobile men, a happy assumption that the facilities and techniques that produced motor vehicles in quantity could do the same for airplanes. Before we become condescending or critical about this error, it is as well to remember that precisely the same illusion persisted twenty-five years later and with less reason.

At any rate, no airframes rolled down the automobile production lines, although automobile men had a hand in building the considerable number that were actually produced. John N. Willys acquired control of the Curtiss Aeroplane and Motor Company, with encouragement from the government because Glenn Curtiss was more interested in design than production; the other major manufacturer of airframes, the Dayton-Wright Company, was the creation of a syndicate from the automobile industry headed by Edward A. Deeds of Delco. The fact that Deeds subsequently was put in charge of aircraft production gave rise to much of the ensuing recrimination about the lapses, real or alleged, in the aviation program. That he made mistakes is certain; it would have been miraculous if he had not. More serious charges were made against him, but none was ever proved, and in retrospect it seems that Deeds was the scapegoat for failure to attain unrealistic expectations. In those more innocent days, Americans still had to learn that military goods cannot be conjured into existence overnight.

There was a different story with aircraft engines, which were still sufficiently similar to automobile engines so that it was practical to build them in existing automotive engine plants. The obvious method of getting into production rapidly was to use tested Allied types, but on investigation this solution did not turn out to be so simple as it looked. The drawings supplied by the Allied governments presupposed a substantial amount of hand machining by skilled craftsmen and were not suitable for American methods of production. Accordingly, while Bugattis and Hispano-Suizas were eventually made in some quantity in the United States, the basic decision was to design an engine capable of being turned out immediately by American techniques and in existing facilities.

The result was the famous Liberty engine, designed mainly by E. J. Hall of the Hall-Scott Motor Company and J. G. Vincent of Packard. They immured themselves in a Washington hotel room for three days at the end of May, 1917, under instructions to come up with an engine that embodied only devices already tested and proved and that was adapted to quantity production. The Liberty therefore emerged as an excellent but very conventional engine, initially eight-cylinder but later raised to twelve and with a horse-power rating starting at 220 and increasing to 440. In all, 24,475 Liberty's were built during the war, almost entirely by automobile firms. The 300,000 cylinders needed for these engines were a Ford contribution, representing a major achievement in the application of mass production techniques to an item that had hitherto required elaborate hand machining.

In short, the concept that the productive capacity of the automobile industry could be the foundation for a massive aircraft program was sound enough once the nature of the problem was fully understood. For engines there was no alternative; of the 42,000 aircraft engines built in the United States during the war, 30,000 came from the automobile industry. The most serious error was the failure to realize that military aircraft could not be turned out in thousands of identical units like automobiles. Provision for changes of design based on combat experience and advances in aeronautics had to be incorporated into the process of production, but it was done belatedly and thereby caused confusion and delay. Had the war continued into 1919, most of the difficulties would have been seen for what they really were—the results of ignorance, inexperience, and neglect of advance planning, rather than of incompetence or corruption.

RETURN TO PEACE

Since the American automobile industry was never completely converted to war production, the sudden cessation of hostilities caused no great disturbance—nothing, for example, to compare with the disaster that struck the nascent aircraft industry when war contracts were cancelled practically overnight. To be sure, there were difficulties. In the wake of the war came the influenza epidemic, labor unrest that included severe strikes in the coal and steel industries, shortages of materials, and uncertain rail service while the nation's railroads disentangled themselves from their emergency wartime operations. Despite these handicaps, motor-vehicle production in 1919 was slightly ahead of the 1917 figure, and in 1920 it passed the two million mark for the first time.

Behind this achievement was an accurate assessment by the leaders of the automobile industry that there would be a great expansion in the demand for passenger cars and in commercial highway transport after the war. Planning for this eventuality was actively pressed by those with the foresight to envisage the opportunities. The most dazzling prospect, of course, was to invade successfully the mass market for low-priced cars preempted by Henry Ford. As of 1919 the leading contender was John N. Willys, whose Overland, priced at about $800, was the second best selling car in the United States. Willys contemplated offering the Overland for $500, including electric starting and lights and a spare tire, luxuries that had not yet appeared on Tin Lizzie. In preparation he had put together in 1917 a combination of car and parts manufacturers loosely controlled by a holding company, the Willys Corporation. Besides the Overland, Willys built the Willys-Knight, the most prominent American car to use the Knight engine.

The Hudson Motor Car Company also had its eye on the mass market. While Roy D. Chapin was managing the highway transport program in Washington he contrived to find time to plan with his business associates for the introduction, after the war, of a low-priced car named the Essex. This step was taken after careful estimates of production problems and assessment of market potential, so that the Essex avoided the hazards of the immediate postwar inflation and depression. Not until 1922 did Chapin present his boldest innovation, the offering of a closed car for only $100 more than the touring car. This step began a new era in American motoring by offering to the public the possibility of riding with style and comfort in all weathers without having to pay luxury prices.

Meanwhile, at General Motors, Durant's Second Empire was in full career. In 1918 the organizational monstrosity represented by Chevrolet control of General Motors was removed by the creation of the General Motors Corporation, which absorbed both the General Motors Company and Chevrolet along with another Durant promotion, a combination of parts manufacturers called the United Motors Corporation. One of the participants was Delco, and so Charles F. Kettering was brought officially into the General Motors fold. Still more important, United Motors included the Hyatt Roller Bearing Company, whose president, Alfred P. Sloan, Jr., became head of United Motors and would in time outshine Billy Durant as the builder of General Motors.

A graduate of the Massachusetts Institute of Technology, Sloan went from college to work for the Hyatt Roller Bearing Company, founded by John Wesley Hyatt, the inventor who created celluloid because he wanted a substitute for ivory as a material for billiard balls and who was now trying to market a tapered roller bearing. Hyatt, however, was no businessman. The company was saved from extinction by a loan of $5,000 from Sloan's father, and Sloan replaced Hyatt as president. He found a lucrative outlet for his bearings in the fast-growing automobile industry and built Hyatt into a large-scale enterprise, until, as Sloan himself pointed out, it became too big to be independent. When Durant proposed that Hyatt join United Motors, Sloan was reluctant, but on thinking it over he realized that his company would be in serious trouble if both Ford and General Motors should decide to manufacture their own bearings. He had to have a guaranteed market with one or the other. So Sloan went into United Motors, and in the 1918 reorganization he became a General Motors vice-president.

Durant also managed, at least temporarily, to hold on to Walter Chrysler. Nash and Storrow had tried to persuade Chrysler to join them, and he had been strongly tempted, but Durant offered him a salary of $500,000 a year to stay at Buick—a remarkable increase in just five years. Then, with the administrative structure of General Motors apparently settled, further expansion proceeded in characteristic Durant fashion. Some of his acquisitions turned out very well. The Fisher Body Company was certainly worth the $30 million General Motors paid for it. It was the creation of six brothers who had initially been wagon and carriage builders in Norwalk, Ohio, but sensibly decided in 1908 that there was a brighter future for them in designing and manufacturing automobile bodies. Frigidaire was picked up for just $56,366.50, the amount Durant personally paid for the Guardian Frigerator Company, a one-man operation run by Alfred Mellowes, who had designed his first electric refrigerator in Dayton, Ohio, in 1915. He then moved to Detroit to manufacture his product. When Durant bought the business, it had sold less than forty refrigerators in two years, all in the Detroit area and all personally serviced by Mellowes. In the process the company had lost some $34,000. Durant changed the name to Frigidaire and in 1919 sold the property to General Motors for what it had cost him. When his fellow directors asked what an automobile manufacturing firm was doing making electric refrigerators, he replied that the two products were similar—each was a box containing a motor. Another innovation of this period, the General Motors Acceptance Corporation, showed a realistic appreciation of the financial problems of mass marketing of motor vehicles.

With this much to his credit, Durant was entitled to some mistakes, and he made them. Some weak automotive properties were taken into General Motors, but the worst blunder was a venture into the manufacture of tractors and farm machinery, taken against Walter Chrysler's advice, and abandoned in 1920 after General Motors had poured $30 million into it. In addition, the construction of the General Motors Center in Detroit had been started; this operation is not to be classed as an error, but it did impose an additional heavy financial burden at a time when the company's resources were already far extended. Durant was gambling that the postwar boom would continue.

So, for that matter, was Henry Ford. Like everyone else in the industry, he saw ahead a rising demand for cars, and in particular a demand for Fords beyond the capacity even of his comparatively new Highland Park factory. Planning was begun in 1916 for a vast plant on the River Rouge in Dearborn, to incorporate the most up-to-date mass-production techniques and to include among other things its own steel mill. Some preparatory work was carried on during the war, and with the coming of peace the project was rapidly pushed to completion. The total outlay on the Rouge installation was more than $116 million, by itself well within the means of the Ford Motor Company. At the same time, however, Ford found himself obligated for $8 million in back dividends and voluntarily assumed the $100 million burden of buying out his stockholders. To get the funds, Henry Ford had to borrow $75 million from Boston and New York banks, much against his will. However, with the primacy of the Model T still almost uncontested—three-quarters of a million were sold in 1919 for profits of more than $70 million—the Ford Motor Company's margin of safety seemed ample.

This period, indeed, was the high noon of Henry Ford's career. His feat in revolutionizing motor-vehicle production was still reasonably fresh, and there was so far no near rival. To the great bulk of the American people (and many others) he was the mechanical wizard with the Midas touch, the Horatio Alger hero who had climbed from farm boy to billionaire by his own unaided genius. He became a sort of Paul Bunyan figure, for whom no task was too great. The most vivid illustration of the Ford legend appears in a Pullman smoking-room conversation during the early twenties, overheard and reported by Frederick L. Smith, former president of the Olds Motor Works, in *Motoring Down a Quarter of a Century*.

"Who invented the automobile anyway?"
"Henry Ford. Started as a racer by beating Barney Oldfield on the ice

at Detroit. Right after that he built a plant to turn out the same kind of car in fifty thousand lots."

"Doesn't he own the Lincoln now?"

"Yeah, owns the Lincoln and the Packard, Cadillac, Buick—all the big ones and a lot of the little ones besides."

"Is it true about his taking over the Detroit City Hospital?"

"I'll say it's true. Bought it and runs it for his employees. Charges everybody a fixed rate for every job and makes it pay."

Among the inaccuracies, the reference to the hospital does less than justice to the Henry Ford Hospital in Dearborn.

It is now a forgotten item of American history that Henry Ford was a Democratic candidate for the office of United States senator from Michigan in 1918 and lost by a narrow margin to Truman S. Newberry, who was subsequently deprived of his seat because of election frauds. Had Ford won, the Senate in 1919 would have been divided equally between Democrats and Republicans, 48–48, so that with the tie-breaking vote of Vice-President Marshall the Democrats would have controlled the chamber. In this situation the chairman of the Committee on Foreign Relations during the debate on the Versailles Treaty and the League of Nations would have been a Democrat and not Henry Cabot Lodge the elder. In this respect it was a significant election; what Henry Ford would have been like as a senator otherwise has to be left to speculation. As a popular idol he was inevitably mentioned as a presidential prospect, and in the early 1920's an organized movement came into existence to give him the Republican nomination in 1924. This however was stopped, after some hesitation, by Ford himself.

For Henry Ford, and still more for his family and friends, the attraction of public life was markedly lessened by his experience when he sued the *Chicago Tribune* for libel for calling him "an ignorant idealist" and "an anarchistic enemy of the nation." The objectionable editorial appeared in 1916, when the *Tribune* and Ford were in sharp difference over the desirability of military preparedness, but the case did not come to trial until 1919. Henry Ford was put on the witness stand for a pitiless exposure of his ignorance of non-automotive subjects. He did not, however, actually say "History is bunk." What he did say was that when he was in school he thought that history was bunk, which is quite a different thing and in fact a fairly common educational experience. Yet, however unpleasant this incident might have been, it did not diminish the glamour of the Ford name in the least. If anything, the effect was just the opposite. The intelligentsia might sneer, but they made their usual blunder of believing that what they thought was public opinion. The average American knew just as little history as Henry Ford and had much the same opinion of it. Ford's deficiencies made him more than ever a figure with whom the common man could feel an affinity: clearly a titan, but equally clearly molded from common clay. Aldous Huxley meant it as satire, but he was hitting very close to the mark when he made Ford the deity of *Brave New World*.

THE CRISIS OF 1920–21

For the American economy as a whole the panic of 1920 ranks as a minor depression. It was sharp but short and was rightly regarded as a readjustment in the wake of the war boom. For the automobile industry, however, it was a major crisis. The market for new cars collapsed, and after a brief effort to hold the line, so did prices. In late September, 1920, Henry Ford cut his touring car from $575 to $440, and the rest of the industry promptly conformed. This was a routine business reaction, but now for the first time both manufacturers and distributors became acutely aware of the problem of the used car. It was bound to come. By the end of 1920, motor-vehicle registrations in the United States passed ten million. So far the steady accumulation of actual or potential secondhand vehicles had not obstructed the sale of new cars, but now, under depression conditions, the effect of the used-car market became a matter of concern. No one had a really satisfactory solution, but the problem of used-car competition was largely responsible for the general adoption during the 1920's of the practice of introducing a new model each year, with enough changes in appearance or technical features, it was hoped, to make secondhand cars definitely out of style. This policy was subsequently termed "planned obsolescence."

The panic struck at the two extremes of the automobile industry. The medium sized companies with good management, like Hudson, Packard, and Studebaker, had little trouble riding out the storm. On the other hand, the big firms—Ford, General Motors, Maxwell, Willys—were caught dangerously overextended and had to resort to drastic measures to avoid disaster. At the other end of the scale the depression shriveled the prospects of the many newcomers who tried to ride the postwar boom into a place in the automotive world. Most were strictly ephemeral; a few achieved distinction. The first of these clearly was the Lincoln, creation of the man who previously had made the Cadillac one of the world's outstanding cars. Henry M. Leland left Cadillac and General Motors in 1917 at the age of 72, largely because he wanted to devote himself to making aircraft engines for war use, but also because of distaste for another Durant regime. With his son he organized the Lincoln Motor Company, which built 6,500 Liberty's. (The name Lincoln was chosen to honor the man Leland most admired and for whom he had cast his first vote in 1864.) When the war ended the Lelands decided to return to the automobile field with a new luxury car. The market collapse caught them just getting into production and short of liquid capital, partly because of an erroneous tax assessment, which failed to allow for depreciation the company was legally entitled to. Before the error was corrected, Lincoln was in receivership.

At this point Henry Ford entered the picture and bought the property for $8 million, to the accompaniment of a fanfare of publicity conveying the impression that he was generously helping out an old friend. A heated and still unsettled argument followed. The Lelands claimed that Ford had promised to leave them in charge and to recompense both their creditors and their stockholders. Ford did pay the Lincoln debts but he denied assuming any other obligations. Since any agreements made were verbal, there is no proof and no definite explanation of why Ford chose to deviate from his policy of concentrating on one model. It seems likely that Edsel Ford was mainly responsible for taking over the Lincoln. He was now officially president of the Ford Motor Company and was trying to persuade his father to give up the Model T, but he had little real authority and seems to have hoped that he would have a free hand where the Lincoln was concerned.

Another prominent casualty of the depression was C. H. Wills. In 1919 Wills and John H. Lee, who had succeeded Dean Marquis as head of the Sociological Department, left the Ford Motor Company along with several other prominent executives. Wills and Lee joined forces to build a car of their own, and since one was generally credited with being Ford's engineering genius and the other the labor relations expert, this news caused a good deal of excitement. Wills announced that he was going to build a car ten years ahead of its time, and unfortunately for himself he did. The Wills Sainte Claire was a beautiful and magnificently designed car, still cherished in the memories of automobile enthusiasts. Its trouble was that it was simply too good. It was high-priced and it was expensive to maintain because no ordinary mechanic could repair it. It appeared on the market squarely in the middle of the depression and could not be sold in sufficient numbers to keep the company solvent, and in this instance there was no rescuer.

Although the big companies had serious difficulties, all managed to survive. Ford had the easiest time, essentially because he dumped his burden on his dealers. The second half of 1920 saw Ford with falling sales, the heavy obligations previously described, and the $75 million bank loan coming due early in 1921. Wall Street eagerly anticipated the Ford Motor Company's being compelled to put some of its stock on the market, but the bankers underestimated Henry. He cancelled his orders for materials and supplies, worked off the inventory on hand, and in January, 1921, shipped some 125,000 cars to his dealers and closed down for six weeks. The dealers were told that this was their first consignment for the new

year and that in accordance with their contracts they must accept
the cars on the customary cash basis or forfeit their franchises.

It is a striking tribute to the dominant position Ford then
occupied that practically all of the 17,000 Ford dealers complied,
some at considerable loss to themselves. A Ford franchise was too
valuable to be abandoned without a major effort to preserve it. So
Ford triumphantly paid off his note and emerged from the crisis
seemingly stronger than ever. To the general public, the folk hero
had outwitted the bankers. Even in informed business circles there
was a tendency to overlook the rather sloppy management of
finances that had preceded the crisis—that is, the piling on of
obligations with no clear accounting technique to balance them
against the company's probable earnings. Nor was much attention
given to the steady attrition of top personnel in the Ford Motor
Company. Couzens was gone, his successor, F. L. Klingensmith,
went out in 1919 along with Wills and Lee, and two years later
came the departure of William S. Knudsen, which would prove to
be the most damaging blow of all.

The General Motors situation was more complex. The company
emerged from the war with a revised corporate structure, an
ambitious program of expansion, and stronger financial backing
than it had previously enjoyed. With good management there was
every reason to anticipate a bright future, and there was first-
class managerial talent available in men like John J. Raskob,
treasurer of the Du Pont Company, who supervised finances,
Walter Chrysler, and Alfred P. Sloan.

The trouble was that there was no co-ordination of the sprawling
General Motors structure. William C. Durant was a man of tremendous dynamism and drive, but he either could not or would not
concentrate on keeping the affairs of General Motors in order. He
swung irregularly between ignoring his subordinates and interfer-
ing with them, and much of his time and effort was devoted to stock
market operations. He was estimated to have had at least seventy
separate brokerage accounts. Chrysler stood it until early in 1920,
when the farm machinery fiasco proved too much for him and he

quit. Sloan, also disturbed by the mismanagement, or rather non-management of the company, submitted a reorganization plan to Durant at this time, basically the one he himself was to apply later. Durant approved the plan but did nothing about it. Sloan then took a trip to Europe to think things over. He decided to resign when he returned, but the depression caught up with Durant first.

When the panic arrived, Durant's finances were badly tangled. He tried to hold the line on car prices and to keep General Motors stock from dropping. He was committed well beyond his resources, although he himself did not know how far. On his own he might have been able to keep his losses short of the disaster point, but he felt that he had to support the market to discharge an obligation to friends who had bought General Motors stock on his recommendation.

Meanwhile the corporation was having its own troubles. In the optimistic mood that preceded the slump many divisions had accumulated excessive inventories at boom prices. They had been warned to cut back early in 1920, but because of the lack of effective control at the top the warning had not been enforced. In addition, some of the expensive parts of the expansion program were not halted as promptly as they should have been. Not all these mistakes were Durant's. There is clear evidence that even before the stock market collapse he wanted to reduce the corporation's heavy commitments by curtailing work on the General Motors Center but was dissuaded by Raskob.

Nevertheless, Billy was the danger point. In the fall of 1920 he was sliding rapidly toward bankruptcy, and if that had occurred, the shock to public confidence might well have brought General Motors down with him. Consequently, when reports of Durant's financial difficulties reached Pierre S. Du Pont, he became deeply alarmed. An inquiry to Durant brought the disturbing admission that Billy simply did not know where he stood. A series of conferences followed in which Durant's indebtedness emerged as approximately $30 million, whereupon a Du Pont–Morgan syndicate was formed to bail him out in exchange for his two and a half million shares of General Motors and his resignation as president. Pierre Du Pont took his place, not because he particularly wanted to but because he had the confidence of the financial community. His executive vice-president, who clearly would actually run the business, was Alfred P. Sloan.

Durant himself was by no means out of the automotive world. Within a month after his expulsion from the company he had founded, he succeeded in raising $7 million from a group of sixty-seven friends and was at work putting together a new combination called Durant Motors. There can be no doubt that he had to leave General Motors. It was his concept and creation, and he started it on its way to greatness, but twice he almost ruined it by his recklessness. Still, it seems a pity that in later years, when Billy's fortune was gone and he was old and ill, all that General Motors could do for him was give him a place on the platform when the corporation celebrated the production of its 25-millionth car in 1942.

Ford and General Motors were able to remain solvent and preserve their organizations intact; General Motors, in fact, emerged from the panic strengthened. Their principal competitors, Willys and Maxwell, were less fortunate. Both had managerial problems. Like Durant, John North Willys had permitted his interests to become so dispersed that he was unable to exercise proper supervision over his automobile business. At Maxwell, authority was divided. The company had previously taken over the Chalmers Motor Car Company, and so the board chairman was Hugh S. Chalmers, former supersalesman for the National Cash Register Company, who knew a lot about selling but very little about production, and the president was Walter E. Flanders, who knew production but evidently not much about engineering. His earlier automotive offering (EMF) had been nicknamed "Every Mechanical Fault," and the Maxwell of 1919–20 had an unhappy propensity for breaking its rear axle.

Interested banking houses brought Walter Chrysler into both companies to take charge of reorganization. The Willys Corporation was put through receivership and liquidated, its component parts resuming their corporate independence. Since it had never had any real cohesion, there was probably nothing more Chrysler could do, although the possibility has to be considered that he might have fought harder if he had been sure that he was fighting for himself rather than for the still powerful figure of John N. Willys. Willys did, in fact, make a spectacular recovery. With the aid of business friends in Toledo he regained control of the Willys-Overland Company and subsequently built another Willys empire. With the Overland continuing to be one of the popular low-priced cars, Willys appeared to have surmounted his difficulties, but events would show that he had passed his zenith as a power in automotive world.

Maxwell was a different matter. There Chrysler had no rival approaching his own stature, and despite the defects in the current models, the Maxwell name still carried weight with the motoring public. If Chrysler wanted his own company, as he did, here was a made-to-order foundation. He was by this time at work with a trio of bright young engineers (Carl Breer, Fred Zeder, and Owen Skelton) on a design for a new passenger car that would take advantage of what had been learned from aviation about high-compression engines and that would bear the Chrysler name. So the Maxwell Motor Car Company went into receivership in 1921 and was reorganized with Chrysler in control, retaining the Maxwell name for another four years until the Chrysler car had been offered to the public and had proved a success. Then the Chrysler Corporation was created to take over the entire Maxwell property.

By late 1921 the panic was over and the automobile was starting a climb to new heights of production and use. On the surface it appeared that this depression had been merely a temporary and not very serious interruption of the growth of the automobile industry; some of the weaker firms had been wiped out, a few of the stronger ones had been shaken up, and that was all. The expanding flow of motor vehicles had not been retarded in the least; the number of cars and trucks on the highways rose from nine million in 1920 to ten and one-half million in 1921. In a general sense this optimistic view was accurate enough. What the depression of 1920–21 left behind was a shift of strength, imperceptible at the time, within the automobile industry. It would take a few years to become apparent and it would not in any way affect the advance of the automobile to its dominant position in American life, but it would determine who provided the cars and to some extent what kind of cars would be offered to the American public.

CHAPTER 6

Coming of Age

As America moved into the "Roaring Twenties," the automobile came into its own. Motor-vehicle manufacturing was by then the largest industry in the country and was still growing rapidly. The continuing expansion of the production and use of motor vehicles was one of the most important factors in the boom of the 1920's, perhaps the most important if its effect on other industries, on highway construction, and on automobile-connected retail and service enterprises is taken into consideration. Automobile production figures rose from two million in 1920 to five and one-half million in 1929. Registrations passed twenty million in 1925 and reached twenty-six and one-half million in 1929, with trucks and buses representing about an eighth of the total. By the late twenties a point was reached at which it was possible to move the entire population of the United States by road at one time, since there was close to one motor vehicle for every five people. Employment in automobile factories was a quarter of a million in 1922 and in excess of four hundred thousand in 1929; during the same period the amount of wages paid doubled, from $400 million to $800 million. About three times as many people were employed in industries dependent on the automobile.

The sale of this swelling flood of cars was made possible by two factors. First, until the mid-twenties there was a downward trend in automobile prices, reaching its lowest point in 1926 when a new

Model T touring car could be bought for $290. Secondly there was a liberal extension of credit to both consumers and dealers. The big companies went into the financing of sales on a large scale, General Motors through its Acceptance Corporation and Ford through a subsidiary, the Universal Credit Corporation (sold in the 1930's to avoid possible antitrust action). The other manufacturers relied on independent finance companies such as the Commercial Credit Corporation and Commercial Investors Trust, and on banks, which were attracted to the opportunities in underwriting installment buying of automobiles. The result was that by 1925 three-fourths of all sales of motor vehicles, new and used, were made on time-payment plans, and the technique was rapidly becoming the accepted method of selling all types of durable consumer goods.

The automobile manufacturers also attempted to regulate the used-car market, but with only qualified success. General Motors, followed by most of the industry, recommended to its dealers that trading in used cars should be managed so as to encourage the sale of new cars. Ford as usual was the exception. Since purchasers of Model T's were usually buying their first car, they were likely to trade in the Ford for a higher-priced model, new or used. Conversely, people who bought a more elegant car in the first place seldom traded it for a "flivver." Dealing in used cars, consequently, did little to stimulate the sale of new Model T's, and Ford dealers were expected to handle their used-car business so that it would pay its own way.

THE AUTOMOBILE AND THE BUSINESS BOOM

This process of expansion promoted a widespread business boom. The motor vehicle was now consuming annually 90 per cent of the country's petroleum products, mostly in the form of gasoline, 80 per cent of the rubber, predominantly tires, 20 per cent of the steel, 75 per cent of the plate glass, and 25 per cent of the machine tools. To these must be added the multitudinous repair and service facilities the automobile had brought into being, as well as the substantial business operations in the manufacture and sale of automotive accessories. In addition, a new Federal Highway Act in 1921 provided further aid to states for road construction, with the specific objective of promoting the development of a national system of highways. Under this act each state highway department (the 1916 Road Aid Act required a state to have a highway department in order to be eligible for federal aid) was to designate up to 7 per cent of its non-urban road mileage as "primary." These roads were planned as links in interstate routes, and for them federal assistance was given on a fifty-fifty matching basis. Initially about two hundred thousand miles of trunk highways received federal support.

Beyond this mileage, the multiplication of automobile owners clamoring for better roads stimulated a greatly increased volume of construction by state and local authorities, especially after the interesting discovery was made that highway users could be made to pay for their roads by the simple and apparently painless method of taxing the sale of gasoline. Oregon led the way in 1919 by imposing a levy of one cent a gallon. Ten years later every state had a gasoline tax, and the average had risen to three cents a gallon. Expenditures on roads during this decade averaged over $2 billion a year from all sources. The federal aid program also led to a uniform system of highway numbering and marking (odd numbers for north-south routes; even for east-west). Thus the motorist no longer had to stop at every crossroad to try to decipher a welter of signs and determine which of several obscure villages lay in the direction he wanted to take.

The figures tell only part of the story. The qualitative effect of the automobile on American industry was fully as important as the quantitative. The continuous-strip mill for rolling sheet steel and the continuous-process technique for manufacturing plate glass were both introduced in the early 1920's for the specific purpose of meeting the heavy requirements of the automobile industry. Henry Ford, in fact, went into the glass business because the established firms were skeptical about continuous process and Ford saw it as the only remedy for the increasingly short supply and high price of plate glass. Safety glass appeared at this time in response to one of the less pleasant features of the automobile, the hazard of shattered glass in the event of accident.

The rubber manufacturers vied with each other in improving the quality of tires. Most of the advances were gradual and unspectacular, such as the general adoption of cotton cord as the base fabric, improvements in the weave of the fabric and the quality of the rubber so as to give better wearing qualities, and more efficient design of treads to give greater traction. The outstanding change was the introduction of the low-pressure balloon tire, riding on thirty pounds of air as against the sixty of its predecessor and adding greatly to the smoothness and comfort of automobile travel.

The petroleum industry continued to search for more and better gasoline. New techniques, first catalytic cracking and then hydrogenation, were developed to replace the Burton process and increase refinery yields. In 1922 Charles F. Kettering and Thomas H. Midgley achieved the outstanding single qualitative advance by discovering after long experimentation that the mixing of tetraethyl lead with gasoline reduced engine knock—this after Kettering had been subjected to a good deal of ridicule for suggesting that the cause of knocking might be in the fuel and not in the motor. He had been stimulated to work on this problem in the first instance by insinuations that Delco's battery-operated ignition system accentuated knock. The octane scale for gasoline was introduced by Graham Edgar in 1926. "Boss Ket" broke another major bottleneck in automobile production in 1923 by developing, this time in co-operation with Du Pont, quick-drying finishes. The chemical industry was also called upon to provide antifreeze solutions superior to the ordinary alcohol that was the earliest and most common protection against winter temperatures. Millions of Americans in those days learned the elementary lesson that alcohol has both a low freezing and a low boiling point.

Road construction was virtually revolutionized by the replacement of gravel and cobblestone with smooth, hard surfaces of asphalt or concrete and by constant improvements in highway design to permit traffic to move with greater speed and safety. Highway development had the unforeseeable effect of touching off a race between road and vehicle that is still in progress, with the vehicle consistently ahead. Not only was the number of cars on the highways steadily increasing, but as roads got better, owners of motor vehicles were encouraged to use them more freely. Old roads were rebuilt and new ones were added; the result seemed to be merely that traffic got progressively heavier. In addition, better roads encouraged automotive engineers to design faster cars and heavier trucks so that a new highway was likely to be obsolescent by the time it was finished.

Not everyone benefited from the automobile boom. The automobile industry gave the railroads a substantial volume of freight traffic; on the other hand, the products of the industry began in the 1920's to cut heavily into the railroads' business. Motor-truck competition made itself most severely felt at first in local hauls and light loads and was not yet a matter of serious concern to the major trunk lines. Passenger traffic offered a more immediate challenge. The number of passengers carried by American railroads reached its peak in 1920 and declined steadily thereafter except for a resurgence during the Second World War. Buses accounted for some of the loss, although like trucks they competed most effectively at first in local rather than long-distance travel. The really irreparable damage to rail passenger traffic, however, was inflicted by the private automobile. Trips, long and short, that in former years would have been made by train if they had been made at all, were now taken in the family car. It was more convenient, as a rule it was cheaper, and the motorist was independent of someone else's schedule. The railroads were badly handicapped in meeting these new competitors. Apart from the greater flexibility and generally lower cost of highway transportation, the railroads were subject to rigorous federal and state regulation, whereas road traffic, commercial or private, was very loosely controlled by state authority where it was under any control at all.

The railroads survived the onslaught of the motor vehicle, with some lasting damage but also with compensation in the form of the freight generated by the automobile industry. City transit systems and interurban electric lines suffered more devastating losses with no offsetting benefits. Most of them gradually withered away, the interurbans first and then the trolley lines on the city streets. The rail transit systems that continued to operate were generally confined to the larger cities and most had to be subsidized in one way or another. Where streetcars remained in existence they were increasingly regarded as an encumbrance to automobile traffic.

The Automobile and Social Change

The total effect of the motor vehicle on American life has still to be measured, if indeed such measurement is even possible. Certainly the automobile brought major social changes, and some of these were becoming evident with the widespread extension of car ownership in the 1920's. It would be an exaggeration to say that the automobile made Americans a mobile people; the people who made their way across the American continent while the motorcar was still a dream were far from static. It would be more accurate to say that an already mobile people was given the means to travel farther, faster, and more freely.

There was no great folk migration involved. Cars were used instead of public transportation to get to and from work, to go shopping, or to visit friends. As the volume of motor-vehicle traffic on city streets rose, the problems of congestion and parking made their appearance and have remained unsolved. In justice to the automobile it should be pointed out that it found rather than created congestion in the larger cities, and that its own advantages of speed and maneuverability were wasted because city streets were not designed for motorized traffic. As with intercity highways, improvements could not be made fast enough to keep pace with the rising torrent of motor vehicles.

On weekends the cars sallied out into the country carrying families bent on recreation, sightseeing, or merely the pleasure of riding in a car. This last practice gave rise to the species termed the "Sunday driver," who wandered aimlessly along the highway, in no hurry because he (or she) was not going anywhere in particular, and frequently displaying a blithe disregard for other traffic. On Sunday evenings the returning travelers converged on the cities, with the result that the narrow roads of the period became choked with long lines of cars, endlessly starting and stopping, overheating, running out of gas, and more often than not taking hours to cover the last few miles.

The vehicle that took the city dweller into the country functioned just as effectively in the opposite direction—to take the farmer into the city. Students of American society may well conclude sometime that the most important influence of the automobile on American life has been alleviating rural isolation and breaking down the age-old distinction between the country and the city dweller. This process was just in its preliminary stages in the 1920's, and a good deal of improvement in both highways and cars would be required to make it really effective. Nevertheless it was in progress. At the beginning of the decade Sinclair Lewis's *Main Street* could focus on the drabness and barrenness of small-town life. The distinction between the small town and the city would have been harder to draw ten years later, although it would still have been there.

Long-distance journeys by motor vehicle were becoming less a major adventure and more an accepted and normal method of travel during the 1920's, although severe handicaps still existed. The mileage of good hard-surface road was growing steadily, but the bulk of it was still in the Northeast. Automobile manufacturers were emphasizing the romance of motoring in their advertising, an outstanding example being the "somewhere west of Laramie" advertisement devised by Edward M. Jordan (1882–1958) of Cleveland, builder of the Jordan car. It used the lure of the West, plus a pretty girl driving a Jordan "Playboy" sports car, as its appeal, but the motorist who actually ventured west of Laramie in those days was likely to conclude that the journey might better have been made by covered wagon. The express highway, moreover, had not yet appeared. Main roads ran directly through the centers of villages, towns, and cities, and there was invariably opposition from local merchants to suggestions that civic centers be bypassed. The motorist who averaged thirty miles an hour in actual driving time, excluding even stops for meals, was doing remarkably well.

Nevertheless the volume of long-distance highway travel was increasing, and with it came a growth of service facilities that represented significant economic and social change. As a matter of course, filling stations and garages sprang up wherever automobile traffic existed in reasonable volume. So did roadside restaurants. More interesting was the fact that the downtown hotel by the railroad station held little attraction for the motorist who had to think about parking his car, wanted to avoid city traffic, and was likely to be reluctant to pay the varied costs of hotel accommodation. Residents of the smaller towns discovered that there was money to be made by renting their spare bedrooms to tourists or, more ambitiously, by building cabins on a convenient piece of vacant property.

The cumulative effect of these changes was strikingly brought out by R. S. and H. M. Lynd in 1929 when they made their study of the typical American community in *Middletown*. At all income and social levels, they found, "ownership of an automobile has now reached the point of being an accepted essential part of normal living." Some families insisted that they would cut down on food and clothing rather than give up their car. The family car was a social rather than an economic need—frequently, indeed, it was a financial burden. It was defended as a means of relaxation and recreation; the family could go for a drive after working hours or take a vacation trip it could not have afforded otherwise.

Not all the social consequences of the automobile could be

regarded with approval. Some of Middletown's residents voiced concern because people were spending their Sundays on the highways instead of going to church and because the automobile appeared to be weakening family life by making it easier for individuals to disperse to their separate interests. Across the nation the motor vehicle was charged with being an encouragement to crime because it enabled criminals to get away rapidly from the scene of their misdeeds. It was also accused of fostering moral laxity because it provided young people with an easy method of escaping parental supervision and at the same time a convenient place to indulge romantic inclinations. In addition, there was a natural concern about the increase in highway accidents—the death toll approximately doubled during the decade, from about fifteen thousand in 1922 to thirty-two thousand in 1930—and there was a human inclination to charge the instrument with the responsibility for this unhappy situation.

All this criticism exemplified man's propensity to blame his technology rather than himself for whatever evil consequences it might produce. The vehicle that took people away from church could equally well take them to it. The automobile itself was not responsible for the materialistic, secular mood of the 1920's any more than it was responsible for crime and moral laxity. If it was used for the wrong purposes, the fault was with the users. After all, motorcars could be employed to enforce the law as well as to break it; and to offset the carnage on the highways was the fact that medical assistance, for illness as well as for accident, could get to where it was needed far more rapidly than in the days of the horse and buggy. The one thing certain was that the motor vehicle was effecting a social as well as an economic revolution in the United States, and revolutions invariably have both good and bad features.

THE AUTOMOBILE INDUSTRY IN TRANSITION

While the automotive conquest of American society was in progress, the automobile industry was undergoing fundamental changes in structure. The day was gone when an individual with technical skill, a little capital, and some business acumen could set out to make cars with some prospect of succeeding. After the First World War the handicaps facing the newcomer were so great as to be insuperable. To break into the mass market required not only a tremendous capital outlay in manufacturing facilities but also an elaborate and widespread dealer network, and even if these were created there was a growing consumer reluctance to buy unknown makes. The buyers of low- and medium-priced cars were becoming habituated to think in terms of trade-in value when they made their purchases, and were inclined to shy away from potential "orphans." The luxury-car field might have offered brighter prospects for a new arrival except that this market was too limited to support the firms that were already competing for it.

Consequently, although several attempts, some under fairly impressive sponsorship, were made to enter the automobile industry during the boom period of the 1920's, none survived. For example, there was the Rickenbacker Motor Car Company, named for and headed by the American aviator of the First World War and promoted by two veteran automobile men, Walter Flanders and Barney Everitt. Despite the combination of experience with the glamour of the Rickenbacker name, the company lasted only five years (1921–26). The Gray Motor Company, managed by former Ford business manager Frank L. Klingensmith, for a time seemed to be making a place for itself in the low-priced market, but it disappeared after just four years of operation (1922–26).

Among the established firms in the industry there was a series of historic shifts in position, with the result that a clear pattern of oligopoly emerged from what had previously been a structure approximating the classical model of free competition. The most momentous change came at the top, where General Motors replaced Ford as the leader of the industry. It was by no means a foreordained development. At the beginning of the boom period of the 1920's, Ford's preeminence was unchallenged and seemingly unchallengeable; in 1921 the Ford Motor Company made three-fifths of all the motor vehicles manufactured in the United States.

General Motors, on the other hand, had just been on the verge of disaster, its strength rested on two of its five models, Buick and Cadillac, and it possessed nothing approaching the glamour of the Ford name. The company's eventual place in the automotive firmament was far from certain.

Henry Ford's contributions to his own defeat were considerable. He stubbornly refused to see that his own great achievements with the assembly line and the Model T were merely a step in the progress of the automobile and not the culminating stage. Consequently he continued to turn out Tin Lizzies essentially unchanged from their prototype of 1908, oblivious to the fact that more attractive and more comfortable cars were available for two or three hundred dollars more than the Ford, or indeed at comparable prices if the customer chose to buy in the used-car market. Since Henry Ford was in no way an economist, he may be pardoned for missing the point that the automobile was introducing a fundamental change in American buying habits: to wit, in consumer decisions price was only one of several determinants and not necessarily the most important.

In the contest with General Motors the decisive factor was that Henry Ford, with his casual attitude toward organization, was pitted against one of the great organizing geniuses of American industry in Alfred P. Sloan, Jr., who became president of General Motors in 1923. Sloan gave to the corporation the coherent structural plan he had proposed to Durant, whereby a clear distinction was made between the operating divisions, which were self-contained and autonomous within the framework of the general policies of the corporation, and the central policy-making and planning bodies. Behind this structure was Sloan's philosophy of business organization, whose principal features may be summarized thus. No one man could successfully manage a corporation the size of General Motors. Policies should be formulated by group judgment based on careful analysis of the data, and although the lines of authority should be clearly defined, authority itself should be decentralized as much as possible. Since subordinate officials ought to be encouraged to make decisions, they had to be given the power to do so.

The Sloan reforms extended well beyond corporate structure and the top-level administrative echelons. Every sector of the General Motors organization came under close and careful scrutiny. For instance Sloan was aware that the sellers' market in motor vehicles was a thing of the past, and that particular attention was needed in the region where General Motors came into contact with the buying public—in the dealers' establishments. He himself spent much time on the road, visiting not only dealers' meetings but individual dealers, sometimes four and five in a day. The result was a strengthening of the General Motors sales organization through improved mechanisms for liaison between the corporation and its dealers and for hearing and adjudicating dealer complaints, more elaborate provisions for financial assistance, and more generous discounts—24 per cent as compared with 17 for Ford dealers.

The difference between General Motors and Ford was strikingly illustrated in the matter of personnel. In contrast to the ruthless battling for power and continuous attrition of executive and technical talent that characterized the Ford organization, Sloan built at General Motors a co-operative and efficient team, including William S. Knudsen, who gave to General Motors the genius for production he had formerly given to Ford and who would in time be Sloan's successor. Knudsen's greatest achievement at General Motors was to rehabilitate the Chevrolet Division, which had slumped so badly after the First World War that Pierre Du Pont seriously considered abandoning it altogether.

When Knudsen took charge Chevrolet was a languid competitor not only of the Model T but of such popular cars in its own price range ($500–$1,000) as Dodge, Essex, Overland, and the Durant Motor Company's Star. It rapidly pulled ahead of the field to become the principal challenger to Ford's supremacy. Ford fought back by trying to dress up Tin Lizzie with frills like spare tires and electric starters, but for all these she still remained Tin Lizzie. General Motors, on the other hand, made the annual model change a definite sales technique, aimed at meeting competition not only from the aging Model T but also from the secondhand car, and this example was followed by most of the rest of the industry. The principal exception was Packard, whose management took the position, quite successfully at the time, that ownership of a Packard conferred sufficient prestige by itself to make tinkering with the appearance and design of the car unnecessary.

Thus the consumer was being offered increasingly sophisticated cars at moderate prices. Lines were smoother, six-cylinder engines replaced fours and the eight was moving out of the luxury class, and items that had recently been accessories were now standard equipment. In the face of this kind of competition Ford's share of the market inexorably declined, until Henry Ford at last recognized the inevitable.

On May 31, 1927 the last Model T (No. 15,007,003) rolled off the assembly line and all Ford manufacturing operations came to a prolonged halt. Chevrolet took first place in car sales and retained it thereafter with only occasional exceptions. Henry Ford appears to have acted in a fit of pique, because he had no replacement for Tin Lizzie in sight when he closed down. Yet faith in his genius remained high; it was taken for granted by the American public that Henry had gone into seclusion in order to work another automotive miracle. Most Ford dealers and many of their customers simply waited patiently for the miracle to occur. What they got was the Model A, put on the market late in 1928. It was a good car, with enough of the Ford spell on it so that it outsold Chevrolet in its first year, but it was not significantly different from its competitors and certainly not superior to them.

At the next level below Ford and General Motors when the 1920's began was an assortment of apparently well-established companies with at least the potential of ranking among the leaders of the industry: Hudson (including Essex), Studebaker, Dodge, Maxwell (later Chrysler), Willys-Overland, Nash, Packard, and Durant Motors. Of these, Durant had the financial instability its founder seemed unable to avoid, and Willys-Overland never really recovered from its collapse in 1921. Packard chose to stay, for the time being, in the prestige-car market. From the rest Chrysler emerged to form what became the Big Three of American automobiledom.

This was the result of a conscious decision on Chrysler's part, along with an ability to grasp opportunities. He was aware that, despite its promising start, the Chrysler Corporation would be a minor and possibly short-lived participant in the automotive world unless it could get established in the mass market. But the manufacturing resources taken over from Maxwell were too limited to enable Chrysler to produce a low-priced car competitively, and the company still lacked the financial strength to build a new plant on the scale that would be required. An extensive marketing organization would also be needed. The solution to the problem was found when the Dodge Brothers Manufacturing Company was put on the market in 1928. John and Horace Dodge had been victims of the influenza epidemic that followed the First World War, and their heirs subsequently decided to get out of the automobile business.

Consequently, after some dickering Dodge was absorbed by the Chrysler organization. The assets acquired by Chrysler were considerable: a first-class manufacturing plant with a well-equipped foundry and other facilities for large-scale production; a car with a well-known name and an established position in the medium-priced market; and a dealer network some twelve thousand strong that could be used as an outlet for other Chrysler products. The Dodge sales organization was considered to be one of the best in the country, and Chrysler's autobiography makes it clear that he wanted the Dodge dealers as much as the Dodge manufacturing capacity. With these resources at his disposal Chrysler was able to introduce the Plymouth in 1928, a step neatly timed to take advantage of Henry Ford's temporary disappearance from the mass market.

With the rise of Chrysler the developing structure of the American automobile industry became clearly discernible. At the top were General Motors and Ford, between them outproducing all the rest of the industry put together. Both were also international automotive powers. Ford had established manufacturing subsidiaries in Europe before the First World War and had regional assembly plants throughout the world. General Motors bought the British Vauxhall and the German Opel companies during the 1920's. Chrysler was well behind the leaders but definitely ahead of the rest of the field. As of 1928 Durant Motors, which was producing a variety of models in the customary Durant manner, was superficially a fourth major power in the industry. However, except for the low-priced Star, which sold one and a half million units over a period of ten years, Billy Durant's third bid for automotive leadership was largely an assortment of rejects and misfits that nobody else wanted, and Durant Motors was coming unstuck well before the boom period ended.

Next in line, sharing 15 to 20 per cent of the automobile market, were Hudson, Nash, Packard, Studebaker, and Willys-Overland. Behind them, struggling for the less than 10 per cent of the market that remained, was a diminishing assortment of smaller concerns. Some bore famous names in American automobile history: Reo, Peerless, Franklin, Hupmobile. Special mention might be made of the splendidly engineered Marmon, whose twelve- and sixteen-cylinder models matched the Rolls-Royce in luxurious smoothness, and the Stutz, whose "Bearcat" roadster was preeminently the sports car of the Jazz Age. During the 1920's Stutz was controlled by the steel tycoon Charles M. Schwab, but his talents were apparently not transferable to automobile manufacturing, as the company steadily declined. On the other hand, one minor concern appeared to be on the way up. This was the Auburn Automobile Company of Auburn, Indiana, a modest producer of high-priced cars since 1903, which in 1924 came under the control of Errett Lobban Cord (b. 1894), a salesman, promoter, and former racing driver and mechanic. Under his management Auburn sales rose from 2,500 in 1924 to 15,000 in 1927. Simultaneously Cord took charge of the Duesenberg Motor Company, founded in 1920 by two brothers, Fred and August Duesenberg, who had got their start as builders of high-powered engines for racing cars and then for airplanes during the First World War. The Duesenberg was the first American passenger automobile to have a straight-eight engine, and it introduced the four-wheel hydraulic brake invented in 1918 by Malcolm Loughead (Lockheed), a member of a family better known as aviation than as automobile pioneers.

But the Duesenbergs were better engineers than businessmen and so their company eventually was merged with Auburn, to the accompaniment of a pronouncement by Cord that he would build the world's most expensive passenger automobile. In 1929 Cord combined an assortment of automotive and aircraft interests as the Cord Corporation and added to his automobile line a car bearing his name and equipped with front-wheel drive. The Cord was an interesting car technically, its one major drawback being that the front-end drive was a complicated mechanism to service and repair. Unfortunately for its promoter, it made its appearance at the worst possible time, just when the market for high-priced cars disintegrated.

In general, the outlook for the small-scale producer was gloomy well before the onset of the depression. Between 1923 and 1927—that is, when the recovery from the 1921 panic was well under way and before there were any signs of the 1929 crash—the number of firms engaged in motor-vehicle manufacturing shrank from 108 to 44. The casualties included historic names like Haynes and Winton, which went back to the birth of the industry. Winton himself had long since lost interest in automobile manufacturing and remained in business as a designer and builder of diesel engines. Among the survivors, those with the best prospects were firms like White, Autocar, and Mack, which had chosen to concentrate on trucks, buses, and other specialized vehicles. In fact, the Fageol brothers of Kent, Ohio, after selling one successful commercial vehicle enterprise to American Car and Foundry, were able to start over again in 1927 with the Twin Coach Company and revolutionize bus transportation. Their design changed the motor bus from an elongated passenger car to a vehicle specifically designed for commercial passenger carriage, with the engine underneath so that the whole body space was available for payload and the driver right in front in the best position to handle his vehicle in traffic.

This, however, was a special situation. In the mainstream of automobile production, whether of passenger cars or standard-type trucks, competitive conditions favored the big company, as they were bound to do when the motorcar became an article of mass production and mass consumption. No one has ever managed to build a hundred thousand cars a year in a machine shop. If automobiles are to be produced in quantity and at low unit cost, the techniques of mass production must be used, and this requires a large-scale operation. These conditions do not necessarily apply to high-priced cars produced in limited numbers, but even in this field the big companies were in a superior competitive position before the end of the twenties. General Motors and Ford could make just as luxurious cars in the Cadillac and the Lincoln as could any of the smaller firms—Pierce-Arrow or Moon, for example—with the advantage of being able to spread some of the overhead cost over their larger organizations.

While the technology of production has to be given first place, there were other factors contributing to the inexorable progression of the automobile industry toward oligopoly. The advantages of size extended to marketing as well as manufacturing, and in the 1920's selling replaced production as the industry's principal problem. Besides being able to finance their selling operations in the way described at the beginning of this chapter, the big companies could maintain larger sales organizations and support more numerous dealers than the small ones, so that as a matter of simple arithmetic they could reach more of the potential buyers. The regional distributors of earlier years disappeared during the 1920's. Selling was far too critical for the manufacturers' sales departments to want any intermediate authority between them and their dealers.

The big producers, moreover, were far better able to advertise extensively in mass media, and because they also had many more dealers who were doing their own local advertising, their appeal to the buying public was stronger and more persistent than that of the small firms. The return from this kind of effort was calculable and striking. Market surveys of this period demonstrated that three-fourths of all prospective purchasers had decided on the make of car they wanted to buy before they arrived at the dealer's sales-room.

In marketing as in production, unit cost declined as volume increased. At the end of the 1920's the advertising and other direct marketing costs incurred in selling approximately a million Chevro-lets was about twenty-five dollars a car, which was at least five dollars less than the cost of selling a Gardner or a Reo or a Chandler. In short, whether in building or selling automobiles the small company had to contend with handicaps that had become inherent in the nature of the business.

Finally, as Billy Durant had foreseen twenty years before, the big concerns could accept losses that would be fatal to their smaller rivals. This point was about to be vividly and painfully demon-strated.

CHAPTER 7

Prosperity and Adversity

As with most other elements of American economic life, 1929 was a watershed in the history of the automobile. Production of motor vehicles in that year reached 5,337,087, a million more than in the previous year and a record that would not be surpassed or even matched for another twenty years. The economic cataclysm that followed the stock market collapse not only curtailed drastically the demand for new cars but had other and more lasting effects on the automobile industry. The decline in production was sharp but temporary; output dropped to a low of 1,331,860 in 1932, but after that conditions slowly improved. On the other hand, the depression accelerated the extinction of the independent producers and brought the United Automobile Workers into existence; these were permanent changes in the structure and functioning of the industry.

In these respects the experience of the automobile industry was in no way unusual, but the impact of the Great Depression is only one reason for picking 1929 as a watershed—the most obvious and probably the most important. There are others worth pointing out. It was a single generation since the first crude Duryea car had made its appearance; the Duryea brothers in fact were still living in 1929, along with other pioneers such as Charles B. King, Freelan O. Stanley, Ransom E. Olds, Henry M. Leland, Alexander Winton, and even George B. Selden. In that time the motor vehicle grew from a dubious experiment of little conceivable value except as a "rich man's toy" to become the bellwether of the American economy and perhaps the most important single influence in American social life. When Herbert Hoover accepted the Republican nomination in 1928, he could announce "two cars in every garage" as an objective shared by his fellow countrymen generally.

During these thirty-odd years before 1929 the automobile changed much more radically than it would do in the same span of time afterward. Had a motorist of 1899 been transported thirty years forward in time and placed in an automobile of that year, he would have been helpless. Vehicles, roads, traffic conditions would all have been radically different from anything in his experience. On the other hand, had the same time machine dropped a 1929 motorist into a car in 1959, he would have felt reasonably at home and would have needed only a little practice to get along.

By the end of the 1920's, in short, the automobile had evolved the mechanical and structural form it would thenceforth retain, subject to improvement and refinement, until some completely new automobile technology replaced it. This is said in full awareness of the introduction after 1929 of the automatic transmission, power steering and braking, streamlining, and other technical advances. These all fall into the category of "improvement and refinement," and practically all had been thought of and experimented with earlier.

The typical new passenger automobile of 1929 was a closed car; the ratio of closed to open cars was nine to one, exactly reversing the corresponding figures for 1919. It was gasoline-powered; at the National Automobile Show in 1924 it was noted that for the first time not a single electric or steam model was displayed. Four-wheel brakes were standard equipment, with mechanical braking systems predominant in the lower price ranges and hydraulic in the upper. Radios and heaters were beginning to appear as optional luxury items.

Engines, as stated before, were mostly six cylinders in the popular models, with a growing trend toward eights. But the advances of the 1920's in motor fuels and the improvement of engine design to give higher compression ratios resulted in greater gains in performance than the mere increase in the number of cylinders would suggest. For instance, the Model A Ford had a four-cylinder engine as did Tin Lizzie, but it had twice the horsepower. Finally, the 1929 car had the low body line of its successors instead of rising high off the ground as had most of its predecessors. The lowering of the center of gravity made it easier to take curves and reduced the risk of the vehicle's turning over. This change was made possible by two developments. One was the introduction of hypoid gearing, first used by Packard in 1927, which permitted lowering of the driveshaft and the rear axle and consequently of the chassis and body also. The other was simply that by 1929 the mileage of hard-surfaced road had become so extensive that it was practical to design and build low-slung cars. It could be assumed that an automobile would normally be operated on a reasonably smooth, hard pavement; it was no longer necessary to design the car so that it could negotiate the deep ruts and other hazards of poorly maintained dirt roads.

The evolution of the automobile industry to 1929 has already been described. It had not yet acquired completely its subsequent oligopolistic form, but the trend was unmistakable. To look at it in a different light, in its first thirty years the American automobile industry grew from a dubious and highly speculative offshoot of machine shops and bicycle manufacturers to the point where its bigger companies ranked among the world's largest manufacturing enterprises and were occasionally extending their operations into other fields. This process was more illuminating of the growth of the automobile industry than significant in its own right. American motor-vehicle manufacturers were usually reluctant to venture outside the automotive area, largely because the phenomenal expansion of their own industry gave them enough to do without looking for additional activities.

Nevertheless, there were some gestures at diversification. Ford got into the tractor business as early as the First World War and, subject to some interruptions, was the only automobile firm to stay in it. General Motors' entry into refrigeration was a whim of Billy Durant's that paid off. In the middle and late twenties there was a flurry of interest in aviation on the part of some automobile companies, stimulated by the advance of aeronautics and the assumption of a close relationship between the two industries because both were based on the internal-combustion engine.

Ford started by buying control of the Stout Metal Airplane Company in 1924 to the accompaniment of much speculation that Henry Ford was going to produce a flying Tin Lizzie. For some years the company built the famous Ford trimotor, the Tin Goose, but it was strictly a transport plane and not an aeronautical Model T. Ford and William B. Stout disagreed on aircraft construction, and finally Ford lost interest and discontinued the operation in 1932. In 1929 General Motors decided that it should be in a position to take advantage of possible commercial developments in aviation and consequently acquired control of the Fokker Aircraft Corporation and a 24 per cent interest in the Bendix Aviation Corporation. Fokker, founded by a Dutch aeronautical engineer who became famous in the First World War, was later renamed the General Aviation Corporation and was absorbed by North American Aviation in 1933. This transaction gave General Motors a 29 per cent interest in North American. By that time the prospect for an immediate, phenomenal boom in aviation had evaporated and General Motors made no further commitment to the airframe business, although it retained its stock holdings in North American and Bendix until 1948.

In addition, the American automobile industry dominated the world market. In the late 1920's the United States built 85 per cent of the world's motor vehicles. About a tenth of the output was exported, this above and beyond what was produced by American-owned firms in foreign countries. The figures become more meaningful when it is appreciated that the number of American cars exported was, for example, approximately twice the total motor-vehicle production of the United Kingdom during this period.

Despite the highest wage scales in the world (Ford was now up to a base rate of seven dollars a day) the American manufacturers were able to compete internationally because of their enormous superiority in the organization and technology of production. For instance, Morris Motors, the biggest of the British firms, did not install a moving assembly line until 1934—not because of any lack of ability to use the technique but simply because demand was too limited to justify the investment. The principal handicap American cars had to encounter in the world market was tax structures based on horsepower, which put a heavy burden on the big American vehicles.

THE ONSET OF DEPRESSION

For the history of the automobile, the first noteworthy feature of Great Depression of the 1930's is that it demonstrated conclusively how firmly imbedded in American society the motor vehicle had become. Between 1929 and 1932, as we have seen, the annual production of new cars in the United States declined 75 per cent. On the other hand, in the same period motor-vehicle registrations dropped only 10 per cent, from 26,500,000 to 23,877,000. In other words, while the American public was deciding that it could not afford to buy new cars, it was contriving to keep those that it had. Economic crisis or no, the family car was not a luxury to be jettisoned during the storm; it was a household necessity which, if it could not be replaced, had somehow to be kept running until better times arrived.

This situation, where an automobile was in effect part of one's household goods, was a novelty in the history of civilization. In the main Americans took it for granted; others did not. As an illustration, when John Steinbeck's novel *The Grapes of Wrath* was made into a moving picture, the film was welcomed by the Communists and exhibited throughout the Soviet Union as an example of the horrible conditions that existed under American capitalism. After about six weeks, further showings were canceled. Russian audiences, it became evident, were less impressed by the plight of the Joads than by the fact that these supposedly downtrodden victims of capitalist oppression owned a motorcar. It may have been a dilapidated jalopy, but it was still a possession beyond the reach of the common man in proletarian Russia.

The preservation of old cars, however, was of little value to an industry that depended on the sale of new ones. The dropping-off of sales from their 1929 peak hit all the automobile companies hard, but what was a difficult period for the big companies was irretrievable disaster for most of the small producers. A few managed to survive by getting out of the passenger-car business. Reo, again managed by R. E. Olds after a few years of retirement, became a manufacturer of trucks exclusively in 1936. Marmon went out of operation in 1933 but in the meantime the Marmon family had joined forces with Arthur W. S. Herrington to form the Marmon-Herrington Company for the manufacture of all-wheel-drive trucks. These were designed by Herrington as a result of his experience as a military transport officer in the First World War. The Hupp Motor Car Company, later reorganized as the Hupp Corporation, became a manufacturer of automotive parts and eventually diversified its operations into such fields as kitchen appliances and electronics.

These, however, were exceptions. Under the blight of depression one famous name after another disappeared from the American automotive scene: Franklin, Moon, Pierce-Arrow, Kissel, Gardner, Peerless, Stutz, Cord. Of these, Peerless had a remarkable record. It began in the late nineteenth century as a manufacturer of clothes wringers, then turned to bicycles and subsequently to automobiles. When the company had to abandon automobile manufacturing in 1931, it was reorganized as Peerless Corporation and three years later transformed its plant into a brewery. E. L. Cord went out characteristically in a confusing flurry of corporate relationships. The Cord Corporation was absorbed by the Aviation Corporation, subsequently known as AVCO, but in the process Cord himself emerged in control of AVCO. Then, however, the whole aviation industry was thrown into a turmoil when the federal government professed to find irregularities in the award of airmail contracts, and in the ensuing reorganization of AVCO, Cord got into a quarrel with the Securities and Exchange Commission and in disgust gave up both his automotive and his aeronautical interests. With his departure manufacture of the Auburn, Cord, and Duesenberg ceased.

A still more spectacular casualty was William C. Durant. Already in trouble before the stock market crash, Billy tried desperately to keep going, but his technique was shopworn. The money market had seen the show twice; it was not impressed by flamboyant announcements of projected new combinations, which failed to materialize, or of the appointment of allegedly top-ranking managerial talent, which turned out to consist of Dodge executives displaced by the merger with Chrysler. The depression provided the coup de grâce. Durant Motors was liquidated in 1933, and two years later Billy, then 75 years old, declared himself bankrupt, listing liabilities of $914,000 and assets of $250 (his clothes).

He was still not finished. In 1935 he started a supermarket in Asbury Park, New Jersey. When an enterprising newspaperman saw him helping to clean up in preparation for the grand opening, the story was published that the founder of General Motors was reduced to sweeping floors for a living. He then started to promote a chain of bowling alleys, designed to take bowling from the cuspidor and sawdust atmosphere in which it then existed and make it a family recreation—in short, to do what others would do later. Durant's aspirations were frustrated by ill health and the shortage of materials caused by the Second World War. He died in 1947, leaving behind the memory of a colorful, likable man who had risen to spectacular heights and then inexorably fallen like the hero of a Greek tragedy. His former business associate, Frederick L. Smith of the Olds Motor Works, summed him up accurately:

It would be a poorly posted analyst who failed to list W. C. Durant as the most picturesque, spectacular, and aggressive figure in the chronicles of American automobiledom. He certainly made some capital mistakes—but the man who makes no mistakes rarely makes anything at all on a large scale.

The medium-sized automobile firms had mixed fortunes. Like everyone else Packard and Nash saw their sales shrink, but they remained solvent. Nash even expanded its area of operations by merging with the Kelvinator Corporation in 1936 as Nash-Kelvinator, thus following General Motors in combining the manufacture of automobiles with electric refrigerators. Both Packard and Nash conceded to the depression by bringing out lower-priced models, with qualified success. Packard in fact appears to have permanently impaired its prestige value by allowing the concept of a "cheap" Packard to get established. Hudson avoided bankruptcy by a monumental effort on the part of Roy D. Chapin, recalled to deal with the crisis after serving briefly as Hoover's Secretary of Commerce. The effort probably cost him his life; he died of pneumonia just as it became clear that the company was safe.

Willys-Overland and Studebaker both had to undergo receivership. For John N. Willys this was his second experience. After his disaster in 1921 he had put together another assortment of automotive companies, producing the popular Overland and a line of higher-priced cars using the Knight engine. In 1929 Willys himself retired from active management to become ambassador to Poland. The crisis brought him back, but there was nothing he could do to keep his company solvent. Before his death in 1933 he did have the satisfaction of seeing it on the way to reorganization, minus its Knight-engined models, which should have been abandoned earlier. Willys was the last major manufacturer to use the sleeve-valve motor, and it seems clear that this was a blunder. By the 1930's the poppet-valve engine had been refined to the point where the extra cost and complexity of the Knight could no longer be justified.

The Studebaker catastrophe was the direct consequence of tragic blunders by president Albert R. Erskine (1871–1933). Here was a long-established firm with an unbroken record of success as a vehicle manufacturer, which should have had as good a prospect as

ORIGINAL PRODUCTION CHRYSLER SIX

This car, Chrysler's first production model, appeared in early 1924.

THE FIRST PLYMOUTH

Introduced in 1928, the Plymouth confirmed Chrysler's position as one of the Big Three.

HENRY MARTYN LELAND, 1843–1932

RANSOM ELI OLDS, 1864–1950

WILLIAM C. DURANT, 1860–1947

HENRY FORD, 1863–1947

(Courtesy The Chrysler Corporation)

WALTER P. CHRYSLER, 1875–1940

(Courtesy General Motors Corporation)

ALFRED P. SLOAN, JR.

(Chase Ltd. Photo, courtesy UAW)

WALTER P. REUTHER

(Courtesy Office of the Governor, Lansing, Mich.)

GEORGE ROMNEY

AUTOMOBILE
STYLING
1896–1965

This series of pictures of Ford products strikingly illustrates men's changing notions, over a span of nearly seventy years, of what an automobile should look like. For the first half of the period motorcars looked pretty much like what they were often called, machines.

From top to bottom on this page are Henry Ford in his quadricycle, 1896; the first production Ford, Model A, 1903; the Model N, 1909; a Model T sedan, 1922, and the Model A of 1929.

On this page from top to bottom: the V-8 model of 1934; the streamlined Lincoln-Zephyr, 1936; the first true postwar model, 1949; a "Fairlane 500" hardtop, 1957; and a Mustang of 1965.

EARLY BODY DROP

On a General Motors assembly line of about 1920 the tonneau of an **automobile** is lowered onto the chassis, a process involving a good deal of hand labor.

THE SAME PROCESS TODAY

In forty-five years, the basic task has not changed, but the methods **have become** almost completely mechanized.

SHOPPING BY AUTOMOBILE

More than five thousand automobiles have brought shoppers to this retail complex at Columbus, Ohio. The development of such suburban shopping centers is one of many economic and social changes brought about by the automobile.

(Picture by Michigan State Highway Department, courtesy Automobile Manufacturers Association)

FREEWAY INTERCHANGE

The requirement in modern superhighway design that automobiles join a stream of moving traffic only when they are already going in the same direction and traveling at highway speed necessitates the construction of elaborate interchanges such as this one near Detroit.

anyone of weathering a prolonged depression. Erskine had been president since 1915 and had handled the company's affairs with competence and judgment. At the peak of the boom, however, he seems to have developed a streak of overoptimism. He tried to expand by buying the Pierce-Arrow Motor Car Company, which proved to be worthless. Then when the depression came, Erskine was convinced that it would be brief. He shared this view with many others, but when he carried his beliefs so far as to pay dividends out of capital in order to maintain confidence, his optimism was clearly running away with his judgment. Events of course proved him disastrously wrong. A desperate last-minute effort to avert bankruptcy by arranging a merger with the White Motor Company failed, and Erskine committed suicide. For a time it appeared that Studebaker would go out of business altogether, but the company was successfully reorganized by Harold S. Vance and Paul G. Hoffman, although it never recovered its previous stature.

Thus the middle group of automobile manufacturers survived the depression, along with one of the smaller producers, Graham-Paige, and the stronger of the truck manufacturers. Nevertheless the status of the independents was perceptibly weaker. Their share of the market dropped from the 25 per cent of 1929 to 10 per cent in 1939. This decline occurred in the face of strenuous efforts to appeal to the buying public in every possible way: styling, colorful names, new technical devices. Essex, for instance, offered a new model called the "Terraplane," which sold well enough to help the Hudson Motor Car Company remain solvent. Studebaker, on the other hand, got nowhere with a low-priced car called the "Rockne," after the famous Notre Dame football coach.

One interesting feature of the response to depression conditions was a renewal of emphasis on the mechanical qualities of the car. These had been the prime subject of advertising when the automobile was young, but in the lush days of the twenties, styling took precedence over engineering. In the thirties, however, the desperate competition for markets turned the manufacturers to the sales appeal of devices that could be claimed to enhance economy or efficiency of operation. Studebaker led the way by offering free-wheeling in 1930, and the rest of the industry promptly followed. Freewheeling, which put the transmission in neutral when the power was cut off, was presented as a fuel-saving technique. But since it sacrificed the braking power of the engine, it cost about as much in extra wear on brake shoes as it saved in gasoline consumption, and it was an additional driving hazard. It was generally abandoned after a brief trial. Overdrive, first introduced by Chrysler in 1934, was a better method of economizing on fuel.

The trouble with this kind of competition was that whatever the smaller companies could do, the big ones could do just as well—frequently better, because they had greater resources for development, testing, and marketing. Chrysler was not only first in the field with overdrive but introduced three-point engine suspension on rubber mountings in the 1931 Plymouth. Reo offered a car with automatic transmission in 1934, but this was one of the last Reo passenger cars, and it was left to General Motors to revive automatic transmission as a feature of the Buick and Oldsmobile in 1937. None of these techniques, it should be understood, was "invented" at this time although the advertising might have given this impression. Practically all had been experimented with earlier, but the 1930's first saw them introduced on regular production models.

There were also valid technical reasons for these changes being made at this time. Automatic transmission may be taken as a sample. Both the torque converter and the hydraulic coupling were tried experimentally on marine engines before the First World War, and the other essential of the automatic transmission, the epicyclic gearbox, was used in the 1890's by the great British automotive engineer F. W. Lanchester, and later by Henry Ford in the transmission of the Model T. It was not until the 1920's, however, that torque converters or hydraulic couplings were refined to the point of being usable for motor vehicles. Another ten years of development, in the United States carried out largely by General Motors, was required to design an automatic transmission suitable for installation on production models. Thus the automatic transmission could hardly have been introduced as a commercially practical device before the late 1930's. It might well have been held up even longer except for the competitive pressure: the company that first put out a car with a workable automatic transmission could expect a definite sales advantage.

THE BIG THREE IN THE DEPRESSION

It should not be thought that the giants of the automobile industry went through the depression unscathed. General Motors, Ford, and Chrysler all shared in the agonies of the period, with production curtailed and revenues diminishing. Nevertheless there was a fundamental difference between the experience of the Big Three and that of their smaller competitors in that the former were at no time threatened with extinction.

It is easy to get the impression, however, that the survival of the Ford Motor Company was more a matter of habit than of any conscious planning. Ford provides an excellent illustration of the fact that a really large business organization can withstand a surprising amount of mismanagement. The company was run by an aged despot, who despised systematic organization and who believed in keeping his executives, including his own son, constantly in conflict with each other. In this policy he was abetted by Harry Bennett (b. 1892), a former prizefighter who made his way into Henry Ford's confidence, apparently by working on his fears for the safety of his grandchildren—this was the time of the sensational kidnapping and murder of Charles A. Lindbergh's infant son. Bennett was made head of a Service Department, with vague powers over all Ford personnel. It was not a revival of the old Sociological Department; Bennett's employees were more likely to be ex-convicts than welfare workers, and the Service Department functioned on the lines of a totalitarian secret police. This was the era when Ford executives were liable to discover that they had been dismissed by finding their offices barred and their effects thrown into the street. Edsel Ford disliked Bennett and disapproved of his methods; Bennett protected himself by using every opportunity to promote friction between father and son. Bennett also had charge of labor relations; how these were handled will be described in the next chapter.

It is difficult to believe that there could have been achievement under such conditions, but there was. The Ford Motor Company produced in 1932 the first low-priced car with a V-8 engine, a feat characterized by Charles E. Sorensen, Ford's production manager and Bennett's principal rival for power, as "the elder Ford's last mechanical triumph." Mass-producing a V-8 engine at low cost was made possible by innovations in foundry technique permitting the entire block and crankcase to be cast as a unit. The V-8 temporarily put Ford ahead of Chevrolet in sales, but Ford management was not equal to the task of holding the lead against its efficiently organized competitors. The lasting effect was a general increase in horsepower among the low-priced cars. In just six years Ford jumped from the 20 horsepower of the Model T to the 65 horsepower of the V-8, although the comparison has to be qualified by the fact that two systems of calculating horsepower are involved. The rating of the Model T engine is a nominal horsepower computed by a formula based on bore measurement and the number of cylinders. This method has been generally employed where motor vehicles are taxed according to horsepower. The figure for the V-8 engine represents brake horsepower, arrived at by measuring engine output at a given number of revolutions per minute with a dynamometer and almost universally used for American cars because it gives a higher and more impressive-sounding horsepower rating. In any event the advance in Ford performance was unmistakable. A Model T in ordinary running condition had a top speed of about fifty miles an hour, whereas the V-8 could match most of the other cars it met on the highway.

This accomplishment was the only bright spot in the Ford picture. Henry Ford continued to deteriorate and a stroke in 1938 further impaired his powers, but he persisted in trying to control the company, although his efforts increasingly became mere capricious interference. An example was his pushing the company into a vague verbal arrangement with an Irish engineer named Henry George Ferguson for the manufacture of tractors using some of Ferguson's designs. Fordson tractors had not been made in the United States since 1928, such production as there was being carried on by the Ford plants in England and Ireland, but the idea of a cheap tractor had always been a passion of Henry Ford's, and in 1938 he imposed it on a reluctant management. At the time the operation lost money, and in later years the company had to pay close to $10 million in patent claims because of the casual nature of Henry Ford's agreement with Ferguson.

Bennett's influence over his nominal chief continued to increase, until it became impossible to tell who was actually issuing the orders. Ford's bitter opposition to unionization hurt the company's popularity and to some extent its sales. It is fair to say, indeed, that during the depression years the Ford Motor Company, except for the V-8 achievement, lived largely on its past reputation: specifically on the existence of a solid core of dealers and customers who remained loyal to the Ford name.

The extent of the Ford decline was such that from 1933 until 1950 the company dropped to third place in total sales. The number of Ford cars produced remained comfortably ahead of the number of Plymouths, but the entire Chrysler line (Chrysler, Dodge, De Soto, Plymouth) consistently outsold the combined Ford-Lincoln output. The introduction of the Mercury in 1938 was an effort sponsored by Edsel Ford to improve his company's competitive position.

The Chrysler record was an impressive achievement. In the pit of the depression the Chrysler Corporation was operating at 40 per cent of capacity, but careful management preserved the company's fiscal health and strengthened its market position, as we have seen, by being first in the field with important technical innovations.

When economic conditions started to improve, the corporation was able to pay off the $60 million indebtedness it had incurred when it bought Dodge. With his company solidly established and clear of debt, Walter Chrysler retired in 1935. He died five years later.

Like the others, General Motors saw its business decline sharply after the stock market collapse. In contrast to its previous crises, however, this time there was accurate financial planning and efficient management to prevent any repetition of the conditions of 1910 and 1921. General Motors, indeed, not only rode through the depression safely but was even able to expand into new areas of operation.

The first of these was diesel engines. For General Motors the impetus to enter this field came predominantly from Charles F. Kettering, who had been experimenting for some time to find out why an engine with the advantages of high thermal efficiency and low fuel cost was not more widely used. The basic problem was that the diesel engine had a very high weight-to-power ratio because of the solid construction required to withstand compression of 500 pounds per square inch. Consequently diesels could not be used efficiently for locomotion on land. The same problem was being worked on in Cleveland, Ohio, by the Winton Engine Company and the Electro-Motive Corporation, the latter a firm engaged in designing railroad equipment propelled by an internal-combustion engine with electric drive. On Kettering's recommendation General Motors bought both companies in 1930.

From this activity came a revolution in transportation. The weight-power difficulty was resolved by adopting two-cycle operation (this idea seems to have originated with Kettering), and major improvements were made in the fuel-injection and cooling systems. The impact of these changes first made itself felt on the railroad system, where in an astonishingly short time the diesel locomotive drove the "iron horse" off the tracks it had dominated since the days of George Stephenson. Adapting the diesel to highway vehicles called for still more refined engineering; diesel-powered trucks and buses were beginning to appear at the end of the thirties, but they came into widespread use only after the Second World War.

The second of General Motors' new ventures was into the manufacture of aircraft engines. This step originated with purchase of the Allison Engineering Company of Indianapolis as part of the acquisition of aviation properties by General Motors in 1929. It was a minor transaction—$592,000 for the entire company—but it was the only one to remain in the General Motors organization. Allison had originally been a machine shop making parts for racing cars and had moved into the manufacture of bearings for aircraft engines. During the 1930's it turned to the design and building of liquid-cooled aircraft engines, and with the coming of the Second World War it expanded to become and remain a major producer in this field.

In 1937 Alfred P. Sloan resigned the presidency of General Motors to become chairman of the board. His successor was William S. Knudsen, who had only four years in the office before he was called to Washington to take charge of war production. When Sloan stepped down, General Motors made 40 per cent of the motor vehicles built in the United States and 35 per cent of the total world output, and it was an important producer of electric refrigerators, diesel locomotives, and aircraft engines. It had five American passenger cars: Cadillac (which also built a slightly lower-priced model, the La Salle, at this time), Buick, Oldsmobile, Pontiac (which replaced the Oakland during the depression), and Chevrolet, consistently the nation's best seller. There was a separate division which made GMC trucks and buses, and Chevrolet also built light trucks. Overseas, General Motors made the Vauxhall in England and the Opel in Germany. It was not only the world's biggest privately owned manufacturing enterprise; it was an industrial empire such as the world had never seen before. The largest single stock ownership was Du Pont, with about 23 per cent. This was not an individual holding, however, but represented a composite of stocks owned by the Du Pont Company and by members of the Du Pont family as individuals. Sloan himself, although a substantial stockholder, had nothing approaching a controlling interest.

CHANGING THE GUARD

The change of top management at General Motors and Chrysler and the progressive decline of Henry Ford's ability to manage his company were evidence of the fact that the first generation of automotive leadership was passing from the American scene. During the thirties, Charles W. Nash and Ransom E. Olds also gave up the presidency of their respective companies, bankruptcy eliminated William C. Durant from the automobile business, and death took other outstanding figures such as Roy D. Chapin, Hiram Percy Maxim, John N. Willys, Henry M. Leland, and Alexander Winton. Founding automobile companies seems to have promoted longevity. Leland died at eighty-nine and Winton at seventy-two. Durant and Ford both died in 1947, aged eighty-seven and eighty-four respectively; Nash followed them a year later at the age of eighty-four and Olds was eighty-six when he died in 1950.

These were colorful individuals whose achievements over the span of a single generation were breathtaking. They represented a cross-section of American society. Maxim and Henry B. Joy were millionaires' sons; Chapin, Sloan, and Durant came from middle-class business and professional families; Chrysler and Ford were farm boys; Nash personified "rags to riches"; Winton and Chevrolet were immigrants. Considering the period in which they grew up, there was a surprisingly large proportion of college graduates: Chapin, Maxim, Sloan, Kettering (who seldom admitted it), Haynes, Packard. The others came up chiefly as mechanics or salesmen, but we have to include, as we have seen, such varied occupations as the manufacture of bathtubs, photographic plates, bird cages, and washing machines.

It is always easy to say, "There were giants in those days." In this instance it happens to be true, but it would be unfair to draw the conclusion that the next generation of automotive leadership was inferior. Pioneering usually looks more glamorous than running the going concern afterward. In any event, the management that was taking over in the 1930's had a very different set of problems to face. Their predecessors worked under conditions of unrestricted competition and in an environment where the overmastering task was to meet an apparently insatiable demand. In the early days, to quote Alfred P. Sloan, "Selling the cars was easy enough; the insistent problem was how to produce." In the depression era precisely the opposite situation prevailed; the automobile industry could produce far more cars than the market was willing to accept.

Moreover, until the coming of the depression the management of the automobile industry had little concern with government other than to urge more funds for better roads. Before the First World War there was also an inclination to press for tariff protection for American cars, but the development of the large export trade of the twenties changed this attitude. Whatever residual support there was for protection vanished after the Smoot-Hawley Tariff of 1930 provoked reprisals in other countries and provided a convincing demonstration that the industry had far more to lose from the closing of its export markets than from the competition of foreign cars in the United States.

The depression and the New Deal brought with them the novel situation of massive intervention by public authority. They also brought labor unrest and an irresistible drive for union organization. The times required a different approach on the part of management from what had been needed previously. Whether the automotive old guard could have adapted to unfamiliar conditions is impossible to determine. Sloan could and did. Ford could not. Most of the others were involved only partially or not at all. It was sheer coincidence that the guard should have been changing at a time of major social and economic upheaval, but perhaps it was better that way.

CHAPTER 8

The Automobile and the New Deal

Because of the key position the automobile had come to occupy in both the economic and the social structure of the United States, it was of necessity deeply involved in the great changes introduced into American life during the period of the New Deal. It was self-evident that the nation's biggest industry and its variety of ancillary enterprises must be restored to health if economic recovery was to be achieved, but there were complicating factors. The automobile industry was a focal point for the Roosevelt administration's ambitious recovery program as expressed in the National Industrial Recovery Act (NIRA). If it worked with the automobile industry it would with others.

In addition, the consequences of the depression in widespread unemployment and wage reductions for those who kept their jobs produced deep-seated labor unrest, which inevitably became channeled into pressure for unionization. This pressure was accentuated when a federal administration came into power committed to the promotion of collective bargaining and strongly sympathetic to the labor side of the bargaining process. The achievement of unionization, however, was complicated not merely by the opposition of the companies but also by interunion rivalries and the fact that the assembly-line worker did not fit the pattern of the predominantly craft-oriented organizations that comprised the American Federation of Labor.

THE AUTOMOBILE CODE

When, to the accompaniment of fanfare, parades, and lavish display of blue eagles, the American economy was urged to organize itself under the code provisions of the NIRA, the automobile industry was in a unique position. Apart from the issue of unionization, which will be considered later, the objectives of the codes in stabilizing production and prices and promoting equitable trade practices did not excite the automobile manufacturers because they believed their industry to be already well enough organized for these purposes. The system of putting a new model on the market each year required that production schedules be geared closely to sales forecasts, so that there was not much a central supervisory authority could do to control production. Prices were administered by the manufacturers, and as far as the low-priced cars were concerned—the bulk of the market—prices still followed Ford's lead at this time. The kind of price competition—uncontrolled price-cutting—which the New Deal wanted to stop was not particularly a problem for the automobile manufacturers. The small independent producers who might have posed such a threat had largely disappeared by 1933, and the few surviving firms had no interest in a form of competition which could only result in everyone's getting hurt. In fact, a formal price structure under an NRA (National Recovery Administration) code was more likely than not to cause trouble, since the other producers could accurately anticipate that Henry Ford would continue his maverick ways and refuse to subscribe to any agreement that would restrict him from doing as he pleased.

Moreover, the industry already had a powerful trade association in the National Automobile Chamber of Commerce, which administered the cross-licensing of patents. It also functioned as a clearinghouse for information on trade practices such as relationships with supplier firms and dealers. These relationships were reasonably uniform throughout the industry and were likewise something the manufacturers preferred to leave undisturbed. The dealers were less well satisfied. The pressure for sales that had been manifest in the late 1920's was greatly intensified by the depression. Both manufacturers and dealers were struggling desperately to hold what they could of a declining market, and in this situation the dealers became acutely aware that the franchise system put control of sales policies and practices, and indeed life-and-death power over the dealer's business, completely in the hands of the manufacturers. As some of them bitterly expressed it, the only right the dealer had under his contract was to buy cars at a discount. The dealers complained of the issuance of new franchises without consideration of the territorial rights of existing distributors, of unrealistic sales quotas, of being forced to take unwanted cars, and of arbitrary cancellation of franchises. The result was an extensive investigation by the Federal Trade Commission, which elicited much information but produced little in the way of tangible results. No evidence of collusive price-fixing or limiting of production on the part of the manufacturers was found, and although the dealers' grievances were adjudged valid, there was no acceptable legislative remedy. By the time the commission finished its report in 1939, most automobile firms had taken steps to correct the worst abuses, and the revival of business had muted the dealers' complaints.

In any event, in early 1933 there was no urgency in the industry to adopt a code. On the other hand, the administration saw the automotive industry as the critical factor in its recovery program, so that President Roosevelt took a strong personal interest in the formulation of an automobile code and the head of the National Recovery Administration, General Hugh S. Johnson (Old Ironpants) demanded compliance with standards that did not yet exist. Consequently the leaders of the automobile industry concluded that they had better draft their own code rather than have one imposed on them by governmental fiat.

A committee of the N.A.C.C. was appointed to draft a code, including a representative of the Ford Motor Company. It completed its work late in July, 1933. As adopted, the automobile code included only the vehicle-manufacturing firms and their subsidiaries. Independent parts manufacturers and distributors were excluded. These groups subsequently worked out their own codes, which was probably the most sensible way to handle the problem. Dealer codes, for example, contained provisions against price-cutting on new or used cars, a practice that was far more directly the concern of the dealer than the manufacturer, since the manufacturer got his list price less dealer's discount anyway. At the same time, given the complex interrelationships of the automotive world, separate codes inevitably meant areas of overlap and friction. During its brief and stormy existence the NRA was constantly bedeviled by bickering among automotive code authorities.

The basic automobile code predictably made little change in the industry's trade practices. It sanctioned the already accepted procedure of offering next season's models in the fall, in the hope that there would be two buying periods (fall and spring), a situation that would reduce the highly seasonal character of automobile production. The major code provisions dealt with wages and hours of labor. The standard work week was set at thirty-five hours; a maximum of forty-eight hours was permitted during peak production periods as long as the annual average was held at thirty-five. Minimum wages were set at forty to forty-three cents an hour, depending on locality. The framers of the code were able to claim that these provisions matched and in some instances bettered the standards of the President's Reemployment Agreement, a temporary measure that employers were invited to sign pending approval of their codes. Indeed, most of the employed automobile workers were at least at the minimum wage scale by the time the automobile code was adopted.

Labor relations were another matter. The industry leaders hoped to avoid unionization and would have preferred to disregard Section 7(a) of the NIRA, giving labor the right to organize and bargain collectively through agents of its own choosing. But Section 7(a) was in the law and had to be included in all codes. The industry consequently tried to take the position that the law did not require ("coerce" was the term actually used) labor to organize. The fate of this interpretation will be discussed later.

The automobile code, like most NRA codes, was never very effective. For one thing, Henry Ford ignored it altogether. Under the law the Ford Motor Company was bound by the code provisions whether it signed the document or not, and it did in fact meet code requirements for wages and hours. Technically, however, the company was guilty of non-compliance, and like the other automobile manufacturers, it was vigorously resisting Section 7(a). Yet the government rather than the company backed away from a showdown. Only half-hearted attempts were made to stop governmental purchases of Ford cars, and no attempt whatever was made to challenge Ford's open defiance of the NRA. Henry Ford was still a great folk hero to large numbers of Americans, and neither Franklin D. Roosevelt, for all his popularity, nor General Johnson, for all his bluster, chose to force an open break. The impasse lasted until the entire code system was brought to an abrupt end on May 27, 1935, by the Supreme Court's unanimous decision in the Schechter Chicken Case (*Schechter Poultry Corp.* v. *U.S.*)

LABOR UNREST

The problem of labor discontent would not vanish quite as readily. Before the Great Depression, the record of the automobile industry in the field of labor relations was mixed. During the era of Henry Ford's greatest achievements there had been the five-dollar day and the Sociological Department as evidence of concern for the welfare of the Ford workers. The rest of the industry did not imitate Ford's paternalism but conformed generally to his wage policy, probably because there was no option if Ford's competitors were to keep their best workers. The high wage rates survived; in 1928 the average hourly wage of automobile workers was seventy-five cents, about twenty cents higher than the average for manufacturing industries as a whole.

This figure, it should be noted, applied only to the automobile firms. Wages and working conditions were uniformly poorer in the independent parts manufacturing companies, which were under the pressure of the oligopolistic trend in the industry. The supplier firms, that is, found their market increasingly limited to a few large automobile concerns, most of whom had their own parts-making affiliates and subsidiaries, so that the independent suppliers were competing with their own customers. This situation explains why the manufacturers preferred that the parts makers should have their own NRA code. It also was a prolific source of disagreement and friction when the issues of labor relations eventually came to a head, since one of labor's complaints was that the automobile firms evaded NRA restrictions by passing on to suppliers work that they could just as well have done themselves.

Until the arrival of the New Deal the automotive industry was predominantly open-shop, a state of affairs entirely satisfactory from the point of view of management. However, although the automobile companies supported antiunion organizations like the Detroit Employers' Association, the failure of the automotive workers to organize has to be attributed primarily to other causes. The most important was that assembly-line production created a type of worker who simply could not be fitted into the categories of existing labor-union organization. He was not a craftsman in the accepted sense of the term; neither, on the other hand, was he an unskilled manual laborer. Only about a tenth of the jobs in the automobile industry required more than one year of training, but at the other end of the spectrum only a fourth of the jobs called for no training at all. Even the term semiskilled is too loose for the majority of the automotive workers, since their skills ranged from jobs that could be learned in a few days, or even a few hours, to those that needed several months.

The response of the American Federation of Labor to this novel industrial situation can be described best as one of monumental ineptitude. A few halfhearted attempts at unionization of the automobile industry were made before the First World War and again in the 1920's, but, along with other handicaps, they received negligible support from the federation. The leadership of the AFL was obviously more concerned with protecting the jurisdictional rights of existing craft unions than with developing an organizational structure that would meet the needs of the automobile workers. At the beginning of the century there had been an active union of carriage and wagon makers that had logically tried to extend its operations to the automobile industry, but it ran into implacable hostility from AFL craft unions and was ruined. By 1930 it had degenerated into a minuscule organization whose sole function was to provide a base of operations for Communist organizers.

Yet even the aggressive IWW made no headway whatever in the automobile industry. The automobile workers simply lacked interest. They had grievances, or at least they had grievances pointed out to them. Because of the seasonal nature of automobile production, the high hourly wage rates became less impressive when they were translated into annual income, which is estimated to have averaged between $1,600 and $1,800 during the boom period of the twenties. There was also a growing awareness that assembly-line production had created a new problem in industrial relations; namely, the effect on the individual worker of prolonged monotonous repetition of the same operation. The evidence of considerable emotional as well as physical strain was fairly impressive, but until the stock market crash the people most directly concerned showed little disposition to complain.

The explanation for this apparent apathy lies in the fact that much of the automotive labor force was made up of newcomers to the American industrial scene. More than half the automotive workers in Detroit in 1930 were immigrants or Negroes, drawn to the promised land of the assembly line by the lure of five and six dollars a day for work that could be performed with a minimum of previous skill or training. If they were disillusioned, they were afraid to show it because they were too easily replaceable; and the few who were even aware of the possibility of organization could have seen little hope of relief from that quarter. In any case, the extent of labor dissatisfaction in the automobile industry during the prosperous years of the 1920's is difficult to measure. Seasonal as employment might be, the aggregate earnings undoubtedly represented a greater cash income than most of the assembly-line workers had previously enjoyed, and it may be doubted whether they were as much bothered by monotony and routine as the people who studied them. To most of them a job was just a means of making a living; its dullness would not matter much—certainly not so much as it would to a member of the intellectual class, especially one with an ideological axe to grind.

The arrival of the depression brought a radical change. Employment dropped along with production, and in time wage rates fell off also. The companies did their best to spread out the available work, but the overall effect of this policy was to create a shorter work week and longer and more frequent layoffs, so that average annual income for those who were employed dropped to about $1,000 in 1932. As conditions deteriorated, grievances that had existed previously but had been ignored now tended to become acute. There were complaints, unquestionably well founded, of arbitrariness and favoritism on the part of foremen. Workers became acutely aware that they had no security in their jobs, that there was no recognition of seniority rights.

Unfortunately there was no machinery for handling problems of labor or even discussing them. A strong, well-established, responsible union would have been a godsend at this juncture to both labor and management, but no such thing existed. The automobile workers were left angry, frustrated, unorganized, and leaderless—a made-to-order situation for the Communists who controlled the tiny Auto Workers Union, the relic of the old carriage and wagon makers' organization. On March 7, 1932, this group staged a march of the unemployed to the Ford River Rouge plant, selected because Henry Ford was the personification of American capitalism. The demonstrators clashed with the Dearborn police and four were killed. Harry Bennett himself was involved in the fighting and was injured—lack of physical courage was not one of Bennett's deficiencies—but there is no indication that he or his service force started the trouble. The Communists did that; it was the whole purpose of the march. Bennett in fact seems to have been honestly trying to prevent the violence from spreading, and subsequent investigation cleared the Dearborn police of anything except possible errors of judgment in handling the mob. A second Communist-inspired march on the Rouge a year later was a failure.

By early 1933 there were sporadic strikes in the automotive industry: spontaneous, almost purposeless expressions of discontent, probably a blind reponse to a feeling that with the election of a new president things ought to be changing. Significantly, in view of the acknowledged disparities in working conditions, these strikes broke out in parts factories rather than in the automobile plants, the worst occurring in the Briggs Manufacturing Company of Detroit, which made bodies for Ford. The strike achieved nothing. The depression was at its depth, the Roosevelt administration was an unknown quantity and not yet in office, and the AFL gave no support.

The NRA Period

The arrival of the New Deal and the enactment of the NIRA changed the situation completely. Management's apprehensions about Section 7(a) were matched or exceeded by labor's expectations. In contrast to its earlier indifference, automotive labor was now eager and anxious to be organized. But what did 7(a) mean? Were company unions acceptable as bargaining agents? Was it obligatory for a minority to accept the choice of the majority? These and other questions had to be worked out, and the process generated further conflict, not only between labor and management but within the ranks of labor itself.

The interpreting and administering of Section 7(a) was ultimately the responsibility of the federal government, but this function was exercised through a complex structure of agencies. The following all had a hand in labor relations in the automotive industries while the NIRA was in effect: (1) the Conciliation Service of the United States Department of Labor; (2) the National Labor Board, established to deal with labor problems under the general provisions of the NIRA; (3) the Labor Advisory Board, created to consult on drafting the automobile code; (4) the Compliance Boards of the NRA; and (5) the Automobile Labor Board, created to deal with the specific problems of the automotive industries. It was a typical New Deal arrangement; Roosevelt seems to have believed that administrators worked best under highly competitive conditions.

These assorted agencies had to deal with constant conflict between management and labor and within the ranks of labor. The automobile companies fought Section 7(a) either by trying to organize company-controlled unions or by resisting unionization altogether. The latter policy was followed by the Big Three, all of whom set up espionage systems within their plants to root out union sympathizers. On the labor side, the existence of a friendly national administration and legislative endorsement of collective bargaining, plus the obvious determination of the automobile workers to be organized somehow, finally moved the AFL to action. It was spurred on also by the more aggressive leaders of its own membership—John L. Lewis, Sidney Hillman, David Dubinsky—who felt that this opportunity must not be lost, not only in automobiles but in steel, rubber, and the other great non-unionized industries.

The federation's trumpet, however, still blew somewhat uncertainly. It would not create a union for automotive workers. Instead, it set up a network of "United Automobile Workers Federal Unions," which were locals under strict control of the parent body. Membership was open to automobile workers who could not be assigned to other AFL unions. It was an unsatisfactory provisional arrangement whose primary function was to protect existing jurisdictional rights and in which the people most directly concerned, the automobile workers, had the least to say on matters of policy. It is surprising that comparatively few automotive workers turned to the competing attractions of the Communist AWU and the IWW.

In the circumstances, with feelings running high and no accepted or effective procedure for negotiation or arbitration, industrial conflict was unavoidable. Strikes and walkouts erupted in unending succession, culminating in an angry outbreak at the Electric Auto-Lite Company of Toledo, Ohio, in May, 1934, which required the intervention of the National Guard. As a rule the grievances cited were questions of wage rates, working conditions, hours, discrimination against union members, and allegations of "speed-up" of assembly lines; but always the paramount issue, whether expressly stated or not, was union recognition. On this front some gains were made among the smaller companies, a few very minor advances were registered at General Motors and Chrysler, but not a dent was made on the Ford Motor Company. As far as establishing collective bargaining was concerned, the NIRA appeared to have been an exercise in futility, with responsibility for this ineffective performance distributed among the vagueness of the law, the chaotic disorganization of the machinery for enforcement, the inertia of the AFL, and the determination of the principal companies not to be unionized.

THE RISE OF THE UAW

The whole problem of labor relations, however, was much too important a national issue to permit efforts at a solution to lapse, or to be dissipated in administrative confusion and fruitless bickering. Likewise, it was politically and economically embarrassing to have constant disturbance in the industry which the administration hoped would lead the way to recovery, preferably along the route chosen by the New Deal. Thus it came about that in the year that saw the end of the NIRA, other developments of considerably longer-range significance were in train. First was the passage of the Wagner-Connery, or National Labor Relations Act, designed to establish conclusively the right of collective bargaining and provide for more rigorous enforcement than had been achieved under the NIRA.

At about the same time the AFL reluctantly issued a charter to the International Union, United Automobile Workers of America. The federation had little choice if it was to hold the automobile workers at all, since many of them were withdrawing in disgust from their "federal union" locals and were establishing independent organizations of their own. The UAW's orientation was definitely toward the industrial union principle, so that when the Committee for Industrial Organization was formed by the Lewis-Hillman-Dubinsky group and soon afterwards separated from the AFL, the UAW went with it. Thereupon most of the independent automotive unions joined it.

The task facing the new organization was great. The AFL federal locals contributed about 23,000 members and the independent unions probably twice as many—in all, perhaps 15 per cent of the approximately 400,000 workers in the automobile and parts industries. Not more than 1,200 members altogether were in Big Three plants. It was hoped that the new National Labor Relations Act would strengthen the hand of the union, but at that juncture the likelihood of the Wagner Act's being sustained by the Supreme Court was dubious and employers were generally ignoring it.

The AFL attempted to provide the leadership for the new organization, but this phase of the UAW's existence was brief. Control of the union was quickly taken by aggressive-minded newcomers to labor organization, such as Homer Martin, a former Baptist minister with a propensity to let his enthusiasms run away with his judgment, and the Reuther brothers, Walter (b. 1907) and Victor (b. 1912), young men in their twenties but ambitious and eager for power. Some of the top figures of the UAW were suspected of being markedly left-wing in their political and economic views, and some undoubtedly were, although the union was never Communist-dominated as were some of the others formed at this time.

Its leaders, however, were prepared to take drastic steps in the face of the stubborn resistance of the Big Three automobile firms. They imported the newly devised European technique of the sit-down strike, in which the labor force stopped work but remained in the plant, so that strikebreakers could not be brought in to keep production going. At the end of 1936 most of General Motors was closed down in this way, and despite court orders and occasional attempts at eviction, the strikers held out. Governor Frank Murphy of Michigan, later a justice of the United States Supreme Court, refused to use force to restore the plants to their owners, preferring to mediate in the hope of avoiding bloodshed. In the end the company gave way. On February 11, 1937, a landmark date in the history of the automobile industry, General Motors accepted the United Automobile Workers as the bargaining agent for its members. Two months later, after a similar experience with sit-down strikes, Chrysler capitulated also. The sit-down strikes were not, of course, the whole story behind the UAW's success. The sweeping victory of Roosevelt and the New Deal in the election of 1936 undoubtedly predisposed Alfred P. Sloan and Walter Chrysler to resign themselves to unionization as inevitable.

Henry Ford was another matter. Apparently convinced that his employees were antiunion and that public opinion would support him, Ford refused to deal with any union, and to Edsel's consternation, put labor relations completely into the hands of Harry Bennett. What this policy meant was dramatically demonstrated in the notorious "battle of the overpass" on May 26, 1937. On that date Walter Reuther and several other UAW organizers were brutally beaten by members of Bennett's Service Department while they were distributing handbills on an overpass leading into the River Rouge plant. Company spokesmen, including the unctuous W. J. Cameron, former editor of the *Dearborn Independent* and at the time spokesman on the Ford Sunday Evening Hour, a radio program of classical music, attributed the attack to "loyal" workers

who resented this outside interference. The explanation was unconvincing. Not even the most loyal assembly-line workers habitually
carried blackjacks and brass knuckles.

Since the Supreme Court had upheld the constitutionality of the
Wagner Act (*NLRB* v. *Jones and Laughlin Steel Co.*) a month
before the battle of the overpass, the Ford Motor Company was
clearly in violation of the law when it refused to permit its workers
to be organized, or even to hold an election to determine if they
wanted to be organized. Yet Ford was able to hold out for another
four years because the UAW chose this time to plunge into a bitter
internal struggle. The immediate issue was dissatisfaction with
Martin's leadership. He was accused of being too complacent about
Communist infiltration into the union, and he blundered badly by
trying to deal on a personal basis with Harry Bennett. Essentially
the revolt against Martin was a contest for power among rival
leaders, and Martin's defeat was important chiefly because it
cleared the way for the subsequent rise of Walter Reuther.

The break at Ford came with dramatic swiftness early in 1941.
The UAW, reunited and strengthened, was successfully recruiting
members in spite of Bennett's terrorism, and complaints against the
company had passed through the ponderous machinery of the
National Labor Relations Board and been upheld by the courts. To
bolster the union was the fact that Ford was falling behind in
competition for defense contracts because of his labor record. On
April 1, the discharge of several union members, a familiar enough
occurrence during the previous four years, touched off a spontaneous walkout by all but a handful of the company's labor force.
Appeals by Henry Ford for protection against violence met with an
icy reception from both federal and state authorities; actually the
violence was limited to fist fights between pickets and non-strikers
trying to leave the Rouge factory, plus occasional and understandable grasping of opportunities to settle old grievances against Harry
Bennett's boys.

Henry Ford and Bennett wanted to resist, but Edsel threw his
weight on the side of negotiation. The strike was halted, and an

NLRB election produced an overwhelming majority for the UAW. It was a bitter disappointment for the elder Ford, who still cherished the illusion that his workers were contented and anti-union. He spoke about shutting down the entire operation and letting the government take over the Ford factories if it so desired, but this was simply petulance from an ailing old man. At any rate, his wife talked him out of it.

So the union conquest of the automobile industry was completed after almost ten years of conflict. The effect was not to solve all the problems of automotive labor, but at least some of the worst abuses that had crept in were ameliorated. There was recognition of seniority rights and restriction on the arbitrary speed-up of assembly lines. On the other hand, nothing much could be done by a labor organization about the seasonal nature of automobile manufacturing. Whether a wage system could be worked out that would offset the irregularity of employment was a problem for the future. For the present the UAW had gained its first requisite—recognition—and the rising war boom permitted, in fact required, the deferment of less urgent issues.

THE TURNPIKE COMES BACK

The influence of the New Deal extended beyond the problems connected with the manufacture of motor vehicles. It is an interesting phenomenon of response to depression that the 1930's should have seen more rather than less activity in highway construction than did the prosperous decade of the twenties. The reason is simple enough. Road-building was an obvious and acceptable method of using public funds to combat unemployment. In Germany the Hitler regime was doing the same thing by promoting a national system of express highways, the *autobahnen*, except that the Germans had an element of military planning in locating their roads that was not present in the American program.

As a matter of fact, what existed in the United States was not, properly speaking, a program at all. It was an assortment of unrelated activities, more concerned with providing jobs and priming the economic pump than with creating an integrated highway system. The Civilian Conservation Corps built access and fire roads in remote areas, the Public Works Administration financed highway construction and other substantial projects such as new bridges and the elimination of grade crossings, and the Works Progress Administration engaged extensively in local road improvement. The Tennessee Valley Authority also did a good deal of highway building and relocation in its area. Meanwhile the regular federal aid program under the Highway Act of 1921 continued, temporarily reduced early in the decade as an economy measure but restored when the emphasis switched to recovery.

This multiplicity of agencies, plus the work of state and local authorities, makes it difficult to estimate just how much road construction and improvement was done during the New Deal era, but it does not mean that there was very much unnecessary duplication of effort. The United States had slightly over three million miles of roads, exclusive of city streets, and somewhat less than half was rated as improved, that is, with as much as a gravel surface capable of all-weather use. There was plenty to be done, and the activities of the alphabetical agencies had the merit of putting needed effort into the betterment of the byways as well as the highways. The significant change of policy was reflected in the expanded role of the federal government. Where federal contributions had previously accounted for about 10 per cent of the total national expenditure on roads, during the New Deal the federal share rose to between 40 and 50 per cent. To a large extent this increase was a matter of necessity, since state and local governments came through the depression with badly depleted finances, but once a grant-in-aid policy has been expanded, it seldom shrinks again.

Most of this highway activity, however, was palliative not only for economic purposes but also as a means of providing for the future of automotive transportation. What was needed most was not the construction of additional mileage of roads of existing types but new roads designed and built for high-speed motor vehicles, with traffic flow channeled to provide for the minimum of interruption and to eliminate conflicting streams of traffic. The direction to be taken was clearly indicated by the Italian *autostrade,* begun in the 1920's, and the German *autobahnen,* as well as by the parkway developments around some American cities. The main roads of the future would be multilane express highways, with limited access, no cross traffic at grade, and separate roadways for traffic moving in opposite directions.

The heavy cost of this kind of construction was a severe deterrent, but it was bound to come. The Commonwealth of Pennsylvania led the way by converting a long-abandoned railroad right-of-way between Harrisburg and Pittsburgh into the nucleus of an express highway across the state. The projected railroad dated back to a power struggle of the 1870's between the New York Central and the Pennsylvania. It was graded and ready for tracks to be laid when the combatants came to terms, and there it lay for sixty years, complete with tunnels (nine of them, of which seven were used by the Turnpike) through the Alleghenies. The state, seeking to combat unemployment, took advantage of this ready-made route; and to finance the project, Pennsylvania returned to the tollroad system of an earlier era. It established a Turnpike Authority to build and operate the highway, with power to issue bonds and to meet its expenses by collecting tolls. The Pennsylvania Turnpike was opened to traffic between Harrisburg and Pittsburgh in October, 1940. It eventually stretched 360 miles across the state without an intersecting road or a traffic light; it had no grade greater than 3 per cent; and its curves were designed for speeds as high as ninety miles an hour. It proved to be successful both financially and as a carrier of high-speed traffic.

As could be expected of this first express highway, experience in its use revealed unanticipated defects in design. Median strips needed to be wider and divider fences stronger. The comparative absence of curves proved to be a quite unexpected hazard, in that continuous high-speed driving on long straight stretches of road produced the condition known as highway hypnosis. Nevertheless the Pennsylvania Turnpike was clearly the prototype for the highway of the future, and other states prepared to follow Pennsylvania's example. The coming of the Second World War, however, interrupted almost all building of new roads, so that these plans had to be deferred.

MOTOR CARRIER REGULATION

Finally, the New Deal succeeded in bringing interstate highway traffic under some degree of federal regulation. This step was also depression-inspired, although it had been advocated for some time by the railroads, which were losing business to the combination of more and better motor vehicles operating on more and better highways. The onset of depression won over the larger trucking concerns to a policy of regulation also. What happened was that thousands of people, many of them truck drivers who had lost their jobs, went into business as highway carriers with equipment usually consisting of a secondhand truck bought on credit. The result was merciless and uncontrolled rate-cutting. These individual operators were satisfied if they could meet day-to-day expenses, and they seldom bothered with luxuries like insurance.

To the desirability of reducing the chaos on the highways was added the hope of alleviating the plight of the railroads, whose overall financial position during the depression was so desperate that even the relief that might be afforded by eliminating a handful of fly-by-night truck operators was not to be disregarded. There was some suggestion that co-ordinated systems of transportation— rail, road, air, water, pipeline—might be the most promising remedy, but in the end the established policy of regulating each medium of transportation separately was retained.

The regulation of commercial interstate highway traffic was embodied in the Motor Carrier Act of 1935, placing certain categories of highway carriers under the jurisdiction of the Interstate Commerce Commission. Vehicles carrying farm products were exempted from the operation of the law, and private trucks, owned by firms not engaged in the business of transportation and used exclusively to carry freight for their owners, were subject only to ICC regulations regarding safety, marking of vehicles, and accounting. Effectively the commission's authority was restricted to common and contract carriers engaged in interstate commerce. (Common carriers are trucks and buses serving the general public; contract carriers operate only under specific agreements or charters.) For these the commission was empowered to issue "certificates of convenience and necessity," giving the right to run on specified routes. Rates were to be "fair and reasonable"; in general, with these particular carriers the ICC had supervisory powers with respect to rates, records, security issues, and so forth similar to those it possessed over the railroads.

The principal immediate effect of the Motor Carrier Act was to eliminate the shoestring operator insofar as he was engaged in interstate commerce. But if the sponsors of the Act expected a comprehensive control of highway carriers, they were disappointed. The great bulk of highway traffic has remained outside the scope of the Motor Carrier Act. Even in commercial transport, only about a third of the interstate business is subject to the route- and rate-making authority of the ICC.

CHAPTER 9

Arsenal of Democracy

It was fortunate for the nation that a reasonable degree of internal peace, if not harmony, had been established in the automobile industry before the full force of the Second World War struck, because this industry and its affiliates constituted the country's largest single resource in manufacturing capacity. The nature of this need was at best vaguely appreciated before the war came. The National Defense Act of 1920, attempting to capitalize on wartime experience, had authorized the drafting of detailed plans for industrial mobilization, but in point of fact very little had been done. The military services spent most of the interwar period in a state of near poverty, and detailed studies of the possible conversion of industrial concerns that had little interest in military production was an activity that could be deferred.

For industry there was no particular incentive to take any independent initiative. The military market was scarcely adequate to support the firms that were organized for it, and in the prevailing mood of the period they had to bear the stigma of being popularly considered "merchants of death." There was therefore no reason for automobile manufacturers, with their enormous civilian market, to be concerned about the problems of making military materials. Until the outbreak of hostilities none did, except to the extent that General Motors had its interests in aviation. The government was still more complacent. As far as the administration anticipated the problem, it assumed that given the continuation of depression conditions, there was ample excess plant capacity and labor, so that wartime needs could be met without disturbing the normal course of the economy. Thus, when war came, both government and industry had to learn their production roles from scratch.

THE EARLY PREPARATIONS

When the German blitzkrieg in the spring of 1940 brought a belated awareness that the threat of a Nazi conquest of Europe was far greater than most people had realized, the United States government began to press more energetically for military preparations. Except in the matter of aircraft production, which will be discussed later, industrial mobilization was still half-hearted. In May, 1940, it was put under the supervision of an advisory committee of the Council of National Defense, and it was a clear indication of where the bulk of the expected production was to come from that the chairman of this committee was William S. Knudsen, president of General Motors. At this time, however, Knudsen had no authority. He could persuade but he could not compel.

After a year's experience had demonstrated the ineffectiveness of this approach to industrial mobilization, President Roosevelt created an Office of Production Management, with Knudsen and Sidney Hillman, president of the Amalgamated Clothing Workers, as joint heads. It was a fantastic administrative arrangement; the only reason it worked at all was that both Knudsen and Hillman were responsible, patriotic individuals. Not until after the United States itself became a belligerent was there an effective organization to control production. In the meantime, getting anything at all accomplished depended entirely on voluntary co-operation on the part of industry, and fortunately this co-operation was forthcoming. Progress was slow and halting for many months; first of all it was necessary to determine what had to be done, and after that to figure out how to do it. There was also the fact that except for a few leaders of government and industry who were aware of the true seriousness of the war situation, there was no great sense of urgency in the twilight era before Pearl Harbor. Even among those who were most committed to aiding the anti-Axis nations, there was a tendency to assume that American "know-how" and productive capacity would produce the necessary rabbits out of an as yet non-existent hat. As it turned out they were ultimately right, except that instead of sleight-of-hand, the trick was performed by a great deal of unappreciated hard work.

The manufacture of motor vehicles continued very much on a "business-as-usual" basis through 1940 and 1941, reaching a total of 4,400,000 and 4,800,000 units in each of these years respectively. This was done despite growing shortages of materials, and at Knudsen's request the industry suspended major model changes so that the resources of the machine tool industry could be devoted to military needs. At the time, or rather on the basis of second-guessing shortly afterward, the automobile manufacturers were criticized for using as much as they did of materials that were becoming scarce and might otherwise have gone into armaments. It seems unfair to hold the industry responsible for the government's failure to formulate a clear-cut production policy or to establish and enforce a rigorous system of priorities. The automobile men must have developed some sympathy for their counterparts in aviation, who until the outbreak of war were excoriated for making military aircraft at all, and then were equally bitterly assailed from the same sources for not making them fast enough.

Yet despite the handicaps there was progress. It was of course a simple matter to make trucks for military as well as civilian use, and before the end of the war more than two and a half million would be turned out. The manufacture of trucks was less glamorous than some of the other war activities engaged in by the automobile industry, but in its contribution to the final victory it probably rates as high as any. The "Red Ball Express," which kept the Allied armies in France supplied after the breakout from the Normandy beachhead, was merely the most spectacular of many occasions on which truck transportation kept advances moving when by ordinary logistic calculations they should have been brought to a halt because of the destruction of rail lines.

There was likewise no major production problem involved in manufacturing the jeep, which was perhaps the most distinctive contribution of the American automobile industry to the war effort and would survive the war to find widespread adoption as a peacetime vehicle. The design of the jeep was the work of Captain Robert G. Howie of the United States Army, working in co-operation with Colonel Arthur W. S. Herrington, who was mentioned previously as cofounder of the Marmon-Herrington Company for the purpose of developing all-wheel-drive vehicles. A prototype was put on display at Fort Benning, Georgia, in March, 1940. Initially the jeep was to be built by the American Bantam Car Company, a firm that had been trying without much success to put a small car on the American market. Within a short time, however, the demand outran this company's production capacity, and the assistance of Willys-Overland and Ford was invoked. With Willys as the principal producer, some 660,000 jeeps were built for war use.

It was also logical that the War Department should turn to the automobile industry for help in building tanks. This was a more complicated production problem than making military trucks or jeeps. Tanks could not be built on automobile assembly lines; they required the construction of new factories, run by men who for the most part had never seen a tank before. The first automobile company to be approached on tank manufacture was Chrysler. It undertook the task in June, 1940, beginning by sending a selected team to the Rock Island Arsenal to examine a tank and take 186 pounds of blueprints back to Detroit. Ground was broken for a new plant in September, and regular production was achieved in the following April. This was just the start; other automobile manufacturers were rapidly drawn in, although Chrysler remained the principal builder of tanks.

A tank was at least a motorized vehicle. Simultaneously the automotive industry was turning its skills and techniques to completely novel and unfamiliar products; artillery and shells, gun mountings, machine guns, fire-control systems, small-arms ammunition, fuses—all the complex equipment of twentieth-century war. The scope of this diversity can be gauged by the fact that of General Motors' eventual $12 billion worth of military production, two-thirds was in items the company had never made before. For the time being however, in 1940 and 1941, most of the effort had to go into planning and preparation, somewhat to the disappointment of an impatient public, which had come to expect miracles from the automobile manufacturers and had no idea of the unavoidable delays incurred in starting from nothing to design and build weapons of war.

THE AUTOMOBILE INDUSTRY AND AIRCRAFT PRODUCTION

Among the wartime activities of the automobile industry, the one that was most highly publicized and drew both the most lavish praise and the sharpest criticism, was the industry's participation in the quantity manufacture of airplanes. Of all the knotty problems to be solved in the mobilizing of industry, this was beyond all question the knottiest. Because of a superficial resemblance between the power plants of the automobile and the airplane, the two industries were widely regarded as related enterprises, but in their techniques of production they were about as far apart as they could be.

Aircraft manufacturing was not and could not have been a mass-production operation. Its highest peacetime output was some five thousand units in 1939; of these more than half were small private planes, representing about one-fifth of the year's production measured in dollar value or airframe weight. The airframe and aircraft engine builders were accustomed to working with small lots, a much higher degree of precision than was required in motor vehicles, and frequent changes in design, whereas the automobile manufacturers changed their models once a year and then concentrated on turning out thousands upon thousands of identical units.

Yet there was a complacent assumption on the part of public opinion, government officials, and even a large segment of the automobile industry that the techniques and facilities that poured out motor-vehicle engines and chassis could easily be switched to aircraft engines and airframes. The experience of the First World War was misunderstood and misleading. There was, for example, a reasonably close relationship between an automobile engine and the 400-horsepower, in-line, twelve-cylinder Liberty of 1918; the same could not be said for the 2,000-horsepower, eighteen-cylinder, air-cooled radial engine of 1940.

Nevertheless the crisis of 1940 made it abundantly clear that the two industries must join forces to build airplanes—more airplanes than anybody had hitherto dreamed of. President Roosevelt picked a figure out of the air and called for 50,000 (the best guess is that he simply took Woodrow Wilson's figure of 25,000 and doubled it). The precise number to be aimed at was unimportant. What mattered was that, although the democratic powers were short of every kind of military material in that desperate summer of 1940, their most acute and vital shortage was aircraft, and if this one was to be remedied in time to do any good, the American automotive industry would have to carry a major share of the load.

The automotive people were perfectly willing to assume the burden and complacently certain of their ability to carry it. Henry Ford blandly announced that there would be no difficulty in turning out a thousand planes of standard design a day if he was left to do it unimpeded by government requirements or labor unions. It was no doubt possible, except that to concentrate on a standard design for aircraft to attain maximum production would have been a good way to lose the war. On their side the aircraft manufacturers were willing to accept assistance, with reservations. First, they were skeptical about the applicability of automobile production methods to their business. Second, while they were accustomed to a feast-or-famine existence, they had no desire to accentuate the inevitable postwar famine by having automotive firms get into aviation and stay there. Automotive companies might be admirable as subcontractors, but that was as far as they should be encouraged to go.

These difficulties caused less trouble than might have been expected, essentially because both industries were staffed by men who realized that there was a vital job to be done. The automobile manufacturers were able to convince their aeronautical associates that they were willing to help build airplanes as a patriotic duty but that their real preference was for building motor vehicles as a long-range occupation. There was a certain amount of patronizing about each other's techniques of production, but that evaporated when experience in co-operation demonstrated that each could profitably learn from the other.

Not that everything went smoothly; that was hardly to be expected under conditions where big and unfamiliar tasks were being undertaken in an atmosphere of emergency. The first appeal to the automobile manufacturers was for help in making aircraft engines, including an arrangement with the Ford Motor Company in June, 1940, to build Rolls-Royce engines for the Royal Air Force. Edsel Ford and Charles E. Sorensen approved, but before anything could be accomplished, Henry Ford's isolationist pacifism flared up and he announced that his company would have nothing to do with building engines for Britain. No appeal would move him, and the Rolls-Royce engines were eventually made by Packard. Later in the year, however, Ford joined with General Motors in a contract to build Pratt and Whitney engines.

By the fall of 1940 it had become evident that automotive resources would have to be employed in the quantity production of fuselages, wing sections, and every other kind of airplane part as well as engines. Military missions to Britain brought back the information that production estimates for two- and four-motored bombers, the most difficult types to fabricate, must be revised sharply upward and production time drastically reduced. The attainment of these goals required the fullest possible co-operation of all participants, and in response to an appeal from William S.

Knudsen, the Automobile Manufacturers Association (formerly the National Automobile Chamber of Commerce) sponsored the Automotive Committee for Air Defense. This organization formally came into existence on October 30, 1940, and terminated its work at the end of March, 1941.

What it did can best be summarized in its concluding report to Major James H. Doolittle of the Army Air Corps, who at this juncture was described as "the man who was trying to promote a peacetime wedding of the aircraft and automobile industries without benefit of a shotgun." In its six months of existence the ACAD reported that it had:

1. Conducted an educational exhibit of aircraft components visited by 2,067 representatives of 1,018 companies.

2. Assisted in placing $1 million worth of orders in the Detroit area for machine shop and tool-and-die work to assist the aircraft manufacturers.

3. Assisted the Air Corps to place "educational orders" for aircraft parts to determine if the firm in question could do the work.

4. Co-ordinated a program whereby Ford would manufacture assemblies for the four-motored Consolidated B-24 "Liberator" bomber; General Motors for the North American twin-engined B-25; and Chrysler, Hudson, and Goodyear Tire and Rubber for the Martin B-26. The plan was that the final assembly should be done by the aircraft companies in new plants to be built by the government, with 75 per cent of the total work being done by the automotive firms.

This program was still in its preliminary stages when the bombs dropped on Pearl Harbor, but at least a start had been made. When war came to America, precious time had been saved—just barely enough if we consider the critically thin margin by which the Axis powers were held in 1942. The aircraft program was able to expand so that President Roosevelt's apparently visionary request was almost met. Output for 1942 was 47,000 aircraft of all types; the 50,000 quota would have been reached if emphasis had not shifted to big bombers. Subsequently this total would be surpassed.

It was not done without delays and disappointments. The outstanding example was the Ford Motor Company's venture into the manufacture of B-24 bombers. For this a vast factory was begun in 1941 at Willow Run in Ypsilanti, Michigan, under the general supervision of Charles E. Sorensen and with ambitious plans for using mass-production techniques on a scale never previously attempted in aircraft manufacturing. These plans caused prolonged disagreement between Consolidated and Ford engineers, and although the Consolidated people eventually adopted some of the Ford proposals in their own plants, they were antagonized by Sorensen's obvious attitude that they were ignorant when it came to production. Moreover, along with the unavoidable problems of shortages of materials and trained labor, the Willow Run operation became entangled in the internecine troubles of the Ford Motor Company: the power struggle between Sorensen and Bennett, the elder Ford's unpredictable interference, and the company's still unsatisfactory labor relations. As late as September, 1943, the Air Force was seriously considering asking the government to take charge of "Will-It-Run."

This solution would have been gratifying to a group of left-wing spokesmen both in and out of the government, who fundamentally wanted to see all war production nationalized. They had been identified with the so-called "Reuther Plan," a proposal made by Walter Reuther late in 1940 whereby idle automotive plants would be devoted to aircraft manufacturing under a joint management arrangement including the government, the automobile companies, and the UAW. The idea found little general support and gradually withered. Its sympathizers, however, continued to hope that the exigencies of war would provide a wedge for nationalization, and they would have liked nothing better than to begin with the Ford Motor Company, since Henry Ford was of course anathema to those of socialist sympathies.

As it happened, by late 1943 Willow Run was over the hump. In the following year the plant was pushing out Liberators at the rate of four and five hundred a month. It was at last a triumph of the mass-production technique, although it seems a pity that all this effort should have been expended on an airplane like the B-24, which Air Force pilots found hard to handle and which was obsolescent by the time Ford got it into full production. However, the decision on what to build was the Air Force's, not Ford's, and it undoubtedly made sense to concentrate on what was available.

The principal casualty of Willow Run was Sorensen. To the extent that he insisted on doing things his way, he contributed to the delay in getting into production, but it was unfair to blame him for troubles that were due to the war itself, and his methods were vindicated in the end. But too much had been expected too soon. Someone had to be the scapegoat, and "Cast-Iron Charlie," his hold on Henry Ford's confidence undermined by Harry Bennett, was it. He had served Henry Ford for forty years as an able, hard-driving, ruthless, and cordially disliked production man, a longer tenure than any other official in the history of the company; now he was tossed aside as casually as any discharged assembly-line worker. He became president of Willys-Overland briefly and then went into retirement.

TOTAL WAR

The aftermath of Pearl Harbor brought with it the startling realization that automotive transportation in the United States was now subject to drastic limitations. For the duration of the war the American automobile owner would no longer be able to indulge his well-established freedom to get into his car at any time and go wherever he chose. It was not just that all production of motor vehicles was stopped early in 1942 in order to conserve steel and other vital materials for war purposes, so that if the family car wore out, the old simple procedure of turning it in for a new (or newer) model could no longer be followed. There were other troubles to be faced as well.

To begin with, the Japanese invasion of Malaya and the Netherlands Indies abruptly cut off almost the entire supply of natural rubber. This possibility had been anticipated, but with the prevailing tendency (pre–Pearl Harbor) to underestimate the Japanese, it had not been taken very seriously. A little stockpiling had been done, but not much, and facilities for making synthetic rubber were still in the pilot stage. There was also some effort to revive rubber growing in Brazil, which had once produced the bulk of the world's raw rubber, but no relief could be expected immediately from this source. The government was compelled to prohibit all non-military use of rubber, so that even if the family car stood up mechanically, it faced the prospect of being immobilized if its tires wore out. A very distinguished special committee (Bernard Baruch, Karl T. Compton, and James B. Conant) urged rigorous measures to conserve rubber and pointed out that the nation's greatest reserve of the product was the tires on its 35,000,000 motor vehicles.

Hard on the heels of the rubber crisis came a shortage of petroleum products in the northeastern states. In this instance the sources of supply were untouched, but submarine depredations along the Atlantic seaboard and in the Gulf of Mexico during the first half of 1942 caused a wholesale destruction of the tankers that normally carried the gasoline and oil to the densely populated, heavily industrialized Northeast. The first claim on tanker tonnage had to be for military needs; after these had been met there was not enough left to provide for the ordinary civilian demand. The railroads performed heroically, but they were already overburdened, and although pipeline construction was pressed, shortages of labor and materials made it evident that relief from this quarter was far in the future.

Yet automobile transportation had to be kept going. It was not just that many of the normal activities of American life had become dependent on the motor vehicle; the war effort itself would be seriously retarded if people were unable to use their cars. The new defense plants and military bases that were springing up were frequently located where there was neither housing nor public transportation. There were valid reasons for picking these sites, and it had never occurred to anyone that people might be unable to come and go by car as usual.

The government's first response to this situation was to establish a national speed limit of forty miles an hour in May, 1942, subsequently reduced to thirty-five. The primary purpose of this measure was to conserve tires. Six months later, a year after the nation had gone to war, a nationwide system of gasoline rationing was adopted. The gasoline shortage remained localized in the Northeast, but it was considered undesirable to discriminate against one section of the country in imposing rationing. In any event the purpose was not only to conserve gasoline but to curtail needless use of automobiles in order to save both vehicles and tires. At the height of gasoline rationing the basic allotment, for pleasure driving only, was two gallons a week; supplemental allowances were made for various necessary uses of cars. In particular, special allowances were given to encourage the formation of car pools by people who had to drive to and from work. The total number of gasoline ration books issued exceeded 25,000,000. There were regrettably widespread abuses of the system, but it worked well enough to keep essential highway traffic moving for the duration of the war.

Upon entry of the United States into the war the automobile industry's defense production activities greatly increased. No longer was there any conflict between the civilian and the military market or any uncertainty of direction and purpose. Instead, an industry with a deep-rooted tradition of free and vigorous competition voluntarily pooled its resources to meet the challenge. Three weeks after the attack on Pearl Harbor the Automobile Manufacturers Association sponsored the formation of the Automotive Council for War Production, for the purpose of facilitating the utilization of the full resources of the automotive industry in the prosecution of the war. Alvan Macauley (1872–1952) president of both the AMA and the Packard Motor Company, became chairman of the ACWP, and another AMA official, George Romney (b. 1907) then, was appointed managing director. Romney, that is, was the executive officer responsible for seeing that the council's functions were carried out.

The council's operations provide the best and indeed the only survey of the automobile industry's multifarious war activities that is at once comprehensive and concise. It functioned through twelve divisions. Three were for industrywide service:

1. Machine Tool and Equipment Service, which listed all machine tools in automotive plants (the total exceeded 350,000) and arranged for interchange so that there would be maximum use of every machine.

2. Tooling Information Service, which performed a similar function for all types of equipment available for making gauges, tools, dies, and jigs.

3. Contract Information Service, which expedited subcontracting.

The nine product divisions reveal the scope of the industry's participation in war production. They were: (1) Aircraft Engines; (2) Airframes; (3) Ammunition Components; (4) Artillery; (5) Small Arms; (6) Marine Equipment; (7) Military Vehicles; (8) Propellers; and (9) Tanks and Tank Parts.

The most useful feature of the automotive industry's wartime performance was not so much the scale on which it could operate, important as that was, as the ability of the automobile men to apply to military equipment the ingenuity in production techniques that had been so spectacularly successful in the making of motor vehicles. An unending list of such achievements could be compiled; the following are samples taken from the reports of the ACWP.

A passenger car producer, getting an anti-aircraft gun of foreign design into production seven months after receipt of the order, cut four months from the time required by the company that invented the gun— time and cost were saved when the military endorsed the company's suggestion that the barrel could be broached instead of processed by traditional rifling methods. This cut the manufacturing time for this part to fifteen minutes from three and one-half hours.

Ingenuity on the part of automotive engineers [engaged in tank manufacture] was outstanding. One company, for example, adopted a flame-cutting process to form the steel sprockets which transfer the engine's power to the caterpillar track. This method allowed twelve sprockets to be turned out every six minutes. About eight hours were formerly required to make only one.

To cut down on welding operations, one company adapted huge presses —formerly used to stamp out automobile body panels—to the forming of armor plate. These presses eliminated sixty-four inches of welding in two places on the tank hull.

On an aircraft wing-panel operation, use of automotive-type machines and tools saved 75 per cent of the time previously required and cut the cost of the wing by $1,000.

Aircraft engine parts, formerly ground one at a time by hand, were grouped into special jigs and automatically ground out fourteen at a time.

It is fair to point out, and it does not detract from the achievement, that these methods could have been employed just as well by the armament industries if they had been engaged in quantity production, but until 1940 they were not. The fact remains that when the need came, the automobile industry was the country's greatest reservoir of "know-how" and skill in the technique of making, accurately and reliably, the largest possible number of items in the shortest possible time. Its record is shown in the accompanying table, which is given in full because it shows more

TABLE 2
PRODUCTION TOTALS, SECOND WORLD WAR

The following list of products produced by motor vehicle, body, parts and accessories companies, is as comprehensive a tabulation of the automotive industry's production for World War II as has been possible to obtain. Compiled in 1947, it is incomplete because it does not embrace all of the end products made by automobile, body, and parts factories, nor does it take into account the huge volume of components, such as vehicle and aircraft sub-assemblies and parts.

4,131,000 Engines

Aircraft	455,522
Marine	168,776
Tank	257,117
Military Trucks	3,250,000

5,947,000 Guns

Carbines and Rifles	3,388,897
Machine Guns	2,276,204
Anti-Aircraft	156,313
Other Guns	125,527

2,812,000 Tanks and Trucks

Tanks	49,058
Amphibian Tanks	5,115
Gun Carriages (Tank Type)	24,147
Gun Carriages, Other; and Armored Cars	126,839
Military Trucks (1940–46)	2,600,687

27,000 Complete Aircraft

Airplanes	22,160
Helicopters	219
Gliders	4,290

Other Items

Trailers	529,647
Aircraft Propellors	255,519
Jettison Fuel Tanks	981,358
Small Arms Ammunition	12,500,000,000
Shells	245,300,000
Shot	1,800,000
Bombs	5,150,000
Anti-Sub Ammunition	780,000
Rockets	2,850,000
Torpedoes	5,289
Mines	2,480,000
Buzz Bombs	1,292
Atomic Bomb Equipment	—
Rocket Motors	1,177,000
Fuses	274,000,000
Cartridge Cases	315,000,000
Containers, Shell, etc.	7,788,000
Ammunition Boxes	2,080,000
Rifle Clips	58,500,000
Ammunition Belt Link	2,620,000,000
Link Loading Machines	64,000
Mine Parachutes	55,000
Mine Anchors	28,000
Ammunition Hoists	415
Shell Extractors	1,228,000
Drop Boxes	28,000
Sand Bags	1,000,000
Squad Tents	11,000
Comforters	390,000
Helmets	20,870,000
Helmet Liners	10,000
Identification Discs	50,000
Buckles	150,000,000
Field Ranges	62,200
Cook and Stock Pots	76,000
Air Raid Sirens	347
Airplane Landing Mats, sq. ft.	50,136,000
Heat Exchangers	304,577
Fire Pumpers	39,539
Fire Extinguisher Pumps	2,196,000
Fire Extinguishers	252,000

Searchlights	97,216
Binoculars	207,400
Periscopes	16,500
Indirect Vision Devices	648,400
Radios	118,000
Radar Computers	2,600
Wire Reels	4,753,000
Marine Tractors	8,418
Motor Tugs	3,025
Life Rafts and Floats	13,000
Pontoons	9,002
Gas Cylinders	1,460,000
Water and Gas Cans	4,313,000
Submarine Nets (miles)	100
Gyro Compasses	5,500
Gyroscopes	300,000
Climb Indicators	5,400
Electric Motors	5,059,000

Automotive Industry Percentage of Total War Output

Complete Airplanes	10%
Machine Guns	47%
Carbines	56%
Tanks	57%
Armored Cars	100%
Scout Cars and Carriers	92%
Torpedoes	10%
Land Mines	10%
Marine Mines	3%
Army Helmets	85%
Aircraft Bombs	87%

SOURCE: *Freedom's Arsenal: The Story of the Automotive Council for War Production* (Detroit, Mich.: Automobile Manufacturers Association, 1950), pp. 199–201.

lucidly than anything else the astonishingly diversified uses to which the industry's productive resources were applied. In all, by the time the Second World War came to an end, the American automotive industry manufactured $29 billion worth of military materials, constituting one-fifth of the nation's entire output of such commodities.

This performance was brought to a halt rapidly but on the whole smoothly. One of the functions assumed by the Automotive Council for War Production was that of intermediary in negotiations for contract termination. At the outset these terminations were predominantly caused by shifts in military requirements as the war situation changed. Then, when the course of events brought eventual victory in sight, both government and industry began to plan for the resumption of peacetime production. They were castigated for doing so by the zealots who insisted that it was improper to think about peace until the war had been won; for dramatic effect these should have been the same people who shrilly denounced planning for war before the shooting actually started, but they probably were not. The fact remains that when the war did come to an end, the advance preparations permitted the enormous production machine to turn from swords to plowshares with far less confusion and disruption than most authorities had feared. The automobile industry faced the postwar world with much happier prospects than its aeronautical cousin. When the reconversion process was accomplished, there was a market for motor vehicles; airplanes in 1945 were definitely a surplus commodity.

The American public demonstrated emphatically what one of its first priorities was going to be. Gasoline rationing officially ended on August 15, 1945. Unofficially it ended the day before, when Japan formally surrendered. On that day the streets of every American community were littered with the scraps of gasoline ration books, while owners leaped into their cars, with the rebuilt motors and the retreaded tires, and drove joyously about until they were ready to head for their dealers and place orders for new cars, deliverable when the assembly lines should catch up with the accumulated demand of four years.

CHAPTER 10

Peace Has Its Problems

When the victory celebrations came to an end and the American automotive world could take stock of its future prospects, its mood was preponderantly one of optimism, with some reservations. For the manufacturers the market outlook was excellent: it would in fact be necessary to go back before the First World War to find a comparable situation, one in which there was a demand for cars beyond the immediate ability of the producers to supply. The demand side is easy to explain. From its 1941 level of 3,250,000 (the highest since 1929), passenger car production dropped to 223,000 in 1942, exactly 139 in 1943, 610 in 1944, and 700 in 1945. In the meantime registrations dropped by four million as automobiles became inoperable for one reason or another and could not be replaced. It is a safe guess that at least as many more passenger cars were ready for the scrapheap by the time the war ended.

Meeting this pent-up demand required time. The war contracts were liquidated satisfactorily enough, but it was no more possible to switch the assembly lines overnight from military matériel to civilian automobiles than it had been to do the opposite five years before. Apart from the necessary reorganization and retooling, there were still acute shortages of materials and other difficulties left behind in the wake of war. It was late 1946 before the government lifted priorities, and price controls remained rather haphazardly in operation for a year after that.

The result was an unparalleled seller's market. Any vehicle that would roll under its own power was salable. (The writer can testify personally to a 1935 Ford bought for $100 in 1941 and allowed a trade-in value, despite worn-out bearings, of $75 in 1946.) The prospects of the automobile business, indeed, were so alluring that for the first time in twenty years there was a determined effort by an important newcomer to break into the ranks of the automobile manufacturers. As an added attraction, a great boom in highway construction was clearly in the making, as projects which had been deferred for the duration of the war were revived. When the new cars arrived, there would be new roads for them to use. Along with this encouraging outlook for the automotive future, there were various imponderables in the situation that would affect the response of the automobile industry to its opportunities. Among them were: whether the trend to oligopoly would continue, or whether the independent producers would survive in the postwar world; whether, among the automotive giants, the Ford Motor Company would be able to find its way out of the chaos into which it had been plunged by the continued vagaries of its founder, Edsel's sudden death, Bennett's machinations, and the firing of Sorensen. The greatest of all imponderables, however, was labor. The aftermath of a great war is usually a period of labor unrest, and the late 1940's conformed to the pattern. In the automobile industry the UAW, now led by Walter Reuther, announced that it expected for its members the same high level of earnings in peacetime as they had enjoyed in war, along with other benefits, some of them attainable only by a drastic revision of management-union relations.

THE POSTWAR INDUSTRY

Among the established passenger car manufacturers, General Motors was the best equipped to make the transition from war to peace. It lost Knudsen, who during the war was given the rank of lieutenant-general and devoted himself to expediting the production of military materials. He died in 1948, worn out by his efforts for his adopted country. His successor at General Motors was Charles E. Wilson (1890–1961), later Secretary of Defense in the Eisenhower administration. He was known to the business world as "Engine Charlie" to distinguish him from another Charles E. Wilson, who was president of General Electric and accordingly identified as "Electric Charlie." General Motors, with its flexible organization and its diversity of operations, was in excellent condition to maintain its automotive leadership.

Chrysler likewise made a satisfactory adjustment. It had no change of management; K. T. Keller (b. 1885), who became president when Walter Chrysler retired, remained in this post until 1950. In addition, Chrysler's role as the country's leading manufacturer of tanks was interrupted only temporarily. The independents—Hudson, Nash, Packard, Studebaker, and Willys—emerged from the war with high hopes for the booming motor-vehicle market of the future. Studebaker, in fact, was the first of the manufacturers to get back to full-scale operation, with a car whose design was apparently inspired by a ferryboat, in that it gave the impression of being double-ended. While the postwar shortage lasted the independents did reasonably well, climbing to 50 per cent of the passenger car market in 1949, but once the Big Three got their assembly lines rolling normally, the inability of the small-scale producer to compete again made itself manifest. It was significant that the independents abandoned the low-priced car market. Even Hudson, whose Essex and Terraplane had had an established position in this market, made no effort to return to it. Willys-Overland perhaps should be considered an exception because it continued to manufacture jeeps for peacetime use, but the jeep was a special case. It was not really competitive with the conventional passenger automobile, and in any event it did not sell well enough to restore Willys-Overland's former glory.

In the immediate postwar years, however, the major question marks in the management of the automobile industry were personified by two Henrys—Henry Ford II (b. 1917) and Henry J.

Kaiser (b. 1882). With the former, the problem was whether he could rehabilitate the Ford Motor Company. Even though he had much to work with, it was not going to be easy. The starting point for this story takes us back to May 26, 1943, when Edsel Ford died, the tragic victim of his father's prejudices. Stomach ulcers, beyond question the consequence of frustration and persecution by the elder Ford and Harry Bennett, turned to cancer, which in turn was aggravated by undulant fever brought on by drinking non-pasteurized milk from the family farm. The company's historians, Allan Nevins and Frank E. Hill, sum up Edsel's death as "stomach cancer, undulant fever, and a broken heart."

The vacant presidency was taken by the eighty-year-old Henry Ford, already the victim of two strokes. It was an arrangement satisfactory to no one except Bennett, who seems to have been maneuvering to secure the presidency for himself. There was consternation in Washington over what might happen to the needed productive capacity of the Ford Motor Company; it was about this point, indeed, that the suggestions of nationalizing the company became loudest. Instead, Henry Ford II, the oldest of Edsel's sons, was released from service in the navy to assist in the management of the company.

He was made vice-president late in 1943, but for a time it seemed to be an empty title. His attempts to exercise authority were blocked by his grandfather's interference, or by what Harry Bennett claimed were the elder Ford's wishes. Young Henry was unable, and more than likely unwilling, to prevent Sorensen's downfall. But the Ford picture was brighter than it looked. Henry Ford II may have come to the company without experience in its management, but both at college (Yale) and in the navy he had made a point of keeping himself as fully informed about its affairs as he could. Bennett made the mistake of underestimating him. In addition, Henry II had allies against whom Bennett's techniques were useless: to wit, the women of the Ford family. Mrs. Henry Ford, the elder, had not interfered in the operation of the business while her husband was in possession of his faculties, but now that he was palpably failing she had no intention of standing aside while her grandson walked the road that her son had been compelled to tread. Mrs. Edsel Ford was the implacable foe of the man who had caused so much misery to her husband and whom she held responsible for his untimely death.

It took time and effort to wear down old Henry's reluctance to surrender his control, but it was finally achieved, and on September 21, 1945, Henry Ford II was elected president of the Ford Motor Company, with a free hand to manage it as he chose. Harry Bennett received his walking papers the same day, although he was given a month to wind up his affairs, which was a greater courtesy than he had extended to the innumerable victims of the Bennett ascendancy. The founder of the company went into complete retirement for the two years more that he had to live, a senile invalid with his great days far behind him.

It was a tragic end to a phenomenal career. For good or ill, Henry Ford *was* the image of America to millions of people throughout the world, and on balance it was a favorable image. He was not just the poor boy who became enormously rich; he was the prophet who struck the rock of mass production and brought from it a stream of plenty for rich and poor alike, who made luxuries like motorcars accessible to the common man, and who saw the secret of prosperity in wages high enough to leave the wage-earner with disposable income. If he was a despot, in his early days he was a benevolent one, and for his great achievements he could be forgiven some foibles and eccentricities. Had he been willing to turn over real authority to Edsel and retire along with the Model T, his reputation would be unassailable. Instead he stayed on, dominated by the prejudices of his rural boyhood and unable to adapt to a fast-changing industrial society which he had done as much as anyone to create; unwilling to let anyone else run his company and progressively less able to do it himself. It is not really surprising that the news of his death startled a good many people because they were under the impression that it had occurred some time before.

The new president of the Ford Motor Company must have been

staggered by what he found when he actually took charge. Conditions were markedly worse than he had envisioned. The Ford Motor Company was losing money at the rate of about $9 million a month. The administrative structure, as far as one could be said to exist, seemed designed to prevent anyone from exercising responsibility, and the legacy of Harry Bennett was present in an atmosphere of mistrust and suspicion and an unwillingness to display initiative or independence of judgment. The accounting system was a joke. One department is credibly reported to have estimated its costs by weighing its invoices. (This is a valid procedure under some conditions. The great mail-order houses can base much of their day-to-day planning on the weight of the morning mail, but it has never been recognized as an acceptable method of cost accounting.)

Ford sensibly decided that he needed help, and furthermore that the logical place to go for assistance in reorganizing an automobile company was General Motors. The man he wanted was Ernest R. Breech (b. 1897), at this time president of the Bendix Aviation Corporation. He had previously been president of North American Aviation, so that his principal executive posts had been in aviation rather than automobiles, but he had held various offices, mainly financial, in General Motors and was thoroughly familiar with its organization. It took a good deal of negotiating to persuade Breech to leave a secure position for a company he knew to be in bad shape, but the challenge of trying to rehabilitate the Ford organization won him over. He became executive vice-president and later moved up to the presidency.

Aid also came from a different and unexpected source. Ten air force officers, ranging in age from twenty-six to thirty-four, who had been concerned with logistics and especially with financial and statistical controls and who wanted to remain associated in peacetime, applied in a body to the Ford Motor Company and were accepted, with no more definite assignment at first than to study and report on various phases of the company's operations. They were promptly dubbed the "Whiz Kids," and they provided the

Ford Motor Company with some high-powered administrative talent. Their leader, Charles B. (Tex) Thornton, left after a year or so to go into the electronics business in Los Angeles and became the founder of the highly successful Litton Industries. The others contributed several vice-presidents and two presidents (Robert S. McNamara and Arjay Miller) to the Ford Motor Company, and McNamara became Secretary of Defense for Presidents Kennedy and Johnson.

The transfusion of new blood had the desired effect. The structure of the Ford Motor Company was comprehensively over-hauled. The deficits were replaced by profits, and in 1950 Ford finally recovered from Chrysler second place among automobile producers. When the fiftieth anniversary of the company arrived in 1953, it could celebrate its past with the assurance that it also had a future. By comparison, Studebaker was simultaneously observing its hundredth year as a vehicle manufacturer, but it was an open question how much longer it would be able to continue.

The crisis and convalescence of the Ford Motor Company were only partially matters of public knowledge. Far greater attention was being paid to the effort of Henry J. Kaiser to get established as an automobile manufacturer. The effort still deserves attention for what it reveals about competitive conditions in the American automobile industry as it began the second half century of its existence.

Kaiser was a colorful figure, a California businessman with a variety of interests who rose to national prominence during the Second World War by impressive production performances, especially in shipbuilding. By intensive use of prefabrication, so that the shipyard itself became in effect an assembly plant, he was able to set records of tonnage and speed in turning out merchant ships. The technique was borrowed immediately from the automobile indus-try; no one thought to give credit to the Venetian shipwrights of a bygone era. Kaiser was also instrumental in starting steel manufac-turing on the Pacific Coast, aided by the wartime demonstration that it was not only costly and cumbersome but also dangerous to have to haul steel across the United States in a time of national crisis.

During the war Kaiser joined forces with Joseph W. Frazer, president of the Graham-Paige Motor Company, to undertake the large-scale manufacture of automobiles when peace came. In 1945 they formed the Kaiser-Frazer Corporation, which absorbed Graham-Paige a few months later. The new venture was launched under promising auspices. Henry J. Kaiser emerged from the war with the reputation of a latter-day Henry Ford. His career offered ample evidence of entrepreneurial and managerial ability. Manufacturing facilities were acquired at bargain prices by purchase or lease of government-owned plants built for war production and now no longer needed, including Willow Run. Credit was also available from government sources, notably the Reconstruction Finance Corporation, which loaned Kaiser-Frazer $44 million in 1949.

With the market situation as promising as it was possible for it to be, if Kaiser-Frazer could build automobiles, it could sell them. New cars were almost non-existent and, because of the four-year span without replacement, even used cars were scarce. For a time it appeared that this combination of favorable conditions would enable Henry Kaiser to create the first new automotive empire since the rise of Chrysler twenty years before. In 1948 the Kaiser-Frazer line (Kaiser, Frazer, Henry J.) accounted for 5 per cent of domestic new-car sales. But that was high tide. Within five years all three models disappeared from the American market. Kaiser-Frazer became the Kaiser Motors Corporation in 1953 and also the owner of Willys-Overland; two years later the company, renamed Kaiser Industries Corporation, withdrew from the passenger car field to concentrate on jeeps and commercial vehicles, all to be built in Toledo by what was now Willys Motors. Kaiser cars continued to be produced in South American subsidiaries. The great Willow Run plant, which had begun with Ford, finished with General Motors. The latter company bought it from Kaiser in 1953 to be used for manufacturing automatic transmissions after General Motors' own transmission plant had been destroyed by fire.

It would be possible to explain the Kaiser experience in general terms as an illustration of the difficulty of breaking into an oligopolistic mass-production industry. It is certainly true that the obstacles facing a newcomer trying to enter the field of passenger automobile production in the United States are almost prohibitively great. Trucks and specialized vehicles are a different matter; here the newcomer and the small firms have brighter prospects. With passenger cars, however, the whole experience of the automobile industry since the 1920's has been that business survival depends on ability to get and hold a position in the mass market.

To do so, the newcomer is faced with a tremendous outlay for the plant and tooling needed for mass poduction, and with the additional heavy expense of creating a marketing and dealer organization—all predicated on the uncertain gamble of breaking into a highly competitive market against firms with established reputations and far greater experience. The worst difficulty, as Kaiser found, is the problem of marketing. Given adequate finances, building the manufacturing facilities is a routine process. Creating a sales organization and finding customers is something else again. Successful dealers cannot be expected to sever their existing connections to join an enterprise whose prospects are speculative at best. The new manufacturer has to recruit from his competitor's discards or from people inexperienced in selling automobiles, and this sales force has to overcome the massive barrier of customer resistance. The American motorist will display an intense interest in a new automotive offering, but he is likely to let someone else take the risk of buying it unless there is an unusual market situation such as existed when Kaiser-Frazer started operations. Normally the American purchaser prefers cars with a reasonably dependable trade-in value in the future. These considerations were fully understood by the business world at the time. It was helpful to Kaiser-Frazer that it had access to RFC financing, but it was also an indication of weakness, because it meant that the private investment and banking community had weighed the company's prospects in the balance and found them wanting.

Yet to write off Kaiser-Frazer as the victim of a general economic pattern is oversimplification. The enterprise began with good prospects, and if it had had something significant to contribute to the automotive world, it might well have solidified its position by the time the output of new cars caught up with the deferred demand. But it soon became apparent that while Henry J. Kaiser's success in his other manufacturing operations was due in part to his drawing ideas on production from the automobile industry, he had nothing to contribute to it in return. The Kaiser cars were conventional, unoriginal designs built by conventional methods. Moreover, while the conversion of war-built aircraft plants provided factory space cheaply, it was a less efficient arrangement than plant specifically designed for the quantity manufacture of motor vehicles. There is a telling comparison in the 1950 records of Kaiser and Hudson. They made almost the same number of cars, 151,000 for Kaiser and 144,000 for Hudson, but where Hudson made $12 million profit, Kaiser showed a $13 million loss. Manufacturing facilities were not the whole story, but it is worth observing that the Ford Motor Company, which had operated Willow Run, considered and rejected an opportunity to buy it from the government when the war ended.

There were other postwar aspirants besides Henry J. Kaiser for a place in the automotive world. The most flamboyant was a Chicago businessman named Preston Tucker, who proposed to produce a rear-engined automobile with sports-car lines, tentatively called the Torpedo. The Tucker Corporation leased a government-built factory in Chicago where the Dodge Division of Chrysler had made engines for B-29 Superfortresses. Tucker, however, ran into financial troubles and went out of business in 1949. A similar effort to market a sports car named Playboy (unrelated to the Jordan Playboy of the 1920's) was even shorter-lived.

A far more interesting experiment in the light of future automotive developments was the Crosley Corporation's attempt to produce what would later be termed a compact. The Crosley was a lightweight car with a four-cylinder engine. It first appeared in 1939, but since it scarcely had time to get on the market before production was halted, it is properly a postwar development. The Crosley had financial substance behind it in that it was sponsored by the manufacturers of Crosley radio and television equipment. It survived until 1952, when the company was bought by General Tire and Rubber and production of the car ceased. It was just a little premature. Had the Crosley still been on the market five years later, when the taste of the American public was turning to compacts, it could conceivably have been a brilliant success.

If it is possible to draw conclusions from these ventures, the evidence indicates that entry into the American automobile industry has become inordinately difficult but not necessarily impossible. Kaiser did after all stay in the motor-vehicle business, although not on the scale initially contemplated. The manufacturers of foreign cars were to demonstrate in the 1950's that the American passenger automobile market could be penetrated. Admittedly they were in a more favorable position than a new domestic producer in that they could exist without American sales, but nevertheless they proved that the American buyer could be wooed away from his accustomed choices. The requisites for a newcomer appear to be: (1) a definite innovation in design or techniques of production; (2) adequate financing; (3) a substantial and well-organized marketing organization; and (4) accurate timing. A ponderous inertia on the part of the existing manufacturers, causing an excessively sluggish response to new developments, may also be essential. The odds against this particular combination of circumstances occurring are certainly heavy, but it could happen.

PRICES AND WAGES

The process of resuming the peacetime manufacture of motor vehicles involved a great deal more than reorganizing factories and waiting for materials to become available. The end of the war was accompanied by a sharp price inflation, which the Truman administration tried rather ineffectually to restrain by continuing the price control structure created during the war. At the same time the inflationary pressures were stimulating demands from labor for higher wages and these demands were resisted still less effectively by an administration which owed a heavy political debt to organized labor.

The immediate consequences in automobile manufacturing offer an interesting commentary on the nature of mass production. After the surrender of Germany in 1945, the industry was authorized to make 200,000 vehicles for civilian use during the rest of the year, if it could find the materials. The collapse of Japan permitted the restriction on numbers to be removed, but material shortages and labor troubles limited the attainable volume of production and forced up unit costs on the vehicles that were manufactured. Mass-production methods will turn out large quantities cheaply; they will not do it for small numbers. The Office of Price Administration, however, used the levels of 1942 to set its ceilings on new-car prices, so that even though the industry was putting warmed-over 1942 models on its assembly lines in order to minimize delays in production, there was a negative relationship between price and cost. The Ford Motor Company, for instance, was restricted to a price ceiling of $780 for a car that cost $1,041 to make. When Henry Ford II pointed this fact out publicly, he was vitriolically assailed by Chester Bowles, then head of the OPA, as a member of a selfish conspiracy to "undermine the American people's bulwark against economic disaster."

The price problem solved itself with the termination of controls in 1947 and the increasing output of new cars to restore the supply side of the market. There was no return to prewar levels; new car prices in the late 1940's were approximately twice what they had been ten years before; but the increase reflected quite accurately the decline in the purchasing power of the dollar.

Labor relations were a more persistent problem. With the

coming of peace there was a near epidemic of wildcat strikes and unauthorized work stoppages both in the automobile companies and in their supplier firms. These were a consequence of the tensions of readjustment to peacetime conditions and could be counted on to subside when a reasonable degree of economic stability was restored. On the other hand, the stand taken by the United Automobile Workers involved basic considerations of long-range policy. During the war there had been a general freeze on wages, but high overtime earnings had given most automotive workers substantial gains in actual take-home pay. The UAW now insisted that this level of remuneration be continued by increased peacetime wage rates. The demand had some merit since prices and living costs were obviously not going to revert to their former levels. The same consideration applied to relatively novel issues in contract negotiations, such as fringe benefits and the tying of wage rates to the cost-of-living index.

The industry, however, was not prepared to guarantee a year-round forty-hour work week or to concede that wage rates should be based on profits. The determination of work schedules and decisions on what to do with profits were regarded as prerogatives of management, and there was a feeling that wage scales should bear some relationship to the productivity of the worker. On this point, the argument that wages should be determined by ability to pay, the UAW prepared to attack General Motors, as the company with the best profit record in the business. If the principle could be established there, it would be a great triumph, although it was never clear how standards established at General Motors could be applied to companies that were having a desperate struggle to survive.

In any event, when a demand for a 30 per cent wage increase was rejected, a strike began at General Motors in November, 1945, and lasted until the following March. The final settlement was for an eighteen and one-half cent raise representing an increase of about 15 per cent, plus some fringe benefits. Negotiations were handicapped by the fact that the UAW was itself involved in a bitter struggle for control between pro- and anticommunist factions. The anticommunists finally won under the leadership of Walter Reuther, but while the fight was on, the contending forces felt obligated to outdo each other in displaying "militancy." Nor was a spirit of compromise stimulated when President Truman publicly endorsed the union's position on the relationship between wages and profits.

The other automobile companies escaped the long agony of General Motors, but they reached approximately similar settlements in the spring of 1946 in the form of a substantial increase in hourly wage rates. At this juncture the union members themselves exhibited a definite preference for straight cash raises rather than greater fringe benefits. The other issues were left in abeyance.

When the next round of negotiations began in 1948, the atmosphere had changed. The manufacturers were anxious to avoid work stoppages. They were getting into full-scale production and were beginning to meet the clamorous postwar demand for new cars. Moreover, they had discovered, as had other industrialists, that higher costs resulting from concessions to labor could be passed on to the buying public without objection from Washington. On its side the UAW was under the chastening influence of the Taft-Hartley Act, passed over President Truman's veto in 1947 in response to an outburst of public indignation against the arrogance and irresponsibility of a number of labor leaders and their unions. In justice to the UAW, it had not been one of the major offenders; nevertheless its leaders had to be aware that there was a need for circumspection.

Once again an agreement with General Motors was to be the criterion for automotive labor standards. This time, however, the bargaining was done in private, by parties who were in a reasonably amicable mood and genuinely wanted to come to terms with each other. The result was a contract of historic importance in American labor relations, since it established a pattern that was widely followed in the next decade. Its most conspicuous features were first, a provision adjusting wage rates in accordance with the cost-of-living index, computed by the United States Department of Labor; second, an annual "improvement factor," calculated to allow for the increased productivity of the worker resulting from advances in manufacturing techniques.

This agreement was to run for two years. When it expired in 1950 it was renewed with some modification for another five years. Meanwhile the UAW negotiated a new contract with Ford in 1949 that incorporated another cherished objective, a company-financed pension plan for hourly wage employees. In the 1949 settlement all Ford employees who had served for thirty years were guaranteed a retirement income of $100 a month, the company making up the difference between that figure and the employee's Social Security benefits.

Because the automobile industry was so much the keystone of the American economy, its labor relations had a peculiar significance. It was not just that disputes and strikes in automobile manufacturing would create a snowballing effect of adverse consequences in other sectors of the economy; it was something more subtle. Consciously or unconsciously the American people had come to look on the automobile industry as the model for others to follow. First it had demonstrated dramatically the possibilities of mass production and mass consumption; then it had led the way in making high wages an American industrial practice; and it seemed to have a limitless capacity for fresh achievements in production and performance. Consequently it was taken for granted that the automobile industry would set the national pattern in labor relations, and this instinctive feeling was largely justified. The cost-of-living formula and the improvement factor were adopted in other industries.

On the whole these labor settlements were beneficial. The automotive workers secured higher real wages and positive gains in job security. On the other side of the picture costs of production were increased and were reflected in higher prices. It seems incontestable that granting automatic pay raises when living costs rose tended to exert a constant upward pressure on the wage-price spiral, since higher wages meant higher costs which in turn had to be met by still higher prices. There was a further consequence, not especially welcome to labor. In a highly competitive industry there was a strong incentive to keep costs down, and the most direct way of offsetting higher wage scales was by intensified mechanization and, as it came to be called, automation.

RECONVERSION COMPLETED

At the midcentury point most of these considerations were still in the future. For the moment there was the comforting prospect that the industry was enjoying internal peace and that the other difficulties of the postwar years had finally been ironed out so that the assembly lines were once more producing at capacity. Output in 1949 rose to more than 5,000,000 passenger cars and 1,000,000 other vehicles, finally surpassing the previous record year of 1929. After the seven lean years the famine had ended. It was once more possible for the ordinary American to go to a dealer and buy whatever kind of automobile, new or used, suited his taste. If it happened to suit his pocketbook also, well and good, but that was a minor question.

If our average American had chosen to buy a new car in 1949 or 1950 and had selected one in the popular-price range, it would have cost him about $1,800. It was most likely to have an eight-cylinder engine rated at about 100 horsepower, although six-cylinder engines were available. Compared with prewar models it had sleeker lines, was slightly longer and lower. It had sealed-beam headlights, and although heater and radio were optional, few automobiles were sold without them. The manual gearshift was still standard equipment but practically all makes now offered automatic transmission if the customer so desired.

Motor-vehicle output in 1950 topped 8,000,000 for the first time in automotive history, but while this record was being made the new era was interrupted by the Communist invasion of the Republic of Korea. American military forces went into action on the other side of the world while at home automobile men patiently put away their plans for expansion of civilian production and began to recall what they knew about the manufacture of tanks, guns, aircraft engines, and wing sections. As it turned out, the Korean conflict did not cause a major disturbance of the civilian economy. There were restrictions on production but nothing on the scale of the Second World War. The manufacture of motor vehicles continued on a somewhat reduced scale, but there was no restraint whatever on their use. The torrent of cars pouring on to American highways went right on rising.

CHAPTER 11

The Broad Highway

In the twenty years that followed the Second World War the outstanding feature of the American automotive world was a great advance in highway design and construction rather than in the evolution of the vehicle itself. Automobiles continued to change, in most respects for the better, but there were no really radical innovations. Roads were a different story. There had been, as we have seen, some parkway and express-highway construction earlier, but it was only after the war that the United States began to get an effective national network of roads built specifically to facilitate the flow of high-speed automobile traffic—roads, in other words, that would encourage rather than obstruct utilization of the potentialities of motor vehicles.

It was high time. In the continuing race between highway and car the latter was emphatically ahead. For all the work that had been done since the first federal highway program in 1916, most American road mileage was still essentially improvement of pre-automotive routes: wagon trails, cart tracks, and cowpaths. U.S. 40, from Washington to St. Louis, followed faithfully the route of the old National Road, which had never been contemplated for use by self-propelled vehicles. U.S. 1, from Maine to Florida, offered a spectrum of conditions calculated to impede rather than assist the flow of traffic. Its northern segment wandered along the Maine coast, offering splendid scenery but also innumerable curves and villages. From Boston to New York it was the Boston Post Road, following the stagecoach route of earlier days and passing through an endless sequence of populous communities. South of New York it took the traveler straight through Philadelphia, Baltimore, and Washington. Eventually it reached the southern tip of Florida, passing en route through a number of localities where justices of the peace and police officials derived much of their income from trapping out-of-state motorists in technical violations of local traffic ordinances.

Even with new roads there had been a tendency to emphasize economy of construction rather than expediting of traffic, so that curves were sharp and grades steep. In an economy where the demand for and production of automobiles was steadily climbing because of the postwar surge in population, accompanied by a general increase in real wages and a rising standard of living, adherence to conventional highway techniques would in a fairly brief span of time have had a seriously retarding effect on both the manufacture and use of motor vehicles. It may be difficult to envisage conditions of worse traffic congestion than actually existed, but such a situation could have developed if there had been shortsightedness in highway planning.

THE TOLLROADS

It was obvious to highway authorities and engineers that what was needed was a network of trunk roads constructed as multilane, limited-access expressways. The technique was well understood; the difficulty was financial, in that such roads were extremely expensive to build. The normal sources of funds for highway construction, even with federal aid increased by the Interstate and Defense Highway Act of 1944, were inadequate for this purpose, particularly in a period when rapidly mounting costs persistently outran revenues. Consequently state after state turned to the example offered by the Pennsylvania Turnpike.

This project had proved to be highly successful both financially and in permitting the smooth flow of a large volume of traffic. There had been grave doubts about the willingness of motorists to pay tolls when alternative free roads were available. The Pennsylvania Turnpike Authority, in fact, had had to have its initial 160-mile section financed by federal funds; 40 per cent of the cost, or $29.2 million, came from a Public Works Administration grant and the rest, $40.8 million, came as a loan from the Reconstruction Finance Corporation.

TABLE 3

TOLLROAD TRAVEL

These are the results of test runs made under the supervision of the Indiana Toll Road Commission to demonstrate the savings on limited-access highways.

Trucks
Chicago–Jersey City round trip via tollroads as compared with U.S. Routes 30 and 22.

Factor	Turnpike Savings
Elapsed time	29 hours, 54 minutes
Travel time	11 hours, 17 minutes
Gasoline consumption	35 gallons
Speed per hour	8.2 miles faster
Gear shifts	2,339
Brake applications	696
Full stops	185

Passenger Cars
Chicago–New York round trip via toll roads as compared with U.S. Routes 30 and 22.

Factor	Turnpike Savings
Driving time	10 hours, 34 minutes
Average speed	14.66 m.p.h. faster
Average miles per gallon	0.52
Gear shifts	834
Brake applications	741
Traffic stops	241

SOURCE: Indiana Toll Road Commission

At the end of the war the atmosphere had completely changed. It was evident that motorists were willing to pay tolls for the privilege of traveling on express highways. For most of them the great attraction was the saving of time. Even with the tolls there was a considerable saving of cost also because of the elimination of frequent starting and stopping. For truck traffic this consideration outweighed the time factor, since non-stop operation and easy grades meant substantial economies in fuel consumption and wear-and-tear on the vehicle. Consequently when the State of Maine began to build a turnpike immediately after the war, it was able to finance the project entirely from the sale of bonds secured by the prospective revenues. The first section of the Maine Turnpike, fifty miles from Portland to Kittery on the New Hampshire border, was opened in 1947.

Once the idea was accepted the arguments in favor of tollroads were impressive. They permitted the building and maintenance of express highways without adding to local taxes; to put it another way, those who benefited from the facility paid for it. The alternative method of placing the burden on the users was to raise the money from gasoline taxes, and this was done in the case of the California freeway systems, which were begun at the same time as the principal tollroads. The objection to gasoline taxes is that their incidence is heaviest on the local population whereas the tollroads found their greatest utility in handling through traffic. If a motorist started at one end of the Pennsylvania Turnpike with a full tank of gasoline, he could complete the 360 miles across the state with one refilling, and out-of-state vehicles have composed half the traffic on the Pennsylvania Turnpike. The California situation was different, indeed unique. There, with a tenth of all the motor vehicles in the country and the majority of these concentrated in the Los Angeles area, the bulk of the traffic was local, so that it was reasonable to finance the freeways from gasoline taxes rather then tolls. Anyone who has driven on a California freeway, moreover, will shudder at the thought of the traffic having to stop for tollgates, especially at rush hours.

The advantages of tollroads, financial and otherwise, were such that an extensive network was projected. At the peak of this twentieth century turnpike boom about twelve thousand miles of tollroads were built, building, authorized, or proposed. About

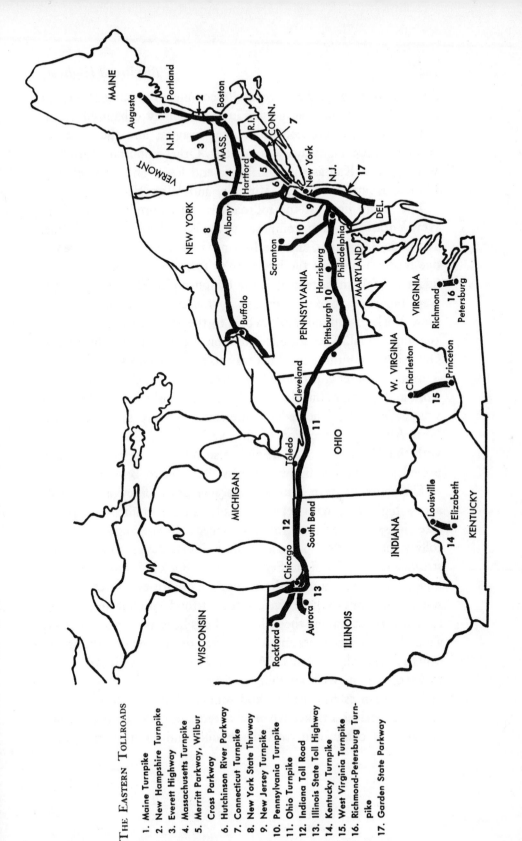

THE EASTERN TOLLROADS

1. Maine Turnpike
2. New Hampshire Turnpike
3. Everett Highway
4. Massachusetts Turnpike
5. Merritt Parkway, Wilbur
   Cross Parkway
6. Hutchinson River Parkway
7. Connecticut Turnpike
8. New York State Thruway
9. New Jersey Turnpike
10. Pennsylvania Turnpike
11. Ohio Turnpike
12. Indiana Toll Road
13. Illinois State Toll Highway
14. Kentucky Turnpike
15. West Virginia Turnpike
16. Richmond-Petersburg Turn-
    pike
17. Garden State Parkway

three thousand miles were eventually completed at a cost of over $2 billion. Most of the mileage was in the intensely urbanized northeastern states, where congestion was heaviest and the need for arterial express highways was greatest. Other important turnpikes were built in Kansas and Oklahoma and lesser ones in Colorado, Florida, Kentucky, Texas, Virginia, and West Virginia.

The "main line" of the tollroads is the 837-mile stretch from New York to Chicago, composed of the New Jersey, Pennsylvania, and Ohio Turnpikes, and the Indiana Toll Road, all completed as one through route in the late 1950's. The largest turnpike system under a single management is the billion-dollar New York Thruway. Begun in 1950, it extended by the end of the decade from New York to Buffalo and beyond to the Pennsylvania state line, 500 miles in all. The original intention was that Pennsylvania and Ohio should continue the Thruway to a connection with the Ohio Turnpike, thereby providing an alternative route between New York and Chicago, but this link was never finished as a tollroad. It was made part of the federal interstate highway system instead. Near Albany an extension of the New York Thruway connects with the Massachusetts Turnpike, also built in the 1950's, which provides an express highway across the state to Boston.

The tollroads have common characteristics. They are limited-access highways, with separate roadways for traffic in opposite directions, and designed for high speeds. Interchanges generally follow the cloverleaf pattern or some similar design so that traffic streams cannot conflict. Service areas, operated as concessions under the supervision of the turnpike authorities, are located at suitable intervals so that travelers can get food, gasoline and oil, and repairs without leaving the tollroads. Tolls have averaged two cents a mile for passenger cars and have ranged up to twelve and thirteen cents a mile for heavy trucks. Aggregate receipts in 1962 were close to $310 million, with another $186 million added by specialized facilities such as toll bridges and tunnels. On most tollroads the motorist receives a ticket when he enters, showing the place, time, and date of entry, and pays the amount indicated on the ticket when he leaves. Some turnpikes, notably in Connecticut and New Hampshire, follow the practice of having tollgates at intervals across the roadway where traffic stops and pays a fixed amount. This arrangement permits local traffic to make short trips on the turnpike without having to pay toll.

Maximum speeds range from fifty-five miles an hour on heavily traveled sections of the eastern turnpikes to eighty in Kansas. In general the tollroads have had better safety records than the conventional highways. As a rule they are patrolled by their own detachments of state police, but this has not been the sole reason for their good showing. The important lesson of the tollroads has been that properly designed highways make possible high-speed movement of traffic with a minimum of accidents.

As might be expected, the financial record of the turnpikes has varied. In areas where traffic is light, revenues have been insufficient to meet the heavy costs of construction, but these conditions have been encountered on only a small part of turnpike mileage. At the other extreme, in heavily populated regions even a tollroad can become congested. When the Pennsylvania Turnpike reached its twentieth anniversary in 1960, it was handling an average of 80,000 vehicles a day, and on occasions of maximum load such as holiday weekends there were tie-ups at places such as the tunnels, where the four traffic lanes had to be squeezed into two. On the whole, however, the tollroads fulfilled effectively the purpose for which they were intended: that is, to provide up-to-date express highways that would pay their own way.

Yet their reign was destined to be brief. When the Interstate Highway Act of 1956 provided for a nationwide system of toll-free superhighways, to be constructed predominantly at federal expense, the incentive to build additional tollroads was abruptly removed. At the time this act was passed a number of states, ranging as far west as Washington, had authorized or proposed some eight thousand miles of turnpike, above and beyond what was already finished or under construction, but only a fifth of this total was actually built as tollroad. At the same time the existing turnpikes were far from being put out of business. About 80 per cent of them were made part of the interstate system while continuing to operate as tollroads. Important new additions were made to various turnpike systems after 1956, exclusive of the completion of work already in progress, and in the 1960's the senior member of the group, the Pennsylvania Turnpike Authority, was so far from contemplating oblivion that it was building new tunnels to eliminate its worst bottleneck and to upgrade the highway to modern standards of construction by providing separate roadways instead of merely a central divider.

THE INTERSTATE SYSTEM

The origins of the interstate highways go back to the Interstate and Defense Highway Act of 1944, in which Congress attempted to anticipate postwar needs. These were going to be considerable, because during the war the nation's roads had deteriorated. New construction had been almost entirely halted, and maintenance had suffered from lack of materials and manpower. The act was far more comprehensive than its predecessors. It authorized the expenditure of $1.5 billion on roads in the three years following the termination of hostilities, on the equal-matching basis of previous legislation. For the first time urban as well as rural areas were made eligible for federal aid, and 40,000 miles of highway were to be designated as interstate routes, to receive the largest share of the funds.

The act was a bold and well-intentioned step toward a full-scale, coordinated national highway system, and it made possible a substantial amount of urgently needed new construction, but it still proved to be inadequate. The trouble was that given the magnitude of the problem and the soaring inflation of the postwar years, even a sum like $1.5 billion was swallowed up with frightening rapidity. By the time immediate requirements for both urban and rural roads were taken care of, there was not enough left for more than a gesture at the development of a new interstate highway system.

There were two possible solutions: an extensive development of tollroads or a really massive federal highway program. The former, as we have seen, was started but the eventual decision was for the latter. By the Interstate Highway Act of 1956, Congress provided for the construction of 41,000 miles of toll-free express highways, with 90 per cent of the cost to be paid by the federal government. Indeed, since the act made special allowances for states with substantial acreage of tax-free public land and for additional improvements such as prohibition of billboard advertising within specified distances from the right-of-way, it was possible for a state like Nevada to receive 95 per cent of its interstate highway costs from federal funds.

To finance this program Congress imposed excise taxes on motor fuels, tires and tubes, new buses, trucks, and trailers, and a use tax on trucks exceeding thirteen tons weight. The proceeds were allocated to a highway trust fund, to be applied to construction of the interstate routes on a pay-as-you-go basis. The entire system was expected to be completed in 1971, and the initial estimate of cost was $27 billion. As of 1965 the work was progressing on schedule, with about half the interstate network far enough advanced to be open to traffic. The price tag, however, had risen to $46 billion, and it was a safe guess that the final cost would reach twice the original figure.

While the superhighways were in progress a still greater expenditure of money and effort was going into the building and improvement of conventional roads, so that practically every part of the United States was becoming readily accessible by motor vehicle. In 1946 the hard-surfaced road mileage in the United States for the first time equaled the non-surfaced, about 1,500,000 miles each, and the proportion of hard-surfaced roads climbed steadily thereafter, reaching 71 per cent of the total of 3,100,000 miles in 1962. Although the creation of this improved highway network was not the only cause of the tremendous increase in the volume of highway travel that followed the Second World War, it certainly was an indispensable prerequisite.

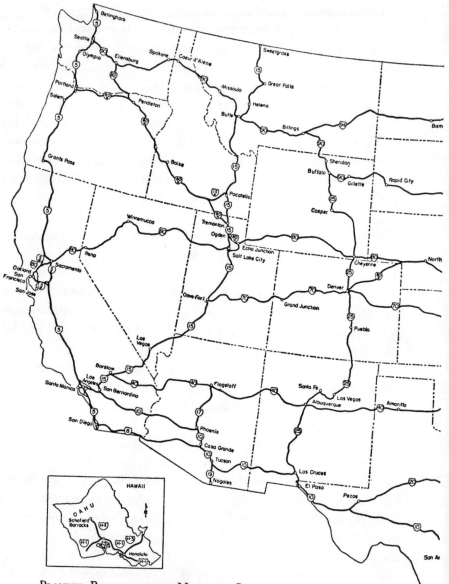

PLANNED ROUTES OF THE NATIONAL SYSTEM OF INTERSTATE
AND DEFENSE HIGHWAYS

The total projected mileage of the national system of superhighways is
41,000 miles. Of this total about half was open to traffic as the present volume went to press.

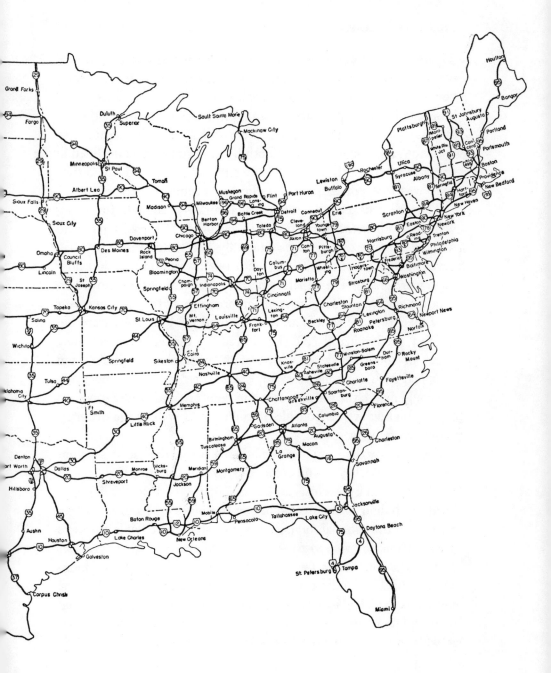

Highway Transport

The increase appeared equally in commercial and non-commercial use of the roads. Indeed, it was only now that the potentialities of commercial highway transport began to be fully realized. In 1948 buses carried more passengers than trains for the first time, although in passenger miles the railroads were still ahead and remained so until 1962. As a matter of fact both bus and train travel declined in the 1950's while airlines and private automobiles gained; the difference was that rail passenger traffic lost ground faster.

The railroads can be criticized accurately enough for being willing, with some exceptions, to abandon the passenger field without a contest, but they admittedly had handicaps. They had never been competitive in cost with bus transportation, and now they were losing the superiority they had formerly enjoyed in comfort and speed. The buses of this era were a great improvement over their predecessors. The vehicles used for long trips were big and fast, predominantly diesel-powered. By the middle 1950's they were air-conditioned, provided with washroom facilities, and equipped with reclining seats adjustable for sleeping. In short, the bus could match the railway coach in comfort, and where travel on express highways was possible, it could do as well as the ordinary passenger train in speed.

Highway carriers also increased their share of the nation's freight traffic. Between 1950 and 1960 the volume of intercity freight carried by truck (exclusive, that is, of strictly local hauls) rose from 173 billion to almost 300 billion ton-miles, or from 16 to 22.5 per cent of the national total. Railroad freight traffic fell in the same decade from 597 to 579 ton-miles, a decline from 56 to 43.5 per cent of the total. Like buses, trucks designed for heavy or long-distance hauling underwent striking developments. They became enormous vehicles, capable of carrying loads of twenty tons and with engines requiring sixteen separate gear ratios. For these trucks, as with buses, diesel power was increasingly used.

One of the outstanding features of the 1940's and 1950's was the widespread use of tractor-trailer combinations, in which the load was carried in a trailer detachable from the power unit, so that the tractor could be employed elsewhere when the trailer was being loaded or unloaded. The truck trailer was somewhat of a rarity before the Second World War; by 1960 well over a million were in service. On the open highways of the West, moreover, trailers towed in tandem offered a further development in truck transportation.

When it came to competing for freight traffic, the railroads were by no means disposed to let the contest go by default, as they had done with their passenger business, and the emergence of the truck trailer proved to be a quite unexpected asset for them. A trailer is after all merely a large container for holding goods in transit; it can be moved equally well on its own wheels or on a railroad flatcar. A single train could easily carry a hundred trailers at an aggregate cost less than that of hauling each one over the road separately. So, in spite of protests and court action by the Teamsters Union, "piggyback" transportation was born in the early 1950's. From its improvised beginnings it grew in ten years to proportions that not only won back for the railroads some of their lost ground but also indicated one means of approach to creation of an efficiently integrated transportation network.

Although long-distance, heavy-duty trucks provided the most dramatic and most important aspect of the growth of freight transport by road, they represented a minor fraction, less than 5 per cent, of the total number of trucks in service. Of the 12,000,000 trucks registered in the United States in 1962, three-fifths were classified as "small," carrying loads less than four tons. These were the ubiquitous pickup trucks, panel trucks, multistop delivery trucks, and all the others whose ceaseless comings and goings are taken for granted on American roads and streets. If their operations are added to the intercity freight movements, then since 1954 more tonnage has been carried by motor truck in the United States than by any other medium of transportation. The distribution of business among types is illuminating. The single-unit trucks, the small and medium-sized vehicles, accounted for 60 per cent of truck mileage and carried 25 per cent of the freight. The big trailer combinations logged 40 per cent of the mileage and carried 75 per cent of the freight, calculated in ton-miles.

Mass Mobility

Impressive as were the advances in commercial transport, they were minor compared with the outpouring of private automobiles on to the nation's highways. It was not that people by and large traveled farther; the family car consistently averaged between nine and ten thousand miles a year. It was just that there were many more people and cars on the roads. Private automobile registrations in the United States were 25,500,000 when the Second World War ended. They doubled in the next ten years and added another twenty million in the decade after that. By 1960 four-fifths of all American families owned at least one car, an increase of 30 per cent in twenty years. The distribution of automobile ownership among income groups ranged from 57 per cent of the households with incomes below $4,000 a year to 95 per cent of the households with incomes about $10,000.

It would be impossible to itemize all the multifarious uses to which this mass of vehicles was put, but a conspicuous one was to take to the road in search of enjoyment. The growing urbanization of American life seems to have created a backlash in the form of an urge to get out into the open, and widespread ownership of automobiles made it possible for this urge to be satisfied. It was no longer a matter of driving just for the sake of driving. People by the million went by car to beaches, lakes, mountains, and forests, in search of recreation or obeying the long-standing adjuration to "see America first."

The impact of this roving host was considerable. Recreational facilities were inundated, not only in the neighborhood of the big cities but all over the country. Recreation, indeed, became an economic enterprise on a scale which would have been out of the question if people had been limited to the proximity of the great centers of population. Tourist traffic was something to be wooed by public authority as well as by private business. State parks, for instance, were practically non-existent in the 1920's; thirty years later there were more than two thousand, and most states also provided picnic and rest areas along their highways, many of them quite elaborate and attractive installations.

For this volume of travel the tourist facilities of the previous generation were no longer sufficient. The somewhat primitive cabins of earlier days were replaced by motels and tourist courts, more than forty thousand of them, varying from simple structures offering nothing more than sleeping facilities to elaborate establishments with their own restaurants and bars, swimming pools, room telephones, and other luxuries. Whatever their differences, all these establishments had one vital characteristic in common; they were designed specifically for the accommodation of people who traveled by automobile. It was absolutely essential that the motorist should have space for his car as well as himself, preferably in the immediate proximity of his room so that loading and unloading could be done with maximum convenience. As the business expanded, chains of motels came into existence, offering some assurance of standards of quality and the opportunity to make reservations from one stage of a journey to the next.

For those who preferred to eschew motels on grounds of cost or preference, there were camp grounds, although never quite enough during the vacation season for the crowds who sought them. More important, there was the trailer. Large house trailers, euphemistically termed mobile homes, became popular during the Second World War as a means of remedying housing shortages in the vicinity of newly built military installations and war plants, and they continued to be used by people affected with wanderlust. The biggest ones needed truck tractors to tow them, but there were smaller types that could be pulled by the ordinary passenger car, ranging all the way down to the simple units, sometimes homemade, that carried only goods. A variation of the trailer was the camper, a structure containing sleeping and cooking facilities and mounted on a small truck chassis. The house trailer and the camper extended the range of the vacationing motorist by enabling him to penetrate areas where commercial accommodations were either scanty or non-existent.

To serve these rambling millions the automobile service associations became organizations with greatly expanded functions. They provided emergency road service and legal assistance for their members, prepared maps and other guides for travel, kept track of road conditions, checked the quality of motels and restaurants, and frequently sold insurance. By far the largest group was the American Automobile Association, which included 750 member clubs and branches. As one sample of its activities, AAA garages were answering close to 70,000,000 service calls a year.

Not all the consequences of this mass movement on the highways were desirable. It was very easy to get the impression that the American landscape was being overrun by a horde of ignorant and wantonly destructive savages, whose idea of enjoying the beauties of nature was to line the roads with empty beer cans, litter the beaches with refuse, throw rubbish into the geysers of Yellowstone, scrawl obscene remarks on imposing rock formations, and toss burning cigarette stubs into woodlands. In justice to the American motorist these acts were the work of the inevitable irresponsible minority. Nevertheless it was physically impossible for millions of people to overflow scenic and recreational areas without changing them radically—in the eyes of purists, without spoiling the unspoiled. Regions whose charm stemmed in part from their inaccessibility were bound to lose some of their quality when concrete and asphalt brought visitors by the thousand. On Cape Cod, for instance, which had always been close to centers of population, the building of an express highway from the canal to Provincetown took on the proportions of a calamity. Nature lovers were deeply and rightly concerned about the preservation of the remaining scenic and wilderness areas of the United States. Apart from the problem of numbers, the planning and construction of superhighways was frequently done with an arrogant and arbitrary disregard both for property rights and the preservation of irreplaceable esthetic or historic features. Too often due process of law was replaced by a bulldozer.

At the same time it was difficult to deplore the social revolution which opened recreational travel to the many instead of the privileged few. Before the great expansion of paved road and automobile ownership, the Adirondacks and the White Mountains were vacation resorts only for the wealthy, the Great Smokies were an unknown region populated by a few primitive backwoodsmen, and for most persons seeing the Grand Canyon except in pictures was as unlikely as climbing Mount Everest. There was a great deal to be said for enabling the American people to enjoy their own country—to say nothing of visiting their neighbors, because automobiles ran just as well on the roads of Canada and Mexico as on those of the United States.

That some of the results were unfortunate is undeniable, but on balance the good appears to outweigh the bad. There is no reason to believe that the scenic beauties of the North American continent were intended to be reserved for a minuscule and favored minority, and there is strong reason to believe that it is eminently desirable for the members of an intensely urbanized society to be able, quite literally, to get out of town. There is even a variety of Newton's Third Law in operation. The threat of the expanding millions to the beauties of nature has stimulated energetic efforts to preserve those that are left. The response of public authorities at all levels to this mass movement on the highways has been—has had to be—expansion of recreational facilities, acquisition of sites for parks to meet the growing demand, and at least gestures toward the preservation of wildlife and scenic and national wonders. It may be that what has been done has not yet been enough. As with the building of roads, it has been inordinately difficult to keep pace with the multiplication of both people and cars. But it is worth something that the effort has been undertaken.

THE PASSING OF RURAL ISOLATION

The combination of motor vehicles and hard-surfaced roads, both in profusion, also brought about far-reaching changes in rural life. It was not the only agency to have this effect. Credit has to be given to the telephone, the radio, and television, and to the extension of electric power to country districts. But the motor vehicle was the agency of direct physical contact, the medium by which the farmer could take himself and his family to town for business or pleasure.

There was far more to the story than the mere facilitating of travel from country to city. From time immemorial the townsman had enjoyed all the advantages in social life, in culture, in education, in medical services. Even the language indicates the gap; the "urbane" individual came from the city. Although the automobile did not close this gap entirely, it certainly narrowed it. The country resident, especially the one who was remote from rail transport, was no longer cut off from the amenities of city life. He had the opportunity to seek them out, or to have them brought to him. By the 1950's it was becoming very difficult in the United States to distinguish on sight the farmer from the townsman. The badly dressed, unshaven individual who might be encountered on the street was more likely to be a college student than a "hayseed" come to town for the day.

In the field of education the motor vehicle, particularly the bus, made it possible for rural schools to approximate urban by allowing children to be transported over considerable distances to consolidated schools. The little red schoolhouse of American folklore was on its way to extinction during the 1950's, at the rate of ten a day. One can grow nostalgic about the barefoot boy making his way to the local one-room school, and perhaps something irretrievable was lost with its passing. Nevertheless the consolidated school had more to offer in educational resources; it could attract better-trained teachers for one thing, partly because the teachers themselves owned automobiles and therefore did not have to fear being lost in the "sticks" out of contact with their profession.

As with education, so with medicine. The old-fashioned country doctor is a cherished figure in American legend, and he represented values which are emphatically worth preserving. It was never necessary for his medical association to suggest, as was done in California in recent years, that he might display his caduceus on something less ostentatious than a Cadillac. Nevertheless it was undeniable that easy and rapid highway transportation made possible better medical service in rural areas. The country doctor delivering the baby or performing an appendectomy in the farmhouse by the light of kerosene lamps was a touching and often a heroic picture, but it was also a dangerous picture, no matter how great the dedication and skill. It was infinitely better that medical aid could be summoned by telephone and arrive rapidly by car and that in case of need the patient could normally be moved to a hospital in time to receive proper care.

Although no claim can be advanced that the motor vehicle provided a solution for the "farm problem," it did profoundly affect the economic pattern of farm life. Before the arrival of the automobile the economic limit of wagon transportation was fifteen to twenty miles. Beyond that the cost of moving goods by highway became so prohibitively high that a village or farm more than twenty miles from rail or water carriage was almost inevitably consigned to a subsistence economy. By contrast, in the middle of the twentieth century, nine-tenths of all farm commodities in the United States were carried to market by motor truck. No community had to be left out of the mainstream of the national economy. In purchasing, likewise, motor transport made the farmer independent if he so chose of the resources of the nearby village store.

This catalog of change could be carried through such specific details as traveling libraries or mobile highway post offices, analogous to railway post offices, in which the mail is sorted en route with resultant expediting of service to small towns and rural areas.

This system of handling mail was initiated in 1951 in response to the shrinking of rail facilities through the abandonment of branch lines and the curtailment of local main-line service.

There were some regrets at these patterns of change from those who saw local distinctiveness and individuality being submerged in a rising tide of monotonous sameness. It was certainly true that when the United States entered the latter half of the twentieth century there was a general uniformity in styles, tastes, and habits, and no doubt there were penalties attached. However, if we consider farm life of the preautomobile era in terms of Hamlin Garland's description of his mother's existence ("life" is too positive a term for it) in *A Son of the Middle Border*, it is possible to argue that the assets outweighed the liabilities. The farm woman of that period, with nothing to look forward to but unending drudgery and drabness, would cheerfully and enthusiastically have exchanged her contribution to local individuality for a uniformity that enabled her to get away once in a while. The automobile was removing the Middle Border and Sinclair Lewis's Gopher Prairie from the American scene, and there were few who could seriously mourn their departure.

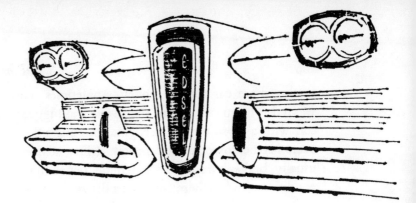

CHAPTER 12

Tail Fins and Compacts

The Korean War was merely a brief interlude in the growth of the American automobile industry. The automotive contribution to the conflict was impressive, to be sure, but there was no need for the all-out effort of the Second World War, and the curtailment of civilian production was minor. The worst obstacle was shortage of metal alloys, and this was overcome in part by substituting plastic components wherever possible. As soon as the war ended automobile manufacturing surged to new peaks of productivity, quite unmistakably carrying the economy with it. Business rose with the automobile industry to the crest of a boom in 1955, marked by the staggering production figure of more than 9,000,000 vehicles for the year, almost 8,000,000 of them passenger cars. This prodigious performance temporarily flooded the new-automobile market. Demand fell off by 2,000,000 a year later, with the result that the whole economy suffered a sharp recession in 1957.

This expansion in production was accompanied by improvements in assembly-line techniques that made it possible to keep retail prices of new cars in a stable relationship to the national price index. Between 1946 and 1955 the average retail price of a new automobile (f.o.b. Detroit) rose from $1,500 to $1,900, an increase of 27 per cent, which was less than the rise in both the general consumer price index and average weekly earnings of workers in manufacturing industries. At the same time the consumer was getting more car for his money—sometimes more than he really wanted. The automobile of the 1950's was bigger than its predecessor, with a more powerful engine, running up to 300 horsepower even in the lower-priced makes. (The advertised figures were usually brake horsepower based on bench tests under optimum conditions, and so there could be a discrepancy between announced rating and actual performance.) By the middle of the decade the majority of all passenger cars were being sold with automatic transmissions, and the proportion grew steadily larger. Brake and light systems became more reliable, and power brakes and power steering came into more general use. Tubeless tires, including the punctureproof type, became available early in the 1950's, and there was a constant improvement in the quality of automotive fuels and lubricants.

The assembly of motor vehicles had come a long way since Henry Ford's pioneering days at Highland Park. The customer of the 1950's could choose among engines, body styles, colors for both exterior and interior, and even hubcaps. He could designate what he wanted in the way of accessories—radio, heater, air-conditioner, for instance—and the car combining his preferences would roll off the assembly line in company with others representing different assortments of choices. Punch-card control systems kept the variety of selections in order. Automatic controls were coming into extensive use throughout the manufacturing process, not only to keep production costs down but because they made for greater accuracy and quality.

TABLE 4

AVERAGE RETAIL PRICES OF PASSENGER CARS

1899	$1,559
1909	1,719
1919	1,157
1929	828
1939	845
1947	1,580
1955	1,910
1959	2,060
1963	2,310

SOURCE: Automobile Manufacturers Association.

The area in which the consumer appeared to have the least choice was price. The automobile manufacturers competed energetically with each other, but in technical features, styling, comfort, and safety rather than in price. In economic terms the industry was an oligopoly operating under a system of administered prices. As is usual in such situations, the largest producer, General Motors, set the price pattern to which the others generally conformed. There was no question of price-fixing; had there been, the lawyers of the Department of Justice's Anti-Trust Division would certainly have made a case of it. The automobile firms simply had too much investment at stake to engage in price wars that could result only in the participants' inflicting lasting injury on each other. General Motors was in a particularly difficult quandary. It could have cut prices for its own cars and still have earned respectable profits, but the effect would have been to ruin its competitors, except Ford probably, and this outcome would hardly have met with the approval of the Department of Justice.

There was, as a matter of fact, little public complaint about automobile price policies. Car prices, we have seen, had moved up no faster than the general price level, and if the improvements in quality are allowed for, the consumer's dollar was actually going farther than before. Besides, the buyer had more leeway than was apparent. He normally had the opportunity to bargain with the dealer on the trade-in allowance for his old car, which could be a considerable factor in the total payment, and although the dealer was expected to be guided by the manufacturer's list price, he was still an independent businessman with freedom to make adjustments. There was always, moreover, a check on any excessive rise in new-car prices: the enormous and uncontrolled used-car market. Consequently criticism of the automobile industry's price policies came mostly from sources that were not actually interested in unrestricted price competition but were using the charge of needlessly high prices either as leverage for higher wage demands, or to justify a greater degree of governmental intervention in the automobile industry.

THE TRIUMPH OF CONCENTRATION

The oligopolistic structure of the automobile industry was further confirmed by shrinkage in the number of vehicle manufacturing firms. Among passenger-car producers, the Kaiser-Willys effort has been noted. Except for jeeps, it ended in 1955. The remaining independents, bearing historic names in American automobiledom, found themselves hard pressed and sought preservation in merger. In 1954 Nash-Kelvinator and Hudson joined forces as the American Motors Corporation, with all manufacturing operations concentrated at Kenosha, while Studebaker and Packard combined as the Studebaker-Packard Corporation.

Of the two, American Motors was to prove more successful by far, a result traceable primarily to the ability and persistence of one man. In 1950 Nash-Kelvinator had acquired as its general manager George Romney, the man who had distinguished himself as manager of the Automotive Council for War Production, and when American Motors was formed, Romney became its president. He was aware that merger alone would not be enough; if American Motors was to succeed it must offer something different that would attract business away from the Big Three. As early as 1950 he had revived the name of Rambler for a low-priced car, and he was convinced that there was a market for a smaller, lower-priced car than the producers in the United States were offering. So American Motors concentrated its effort on the Rambler, to the extent of discontinuing both the Nash and the Hudson in 1957. It was a gamble, and for several critical years it appeared that Romney would lose.

Studebaker-Packard seemed to have about the same prospects as American Motors at the time of its formation. The two groups started at the same level in total sales, approximately 100,000 in 1954. The Studebaker-Packard structure, however, was inherently weaker. Packard, never a large-scale producer, was struggling to hold a place in the luxury car field and was faring badly in competition with Cadillac as a prestige automobile. The Packard plant in Detroit was closed in 1956 and production transferred to the Studebaker factory in South Bend; two years later the Packard name passed into history. The Studebaker half of the combination had its own weaknesses, centering on the fact that the company had never come back to real financial health after its catastrophe in 1932.

Consequently this merger failed to achieve the hoped-for results. There was a time in the middle 1950's when the Curtiss-Wright Corporation was negotiating for the acquisition of Studebaker-Packard, mainly so that the latter's $35 million deficit could be used to offset Curtiss-Wright's profits for tax purposes. This plan, however, was eventually dropped. All it achieved was to provide a startling illustration of the effect of the tax structure on business policy; it takes some readjustment of customary economic ideas to realize that there are conditions in which a company can lose money on this scale and be a desirable acquisition. Studebaker production in South Bend lasted until 1964, when the company gave up the attempt to compete in the American market and moved its automobile manufacturing to Hamilton, Ontario.

The trend to concentration also appeared in truck manufacturing, with the White Motor Company as the focus. For White this development was an impressive performance for a company that had had a difficult time during the depression years of the early thirties and was under the constant pressure of competition from the automotive giants, including three General Motors divisions engaged in the manufacture of commercial vehicles (GMC Truck and Coach, Chevrolet, and Pontiac).

White's expansion began in the 1950's, the first major step being the acquisition in 1953 of the Autocar Company of Ardmore, Pennsylvania, one of the oldest of American motor vehicle manufacturers (1898) and one of the earliest (1908) to give up passenger-car production and concentrate on trucks. Next came Reo (1957), and Diamond T (1958), to make White by far the largest of the dwindling number of firms engaged in the manufacture of commercial vehicles. For this achievement credit goes principally to Robert F. Black, who became president of the White Motor Company in 1935 and successfully pulled it out of its depression difficulties—summed up in automotive circles as "Black took White out of the red." His success was based on a calculated realization that his company could not compete in mass production. He told the author in 1956, "If all trucks could be built like passenger cars, we would be out of business." It was necessary for White to lead the field in research and design of motor trucks and to manufacture to quality specifications. So the company pioneered with the cab-over-engine truck, the pancake bus engine, and other innovations. The results speak for themselves; when conditions were ripe, White was able to absorb its competitors. There is a certain irony in the techniques of motor-vehicle manufacturing. The passenger car, which has become a status symbol as much as a medium of transportation, is turned out in impersonal volume by the assembly line. It is the unglamorous, heavy-duty truck that is custom-built to specifications.

In the upper brackets of the industry the Big Three continued to fight for the passenger-car market, with General Motors easily in the lead. The Ford car and the Chevrolet staged a furious race year in and year out for leadership in sales, with Chevrolet usually having a narrow edge, but the full General Motors line outsold the combined Ford offerings by a substantial margin. General Motors had a secure hold on half the entire automobile market and sometimes went higher. It so dominated the industrial scene, indeed, that when its president, Charles E. Wilson, was nominated as Secretary of Defense by President Eisenhower, he could say with a clear conscience to the Senate committee which investigated his qualifications, "What's good for the country is good for General Motors and what's good for General Motors is good for the country."

General Motors' problems in this period came from the judiciary rather than from questions of production and sales. After prolonged investigation and litigation, the United States Supreme Court in 1958 finally ordered the Du Pont Company to divest itself of its General Motors holdings, which came to 23 per cent of the outstanding General Motors common stock, or 63,000,000 shares. It was a difficult decision for a layman to comprehend. There was no suggestion that Du Pont had ever exercised any improper influence over General Motors in their forty-year relationship. The decision was based on a section of the Clayton Act of 1914 prohibiting the holding of stock interests that might restrict competition. The majority of the court held that Du Pont's stock holdings might give it a preferential position in the sale of automobile paints and lacquers to General Motors. There was no evidence that Du Pont had ever acted in this way nor was there allowance for the fact that the Du Pont Company was the pioneer and principal American producer of quick-drying automobile finishes, so that under normal business conditions it would have had a preferential position anyway.

The decision produced consternation in the financial community. In the best of circumstances disposing of 63,000,000 shares of General Motors stock would have posed serious problems. In addition, because this stock had all been acquired between 1916 and 1921, there was a frightening capital-gains tax liability. A proposal that Du Pont place its General Motors stock in a non-voting trust was rejected by the court. Eventually a special act of Congress was required to remove some of the capital-gains liability and make possible the sale of the stock without crippling losses, and by 1964 the stock had been duly disposed of. Such penalties as were involved fell on the Du Pont stockholders and not on General Motors; its automotive supremacy was left unimpaired. In 1964, in fact, General Motors established an all-time record in profits of $1.7 billion.

The 1950's saw the Ford Motor Company firmly and profitably reestablished in second place among automobile manufacturers and energetically but unavailingly trying to narrow the gap between it and General Motors. The Ford weakness was, or seemed to be, in the middle price range, where the Mercury had to compete with General Motors' Buick, Oldsmobile, and Pontiac and Chrysler's

Dodge and De Soto. The Ford firm did not arrive at its conclusion hastily; if anything, it took too long. In the face of suggestions that what was really wanted was a smaller and cheaper car than was being offered, the company conducted an extensive market research, which concluded that there was insufficient demand for a small car but a bright prospect for one in the range between the Lincoln and the Mercury. The result was the Edsel, in which the Ford Motor Company invested $250 million, including whatever it paid the poet Marianne Moore to think up names for it that were never used. It was a well-engineered but rather awkwardly styled car, and it lasted just two years after it was put on the market in 1958. Its failure was due fundamentally to its timing; 1958 was a recession year, when the prospect for a new high-priced automobile was poor in any event, and somewhere between the planning and the unveiling of the Edsel public preference turned away from the big, ornate cars that had dominated the scene for several years. The experiment served to provide a vivid explanation of why the automobile industry had evolved into its pattern of domination by a few very large firms; only a big company could make a mistake costing a quarter of a billion dollars and live.

A brighter and definitely more momentous landmark in Ford history was the first offering of Ford Motor Company stock to the public. This event occurred in 1956 as the result of a decision of the Ford Foundation that it was unwise to have the Foundation's entire resources, enormous as they were, represented by common stock in the Ford Motor Company. The Ford Foundation dates back to 1936, when it was created in order to avoid the possibility that the family might be forced to sell control of the company in order to pay inheritance taxes. In view of the deaths of Edsel Ford and his father within four years of each other it proved to be a wise move. The Foundation was of minor importance for its first ten years, but then in consequence of those two deaths it came into possession of 90 per cent of the stock of the Ford Motor Company, and because of the successful rehabilitation of the company, the Ford Foundation suddenly found itself the world's largest private philanthropic enterprise.

The difficulty was that the stock was non-voting; the Foundation depended on the management of the company but could not control it. Hence the decision to diversify. A transaction of this magnitude naturally required delicate legal and financial handling. Among other things, it was necessary to reclassify the stock so that the purchasers could have an equitable voice in company affairs without sacrificing the proper interest of the Ford family. However, it was all worked out, and the offering of the stock demonstrated that the Ford name had lost none of its glamour. Brokerage houses were swamped with orders for the 10,000,000 shares that were available, and the issue, offered at $64.50, went as high as $70.00 a share in the first few days. Subsequent offerings left the foundation, in 1961, with half the total common stock of the Ford Motor Company, the family with a ninth, and the rest in the hands of the public.

Of the three giants, the Chrysler Corporation experienced the greatest difficulty in maintaining its position during the 1950's, for reasons that cannot readily be explained in terms of clear and tangible occurrences. There were errors of judgment in styling and there were managerial troubles, along with unaccountable shifts in consumer preferences. The visible evidence of Chrysler's troubles was that the company's bread-and-butter model, the Plymouth, lost the third-place position it had held comfortably for twenty years and was persistently outsold by one or the other of the General Motors medium-price lines: Oldsmobile, Buick, or Pontiac. The once-popular De Soto also lost its appeal and was discontinued in 1960.

The process of concentration applied primarily to the actual production of motor vehicles and not so much to the fabrication of parts. The independent supplier firms showed a remarkable capacity to survive in the automotive world. Even mighty General Motors went outside its own organization for half the components of its cars. The manufacturers retained this policy consciously. With some parts, cost calculations showed that it was cheaper to buy on the open market than to install facilities for making them; with others, the supplier company's experience and "know-how" were worth preserving. Moreover, although the automobile company might be making the item itself, it was desirable to keep competitors in existence as a check on the efficiency of one's own operations.

Consequently, while the industry was admittedly dominated by a handful of giant corporations, in the early 1960's there were almost three thousand companies in the United States classified as manufacturers of motor vehicles and parts, and after due allowance for subsidiaries of the big companies, there was manifestly still a multitude of small-scale independents. Outside the automotive industry there were many more suppliers. Tires, for instance, have always been made by rubber manufacturers, although some have been sold under the names of automobile companies. The Ford Motor Company reported in 1963 that it had thirty thousand separate suppliers scattered throughout the world who took fifty-six cents of each dollar the company earned and contributed products which, to quote the company's annual report, "may range from a lockwasher to an entire steelmaking furnace capable of producing seven thousand tons of steel a day."

CONSPICUOUS CONSUMPTION

The Plymouth can fairly be described as a victim of the competition in power and glitter that characterized American automobile manufacturing in the middle 1950's. It continued a little too long to look like a low-priced car at a time when its rivals were trying to eliminate all differences in external appearance between automobiles of varying price ranges. The idea seems to have been that the decision on the purchase of an automobile was based as much on prestige considerations as on convenience of transportation, so that sales would be stimulated if every buyer of a new car could be given the feeling that he was getting something equivalent to a Rolls-Royce. The idea was valid enough, but the method chosen for its execution had the unfortunate effect of giving most new American automobiles an ostentatiously nouveau riche quality from which Rolls-Royce designers would have recoiled in horror—and probably did.

What happened was that lower-priced cars became big and gaudy, whereupon the vehicles in the higher price ranges felt compelled to compensate by becoming bigger and gaudier. Engine horsepower even on the standard models rose to new heights, and body designers were lavish with chrome and gleaming finishes to the point where the glare from car surfaces became a potential driving hazard. Body styles featured grandiose and eye-catching tail fins, justified on the ground that they were needed to house the complex of lights now installed at the rear of an automobile: tail, stop, back-up, and directional. There were even occasional claims that these elaborate fins had a stabilizing effect on the vehicle's motion—which might well have been so if the car had been airborne.

At the peak of the automobile boom of the 1950's, therefore, the American passenger car was exemplifying Thorstein Veblen's concept of conspicuous consumption on a scale never anticipated by him. Most of the trappings were purely for show and had nothing to do with improving the vehicle's qualities as a medium of transportation. The higher horsepowers were defended as providing a reserve of power for emergencies, and they did on occasion serve this purpose, but whether the availability of greater speeds prevented more accidents than it caused is debatable. The big cars had an advantage in riding comfort, especially on long trips. On the other hand, the profusion of big cars complicated traffic and parking problems, since fewer vehicles could be accommodated in a given area.

In a boom period with a high level of employment these vehicles seemed to be what the American people wanted, and so they were built. To be sure, sales of small foreign cars on the American

market were rising, and Chevrolet and Ford had been more successful than they had anticipated with their quasi sports cars, the
Corvette and Thunderbird, the former introduced by Chevrolet in
1953 and the latter by Ford in 1954. But this sector of the market,
the foreign and sports cars, was written off as purely prestige
buying on the part of a specialized group of consumers. Nor, in the
middle of the decade, did Romney's efforts with the Rambler seem
likely to bear fruit. It was this expansive mood that led Ford to
decide on bringing out the Edsel.

Even in labor relations there was a perceptible disposition to
emphasize external appearances. There were some contract negotiations in the early 1950's whereby cost-of-living increases were
incorporated permanently into base wage rates, a predictable revision of the original arrangement. But the grievances and hostility of
earlier years had at least temporarily subsided and the next major
round of negotiations in 1955 concentrated on Walter Reuther's
proposal for a guaranteed annual wage to offset the seasonality of
automobile manufacturing. Ford was the first company to reach an
agreement on this problem, and the terms of this settlement were
adopted generally throughout the industry. The company contributed five cents a worker for each hour of employment to create
a fund from which payments would be made to supplement state
unemployment benefits up to an agreed percentage of the worker's
normal earnings. Payments ran for a maximum of twenty-six
weeks, depending on the recipient's employment record and the
amount available in the fund.

This settlement was hailed as a great advance in industrial
relations, but it does not stand up under critical examination.
Although it would work well enough under the full employment
conditions in the automobile industry at the time, it required very
little calculation to make it evident that in a depression with
large-scale layoffs the fund would be depleted far more rapidly
than it could be replenished. One happily erudite Ford official
paraphrased Voltaire's description of the Holy Roman Empire and
observed (in private) that what the UAW had secured was neither

guaranteed nor annual nor a wage. Nevertheless it sufficed to keep labor peace in automotive circles for almost another decade.

THE COMING OF THE COMPACTS

What came to be known as the great horsepower race was bound to end sooner or later. There was a useful limit to the size and power of the ordinary passenger automobile, and after the banner year of 1955 this limit was passed. Cars were becoming more and more expensive both to buy and to operate, much of the cost was manifestly in frills, and when humorists could remark, with enough accuracy to sting, that the buyer of a new car had to be able to afford not only the vehicle but a new and bigger garage to house it, the situation was palpably ridiculous. Yet consumer reaction was surprisingly slow. The manufacturers could protest with considerable justification that they were giving the customer what he seemed to want and offer in evidence the fact that their least luxurious models were their poorest sellers.

There were some straws blowing in the wind. Sales of small foreign cars were still climbing, although their total of 60,000 in 1955 was less than 1 per cent of the sales of motor vehicles in the United States. Nevertheless it was impossible to dismiss the standard Volkswagen, Hillman, Renault, or Morris as appealing exclusively to the sports car enthusiasts. At the time, however, they were explained away in terms of status-seeking or as second cars for the growing proportion of multicar families in the United States. It might have been considered significant that the Rambler sold 80,000 in 1955, double its previous record, but this too was disregarded, because everything automotive sold well in 1955 and American Motors was still losing money on Romney's experiment.

The awakening came when automobile production slid from its 1955 peak and the national economy slumped into the 1957–58 recession. As depressions go, this one was moderate, but it served to revive the neglected habit of looking at price tags and considering costs of upkeep and maintenance. So, paradoxically, an economic condition which troubled the major manufacturers saw American Motors prosper. Romney's persistence and faith finally had their reward as Rambler output went into six figures and continued up until it approached the half million mark in 1960. Simultaneously imports of foreign cars skyrocketed to 700,000 in 1959, which was about 10 per cent of the aggregate domestic production of motor vehicles for the year, or 12 per cent if only passenger cars are counted. Almost half the total came from West Germany, principally the highly popular Volkswagen. The United Kingdom ranked next, and then in order France, Sweden, Italy, and Japan. Of these, Swedish and Japanese automobiles were newcomers to the American scene.

TABLE 5

MOTOR VEHICLE IMPORTS IN 1963 BY COUNTRIES OF ORIGIN

COUNTRY IMPORTED FROM	TRUCKS, BUSES & CHASSIS		PASSENGER CARS NEW		PASSENGER CARS USED		AUTOMOTIVE PARTS VALUE
	Number	Value	Number	Value	Number	Value	
Belgium......	20	$ 354,000	17	$ 50,650	1	$ 2,000	$ 1,875,507
Canada......	1,665	1,225,043	921	680,537	169	124,815	18,961,974
Denmark.....	—	—	60	87,166	—	—	29,371
France.......	8	9,852	28,531	23,384,874	30	30,242	3,593,524
W. Germany..	13,873	15,427,080	274,105	276,291,422	14,151	17,332,057	33,140,818
Italy.........	1	1,280	12,973	17,012,369	20	60,935	1,777,400
Japan........	443	466,168	7,038	6,807,549	—	—	1,463,692
Netherlands..	—	—	311	277,785	3	3,200	331,878
Sweden......	1	16,396	16,901	23,993,675	15	16,267	2,155,990
United Kingdom...	216	493,236	68,092	96,366,837	268	337,980	18,298,202
Other........	1,407	530,501	75	100,963	12	24,235	1,006,317
Total....	17,634	$18,523,556	409,024	$445,053,827	14,669	$17,931,731	$82,634,673

SOURCE: U.S. Department of Commerce.

The domestic manufacturers met this challenge by themselves, without going to the government for aid. There was no suggestion that the influx of foreign cars should be curtailed by tariffs or otherwise; on the contrary, the automobile industry, through the Detroit Chamber of Commerce, openly advocated the removal of barriers to international trade. This position was arrived at by harsh experience. American automobile manufacturers had discovered that the restriction of trade was a game that could be played multilaterally, and that exports of American motor vehicles were the first victims of reprisals against United States tariff policies. Far from trying to prohibit the foreign invasion, the American companies joined it. General Motors and Ford had long been European producers and were perfectly willing to sell their European models on the American market, although neither actually did so on a scale comparable to the genuine foreign manufacturers. Chrysler moved into the picture by acquiring interests in the French Simca Company in 1958 and the British Rootes Group (Hillman, Humber, Singer, Sunbeam) in 1964.

The most effective response of the American manufacturers to the challenge of the small car, foreign and domestic, was to go into the compact business themselves—a reaction that had been pessimistically anticipated by the European producers. They had calculated, with commendable accuracy as it turned out, that when their American sales amounted to 10 per cent of the total number of motor vehicles sold in the United States, the threat would then be sufficient to bring the big American companies into the small-car field, with resources in economic strength and productive capacity beyond the ability of the Europeans to compete with. Events would disprove the gloomier forebodings of the Europeans. The high level of 1959 was not repeated in the ensuing years, but European firms retained a respectable volume of United States sales.

The late 1950's and early 1960's accordingly saw a dramatic shift in the pattern of American automobile production as a profusion of compact models was thrust before the buying public. Studebaker, under the pressure of necessity, hastened to follow the American Motors example, but without the same satisfying results. The Scotsman (1957) and the Lark (1958) gave Studebaker a temporary respite. But although the Rambler remained energetically in competition after the Big Three compacts appeared, the Studebaker entries faded rapidly.

From this time compacts came and went in bewildering variety. The more prominent included Chrysler's Valiant and Dart, Ford's

Falcon and Comet, and General Motors' Corvair, Tempest, and Chevy II. All featured economy and ease of operation, but all were bigger than the foreign cars they were meant to supplant. Occasionally claims for the compacts were carried to the point of absurdity (the same could be said of some of the advertising for standard automobiles). Corvair, for instance, was clearly inspired by the Volkswagen when it was designed with an air-cooled engine in the rear, but some of the Corvair advertising gave the impression that this was the first time in automotive history that anyone had thought either of building an air-cooled engine or of putting it at the rear of the car.

The compacts made more sense than some of the behemoths that had preceded them, but with all the fanfare that was lavished on them, their sales record revealed that the American preference for big cars was essentially unimpaired. The standard Chevrolet and Ford models easily outsold their smaller brothers. At Chrysler the Plymouth was still having its troubles in the early 1960's, but both it and the regular Dodge remained ahead of the Chrysler compacts. As far as it was possible to draw conclusions from a limited experience, the evidence indicated that although small cars had a firm hold on a segment of the American automobile market, it was a minor segment. Indeed, as the American-built compacts vied with each other for public approval, there was an observable tendency for each year's model to be a little larger and a little more ornate than before. If this trend continued there was an intriguing prospect that some enterprising manufacturer might copy Romney's example and this time come out with a compact compact.

THE AUTOMOBILE CULTS

The rise and fall of consumer preferences among the tail-finned models, the compacts, the foreign cars, and so on demonstrated that if the automobile had brought uniformity to many aspects of American life, the American people compensated by requiring diversity in their automobiles. There was not one automobile market; there were many, each with its own body of devotees. The largest single demand was for the conventional passenger car in varying sizes and prices, but there were communities in which eating with a knife would have been more acceptable than driving anything but a station wagon and others in which the convertible was a sine qua non.

Then there were the groups with special enthusiasms. There was a sports car cult, whose members enjoyed riding in small, high-performance vehicles, sometimes making a show of driving exposed to the elements in all weather. There were those who were addicted to foreign cars merely because of their snob appeal. They usually justified their perference by arguing that foreign cars were better built and did not have "planned obsolescence" incorporated into their design. The argument was valid for styling but not for performance or durability, because there is no convincing evidence that foreign cars last longer or run better than comparable American vehicles.

Among teen-agers there was a wide variety of automotive enthusiasms. There were those who delighted in "jalopies"—old cars, preferably as dilapidated as possible, whose continued functioning could be explained only in terms of the miraculous. In contrast to these were the customizers, who sought individuality in their cars by modification of the bodies. The changes could take such forms as reworking body lines, removing chrome or grill-work, lowering the front or rear end, or painting in unconventional patterns. Frequently the results showed artistry; sometimes they were grotesque. Lowering bodies was carried to such extremes that some states legislated against the practice. California, for example, stipulates that "no modified motor vehicles may be driven on the highway if any portion of their bodies other than the wheels are [*sic*] lower than the low point of any rim of the wheels." Another important group was the "hot-rodders," who took conventional cars and gave them extra power by reboring cylinders, installing extra carburetors or fuel-injection systems, and other methods. These "souped-up" vehicles were frequently used for drag-racing, which consisted of starting from a standing stop and trying to achieve maximum acceleration in a specified distance, usually a quarter of a mile. Since indulging in this sport on public highways was undesirable, many communities provided space for drag strips on which drag races could be held under controlled and orderly conditions.

Automobile racing retained all the popularity it had had since the days of the horseless carriage, but it had developed in a variety of different forms. The standard style of racing, with specially built racing cars, held its place although there was no longer a pretence that it was a method of testing cars. In addition, a multitude of small tracks came into existence for sports- and stock-car racing. The latter title was a misnomer. The vehicles entered in those contests were no more regular stock cars than those that ran in the Indianapolis 500 every Memorial Day. They were completely rebuilt for racing purposes, with high-powered engines and body structures remodeled for greater stability and safety at high speeds.

Finally, the automobile was acquiring a history. The fiftieth anniversary of the Duryea car came in 1943 and was overshadowed by the Second World War, but afterward there was a steady succession of golden jubilees: the first automobiles in Detroit (1946); the beginning of automobile manufacturing in Hartford (1947); Ford and Buick (1953); General Motors and the Model T (1958). It was now possible to cherish an automobile because it was old rather than because it was new; the lovers of antique cars, indeed, possessed a fervor that the owner of a gleaming new model fresh off the assembly line could never experience. Part of this enthusiasm manifested itself in the preservation of old cars in museums or in collections of private individuals or societies. The museums varied widely. Some were well organized and professionally managed. At the risk of seeming to discriminate, mention can be made of the Smithsonian Institution, which possesses the original Duryea, Haynes, and Winton cars, the Ford Museum in Dearborn, probably the largest of the collections, and the Thompson Products (now Thompson-Ramo-Wooldridge) Museum in

Cleveland. At the other end of the scale were numerous so-called auto museums along the highways, which were often simply tourist traps containing an assortment of junk.

There was also a substantial effort to promote study of automotive history. Much of this work was strictly antiquarian, performed by local organizations of automobile "buffs." There were societies of national scope, such as the Antique Automobile Club of America, which published magazines and promoted a certain amount of scholarly research. Recognition of the historical significance of the automobile was further emphasized when the Ford Motor Company opened its archives to students in 1951 through the medium of a department directed by a trained archivist, Henry E. Edmunds. At the same time the company sponsored a massive historical project covering the career of Henry Ford and the history of the Ford Motor Company, under the supervision of the distinguished American historian Allan Nevins. It was completed in three volumes in 1963. A further step on a broader scope was the designation in 1954 of the Detroit Public Library (certainly a logical choice) as the principal repository for materials on automotive history in the United States. The library's Automotive History Collection was assisted by the Automobile Manufacturers Association and has built up the most complete collection in the world of books, periodicals, and documents on the history of the American automobile and the automobile industry.

The true antique car enthusiast, however, was not interested in having his idols either mounted immobile in a museum or enshrined in the pages of a book. He wanted them out on the highway where they belonged. Most states by the 1950's made special provision for vehicles more than twenty-five years old to be registered as antique automobiles so that they could be legally operated. Enough of them were running so that the rubber companies unexpectedly found a profitable sideline in setting up sections of their plants to revive the manufacture of smooth-treaded, large-diameter, high-pressure tires.

For the antique-car devotees of the 1950's and 1960's a vehicle only a quarter of a century old was practically modern. The prized cars were early Model T's, curved-dash Oldsmobiles, Stanley Steamers, and others of comparable vintage. A surprising number of these were resurrected and rebuilt, and there were even new models built to the original design, to the accompaniment of anxious deliberations in antique automobile clubs concerning the authenticity for a particular car of artillery wheels or wire wheels, steering wheel or tiller, horn or siren, and innumerable other details. The clubs held meets to demonstrate the capabilities of their cars, at which the men were properly attired with long dust coats and goggles and the women wore the veils and scarfs of the horseless carriage era. The Glidden Tours were revived; at appropriate seasons one could see on American highways lines of colorful old cars chugging along on their prescribed routes. The big difference was that the participating vehicles usually reached the scene on trailers rather than under their own power. It was nostalgic, it was entertaining, and it underlined how in just over fifty years the automobile had implanted itself deeply in American culture.

CHAPTER 13

Metropolis on the Freeway

The "average American" is a fiction of journalists, politicians, and social statisticians. But in the composite of characteristics that would make up this hypothetical individual, three would definitely emerge for the second half of the twentieth century: first, he lived in a metropolitan area and most likely in a suburb; second, he owned an automobile; and third, he and his family were almost completely dependent on their car for transportation beyond walking distance, or frequently within walking distance. The most important single supplement to the family automobile was another motor vehicle, the bus. After that, especially in large cities, came the taxicab.

The growth of the city is a well-documented aspect of modern life. In the United States the proportion of the population classed as urban—living in communities with more than 2,500 persons—rose from 40 per cent in 1900 to 70 per cent in 1960. Among urban communities the great metropolitan centers had a faster growth rate than the small towns, and their suburbs grew fastest of all. Suburban expansion began to outpace that of the cities as early as 1910. It mushroomed after 1920 until at midcentury one-fourth of the people of the United States lived in suburbs. By that time some central city areas were actually declining, and those that continued to grow did so at a rate never more than half as fast as that of their surrounding suburbs.

For this phenomenon the motor vehicle has been almost exclusively responsible. Modern Suburbia is a creation of the automobile and could not exist without it. It is true that with some American cities, notably New York, Chicago, Philadelphia, and Boston, suburban growth originally extended along a network of rail and rapid-transit lines, and in these metropolitan areas communication between city and suburb has remained heavily dependent on mass transportation by rail. Yet even in these four cities the great suburban expansion of the mid–twentieth century was accompanied by a shrinkage of rail commuter service, to the point where it was threatened with extinction. New suburbs grew with little reference to the mass transportation media. In any event the commuter, whether he lived in Wellesley Hills or Winnetka, Bala Cynwyd or Cos Cob, relied on a motor vehicle of some kind to get him to and from the railroad station. By comparison, a metropolis like Los Angeles, often and accurately described as a collection of suburbs in search of a city, grew up on highway transportation. Admittedly Los Angeles had an extensive electric interurban network in the early part of the century, but no one will seriously suggest that the Pacific Electric had much to do with the expansion of Los Angeles after 1925. The city was conspicuously a product of the automobile.

Los Angeles might be considered an extreme example but it was nonetheless an example of the fact that urban growth in the United States was predicated on motor-vehicle transportation. The extent of this dependence was not realized until the Second World War, when the critical shortages of rubber and gasoline stimulated investigation to determine the minimum possible use of private automobiles. The result was staggering. As of 1940, 13,000,000 persons, close to one-tenth of the population of the United States at the time, lived in suburban communities without access to any kind of public transportation system. In view of the accelerated expansion of Suburbia after the war, this proportion has become considerably higher. For good or ill the contemporary American metropolis is now so constituted that it could not live if movement by motor vehicle were to cease for any reason whatsoever.

TRAFFIC AND TRANSIT

Contrary to what is generally believed, the automobile did not create congestion on city streets. That is as old as cities themselves. Ancient Rome had ordinances restricting vehicular traffic for the convenience and safety of the citizenry. The effect of the automobile was to create a traffic problem much more complicated than had ever existed before.

The crux of the problem in the United States was movement between city and suburb. To the American motorist it must have seemed that congestion was a malignant and ubiquitous plague that pursued him wherever he went, but in fact if a method could be found for dealing with the flow into Metropolis in the morning and out again at might, other traffic difficulties would be considerably easier to remedy. A study of urban problems made in the 1950's by *Fortune* and published in 1957 under the title *The Exploding Metropolis* revealed that in the twenty-five largest American metropolises three-fifths of the people who entered the downtown business district every day did so by car. This average represents a range from 17 per cent for New York City to 78 per cent for San Antonio, Texas. Los Angeles, which might have been expected to lead the list, had a 66 per cent level; on the other hand, in metropolitan Los Angeles 95 per cent of all local passenger travel was by private automobile, the highest figure for any urban area in the world.

The New York situation is exceptional. The metropolitan region is elaborately equipped with rapid-transit lines and commuter railroads, and it would be a physical impossibility for the millions who enter and leave Manhattan Island daily to do so by automobile, both because of the restricted area of the island and the limited means of access. Yet it is safe to say that the difficulties of getting into New York by automobile and of finding a place to put the car after getting there are far more responsible for the low incidence of private automobile use than is the existence of the extensive mass transportation system. One item of evidence is that New York has fared no better than other large cities in the matter of declining patronage and revenue for the public transportation services. Another is that the low relative inflow of private cars is offset by extensive use of taxis, which comprise about half the motor vehicles in downtown Manhattan.

Whatever the variations from one metropolis to another, the traffic problem was there. The first obvious remedy was to improve existing streets, build new ones, and adopt various measures for expediting the movement of vehicles. These last took such forms as one-way streets, synchronized traffic lights, restriction of parking on main arteries, and techniques for reversing traffic lanes so that the flow would be inbound in the morning and outbound in the evening. Most ambitious—and expensive—was the construction of expressways. These, like the original Los Angeles freeways and the Detroit expressways, were principally designed to facilitate movement in and out of the central city. Some were built as bypass routes to keep through traffic out of the cities altogether, the classic being Massachusetts' Route 128, which swings in a great arc around Boston from Nantasket on the south shore to Cape Ann on the north and is, as far as is known, the only highway to have a railroad station named for it. Where it intersected the main line of the New Haven Railroad, a station called Route 128 was built at which all trains, express and local, stopped for the convenience of the heavily populated southern suburbs of Boston. The great advantage of the station was that it was easy to reach by automobile and had ample parking space.

About fifteen hundred miles of metropolitan freeways existed in 1955, mostly in California. The cost, never less than a million dollars a mile, and the complexities of building through urban areas made state and local authorities hesitate to undertake such projects except where there was compelling need. When Illinois decided to construct an express belt line around Chicago, it made it a tollroad. The Interstate Highway Act of 1956 removed the financial barrier by including provision for an additional five thousand miles of urban expressway, and a marked increase of activity ensued.

To the weary motorist inching along in rush hour traffic it must have appeared that all this expenditure on new highways and traffic control systems was simply being poured into a bottomless rathole, and he would have found widespread concurrence among traffic experts. No matter how fast or on what scale improved facilities were provided for getting into Metropolis, they could never keep up with the volume of vehicles using them. It was common for a new section of Los Angeles freeway to be opened and have its first traffic jam within twenty-four hours. The pressure on urban arteries came from two sources. First, there were just many more motor vehicles; between 1950 and 1963 total automobile registrations in the United States rose by a factor of two-thirds, from 49,000,000 to 82,000,000, or at the rate of 5 per cent per year. This increase was calculable and could be allowed for in highway planning. The unknown variable was the number of existing vehicles that would be attracted into the cities by more and better roads. Surveys of the New York traffic problem in the middle 1950's indicated that only one-fourth of the potential total of cars in New York's Suburbia were driven into the city. Even if no more cars were added, the main effect of building more express routes into New York City would be to draw an unpredictable flow of automobiles from this enormous reservoir of the remaining three-fourths.

Was it worth while even trying to keep up with the insatiable demands of the automobile? There was a substantial body of opinion that held that it was not; that the automobile was an inordinately wasteful and expensive method of providing for the transportation needs of Metropolis. Traffic surveys of major cities have shown with a striking consistency that car occupancy in rush hours averages between 1.4 and 1.8 persons. Elementary common sense seemed to dictate that the billions being spent on freeways would be better employed in creating really adequate systems of mass transportation. The appeal of this position was strong enough so that when the 1960's arrived, nearly all major American cities were discussing plans either for developing new rapid-transit facilities or rehabilitating those that they had.

It was an attractive solution to traffic woes, but it was not as simple as it looked. Existing urban transportaion systems were in poor condition physically and financially; they were used from necessity and not from choice. By and large they were not competitive in any way with the private automobile. According to the findings of *The Exploding Metropolis*, in the middle 1950's automobile traffic had a definite advantage over public transportation in speed. In every city of more than half a million population private cars moved during rush hours in the most congested sections at an average rate of twenty miles an hour, a figure not only astonishingly uniform but undoubtedly higher than would generally have been guessed. The average for all media of public transportation was thirteen miles an hour. The comparison is unfair to the public transportation systems, since these include streetcars and buses, neither of which is as maneuverable on crowded streets as the private car. Bus service came out slightly ahead of the automobile in Detroit, where express buses have definite traffic lanes assigned to them, and rail travel on separate rights-of-way had a clear advantage. The New York subway did slightly better than the automobile at rush hours, and commuter trains went almost twice as fast—thirty-six miles an hour for the much abused Long Island Railroad. Since these speeds are for peak congestion periods, allowance has to be made for the fact that at other times the automobile would do considerably better than twenty miles an hour, and the performance of the bus would improve also. The commuter train and the rapid transit, on the other hand, would show no appreciable gain and might even have a lower average speed for off-peak hours because there would be fewer express runs.

There are valid and compelling reasons for trying to replace the endless lines of motor vehicles on city streets and expressways with efficient mass transportation, but experience so far has made it manifest that the automobile will be an extraordinarily difficult contender to eliminate. Its disadvantages as a means of commuting between city and suburb can be freely conceded; nevertheless no existing or proposed system of mass transportation offers any real promise of dissuading the inhabitant of Metropolis from using his car if he possibly can. Whether the trip in town is made to go to work or to shop or for entertainment, the automobile allows flexibility of schedule, it avoids the nuisance of getting to and from stations or bus stops, and it is invariably pleasanter than riding in crowded, uncomfortable, and usually dingy public vehicles. The out-of-pocket cost, which is all that most motorists take into consideration, is unlikely to be enough higher than that of public transportation to offset the convenience of the automobile, and if two or more people ride in the car, the cost factor is normally in its favor. Exact figures are unavailable, but the *Fortune* study referred to estimated that even with a generous allowance for depreciation and highway taxes the cost of commuting by car in 1955 was six cents a mile as compared with an average of four cents for public transportation.

To compete effectively with the private automobile a transit system would have to be capable of scheduled speeds that would get a passenger to his destination in less time than he would require to make the trip in his own car on a freeway under favorable traffic conditions. Movement by rail on a separate right-of-way is the best existing method of achieving this goal, although a possible alternative might be high-speed buses operating on traffic lanes reserved exclusively for their use. Such service, whether by rail or bus, would also have to be frequent, convenient, comfortable, and attractive, and it would have to be offered at a price low enough to make it worthwhile for people to leave their cars at home. Transit facilities meeting these standards do not now exist but they are attainable if communities are prepared to face the cost; a system incorporating the qualities just described is technically feasible but it cannot be expected to pay its own way. In essence, metropolitan populations must choose between paying taxes to provide up-to-date mass transportation and paying them to build more express highways and parking facilities for their automobiles. The first choice may be the better one on several grounds, but the notion that it will be less expensive is illusory.

Another suggested remedy for urban traffic congestion is to keep automobiles out of the downtown business district altogether. Some cities, of which the best examples are Toledo, Ohio, and Pomona, California, have established central "malls" accessible only to pedestrians, with encouraging results both esthetically and commercially. But neither Toledo nor Pomona is of metropolitan size; the latter in fact is part of the greater Los Angeles metropolis. Neither, therefore, has to deal with the problem of moving enormous masses of people in and out every day. In the case of the Pomona mall, with which the author is familiar, the provision of generous parking areas immediately contiguous makes it evident that the patrons are expected to come by car. A major city would have to tear down a large part of its downtown section to provide parking space on a comparable scale. Indeed, proposals of this kind for the metropolitan centers have assumed that at least half the people coming into the mall area would use public transportation, so that implementation of the idea becomes contingent on resolving the larger question of providing adequate transit facilities. The concept of the central mall has its own indubitable merit, but it offers no quick and easy cure for crowded city streets.

MOTORIZED SUBURBIA

If the automobile brought blight to the inner city, it gave life to Suburbia. Besides being the principal means of transportation between suburb and city, it accounted for practically all movement within suburban communities themselves. Figures cannot tell the whole story, but it is an eloquent testimony to the automotive character of Suburbia that it has the highest incidence of automobile ownership in the United States; 87 per cent of suburban families own cars, as compared with just under 80 per cent for the nation as a whole. It is an interesting commentary on the structure of Metropolis that it has the low figure on the scale; in cities with more than half a million population the percentage drops to 61 within the city limits. This discrepancy can be explained on the ground that the higher-income families move to the suburbs while the low-income groups stay in the central city, but there is more to the story. Apartment dwellers in sections like Manhattan or in-town Washington, D.C., may be able to afford a car. But with ample taxi service or public transportation available for local travel, automobile ownership can well be dispensed with in order to avoid the nuisance and cost of parking and garaging.

The head of a suburban family might use an automobile to get to his job in the city, or he might drive his car to the railroad or bus station and park it there. If he used public transportation, there was a strong probability that his wife drove him to the station and met him on his return, meanwhile using the car for other family activities. (Since the husband and father spends most of his day elsewhere, Suburbia is definitely a matriarchy. This social phe-nomenon may be ranked as one of the major consequences of the automobile.) Suburban children go to school in motor vehicles, either driven in the family car or riding in school buses. When they are old enough they may and frequently do use their own cars, although studies have shown an inverse correlation between aca-demic performance and the amount of time devoted to an automo-bile. The housewife drives to supermarket and shopping center and to civic and social activities. When the family is reunited in the evening, the car is available for visiting friends, going to the movies, or attending the meeting of the P.T.A., unless it has been taken by a younger member of the family to go on a date.

Considering their multifarious requirements for automotive transportation, it is understandable that suburban families should have not only the highest percentage of car ownership but also the highest percentage of multiple-car ownership. In 1963 one-fifth of all suburban households owned two or more automobiles, and these constituted two-fifths of all the multiple-car households in the United States.

There is a discernible relationship between suburban growth and the increase in two- and three-car families. Whereas the expansion of suburbs has been proceeding at an accelerating pace for most of the twentieth century, the real explosion of Suburbia occurred after the Second World War. During this same period multiple-car ownership at least doubled. For the ten years between the beginning of 1954 and the end of 1963 the total number of households in the United States with more than one car rose from 4,000,000 to almost 9,000,000. In percentage terms this was an increase from 9 per cent of all households in 1954 to 15.6 per cent in 1963, or from 12 to 20 per cent of car-owning households. If more than one car was needed only occasionally and multiple ownership was too much of a financial burden, rental agencies existed to fill the gap. These were not exclusively a suburban phenomenon; the larger agencies functioned on a nationwide scale. They reflected, however, the growing number of families, predominantly suburban, whose living conditions demanded that one car be available for family activities while another was in use for business.

The primary outward thrust of Metropolis was one of people seeking room and a community to live in rather than the mass impersonality of the great city. The automobile was the instrument that made it possible for millions, for the many rather than the few, at least partially to realize these desires. The "suburban sprawl" that surrounds every large American city, the acres upon acres of monotonously uniform "developments," could be accused of turning a dream into a nightmare; yet whatever the deficiencies of the rows of "ranch houses" and synthetic Cape Cod cottages, the occupants were certainly better off than as if they had been jammed into city tenements.

The mass movement to the suburbs naturally carried with it the various business enterprises necessary to provide for these vast numbers. There was nothing unusual about business moving to where its customers could best be found; the distinctive feature of this migration was that it had to accommodate customers who preferred to do their shopping by automobile. Until the 1940's suburban retail stores were either strictly local establishments or minor branches of downtown department stores. It then became increasingly evident that the suburban housewife would shop by preference where she could drive and park conveniently rather than face a tiring and time-consuming trip in town either by car or by public transportation. If the customer was not going to come to the store, the store of necessity had to go to the customer.

The answer was the suburban shopping center, located where there was plenty of room and easy access by road—preferably close to an express highway. The typical shopping center was built around a large, fully-equipped branch of a major department store or mail-order house. If the center was very big it might have two or more of these establishments. Around the core were ancillary enterprises: specialty shops, drug stores, restaurants, and so on. Surrounding the whole complex was the ample parking lot, the element on which the rest of operation depended, because the customers would come by car or not at all. There were 1,800 of these shopping centers in 1955, and their number was growing fast as both Metropolis and Suburbia continued to expand. A super-market might or might not be part of a shopping center such as has been described; it was more usual for a supermarket to be the nucleus of a separate center of its own. In any event the super-market was also a creation of the automobile. It could easily outmatch the corner grocery store in price and variety of selection, but to do so it had to be able to operate on a large scale. It had to draw customers in numbers from a considerably wider area than could be covered on foot, and they had to buy in quantity. These conditions presupposed shopping by car. The parking lot was an essential adjunct to the supermarket also. The total effect was a revolutionary redistribution of retail business in Metropolis. Before the Second World War less than 5 per cent of the retail purchases in large city complexes were made in suburban outlets. As early as 1950 this proportion had risen to a third, and it was still going up.

The vehicular orientation of suburban life was reflected in a development of business enterprises which went beyond the provision of parking space and were organized so that the patrons need not get out of their automobiles at all. The drive-in theater and the drive-in restaurant are not, strictly speaking, suburban phenomena, since they can now be found in every kind of community. They first appeared on the outskirts of urban areas, however, and the heaviest concentrations continued to flourish in Suburbia. There were more than 4,000 drive-in theaters in the United States in 1964 and about 30,000 drive-in restaurants. The latter total fluctuated markedly because many of the drive-ins were hamburger stands operating on a shoestring and with a very short life expectancy. The drive-in business technique has been widely adopted. Even the traditionally staid banking community has yielded to the domination of the automobile by installing drive-in tellers' windows, most frequently in suburban banks.

FREEWAY INDUSTRY

The suburban exodus was originally exclusively residential and long remained so. It was a migration of people looking for homes where they could live under better conditions than the cities could offer. The retail business enterprises that accompanied the movement did not affect its character; they were manifestly needed to serve the residents of Suburbia. Industry was in a very different position. In the initial stages of suburban expansion industry was emphatically not wanted, and it had little incentive in any event to move to places where the local labor supply was negligible and transportation facilities for moving freight were poor.

The advent of metropolitan expressways brought a marked change. For an industry whose hauling requirements could be adequately taken care of by truck, there were now distinct advantages to locating on the freeway in an outlying area. Land was cheaper and taxes lower than in central city industrial districts, and shipments by road could be made faster and more dependably since they did not have to contend with crowded city streets. The work force likewise had easy access to the plant by automobile.

Consequently, the 1950's saw a noticeable tendency for light industry—for instance, electronics plants or firms engaged in research and development—to spring up along the outer sections of metropolitan expressways. Besides residential tracts and shopping centers, Suburbia began to sprout "industrial parks," choice sites in which a variety of small factories could be placed. To make them acceptable to their communities, the industrial parks were carefully designed and landscaped; many of them, indeed, were esthetically superior to adjoining subdivisions of identical tract houses. Some of these suburban industrial centers had rail transportation available, but for the most part they, like Suburbia itself, depended on the motor vehicle.

This industrial expansion into suburban areas was welcomed, within limits. Living in Paradise Estates might be all that was expected of it, but providing schools of the desired quality and other public services, such as sewers, where none had existed before, had an inflationary effect on tax rates. If the community could include some nice respectable industrial plants, the kind that did not make loud noises or emit vast quantities of smoke and fumes, these could assume some of the tax burden that would otherwise fall on residential property. Preferably they should also be industries that either required a small labor force or could draw it from some other community, so that Paradise Estates would not have a welfare burden if business was bad. There was thus a happy meeting of minds. The light industries and the "think tanks" could benefit most from locations on suburban freeways, and they were also the type preferred by suburban residents.

It is clear enough that the motor vehicle is primarily responsible for the pattern of development of suburban life in the United States, in both its social and economic aspects. There is a less conspicuous reciprocal effect, whose implications have not yet been fully realized. This is the likelihood that this movement of commerce and industry into the suburbs is anchoring the automobile

still more firmly on Metropolis. The suburbanite's need to travel
into the downtown business district for shopping purposes was
approaching a possible vanishing point. If the rise of freeway
industry meant that the commuter movement between home and
work was to change in significant volume from its accustomed
suburb-to-city flow to a flow from suburb to suburb, then much of
the case for subsidized mass transportation would lose its meaning.
In fact, no conceivable public transportation system could provide
for the necessary travel as efficiently or as economically as the
private automobile.

THE TROUBLED CENTER

The same forces that stimulated growth and vitality on the outskirts of Metropolis threatened the middle with rot and decay. This
condition applied both to population and to business activity. Plans
for arresting this downward trend invariably and necessarily
devoted much attention to the automobile. It could hardly be
considered the sole cause of urban troubles, but no twentieth-
century American city was going to make much progress with its
other problems until it had figured out what to do with the motor
vehicle.

The questions of traffic control and the relief of congestion that
have been discussed previously were only part of the story,
although the major part. For most American cities the prospect of
replacing automobiles with rapid-transit facilities was a distant and
uncertain one if it existed at all. Meanwhile, if people were to come
into the downtown area to do business, they were going to come by
car, and provision had to be made to accommodate them. Along
with arrangements for expediting traffic, parking had somehow or
other to be made available. A traffic study of Boston in the middle
1950's showed that a daily average of 150,000 motor vehicles
entered the business district, an area in which, counting all garages,
parking lots, and curbside space, there was room for 110,000 cars,
including those that parked illegally. For Boston, one remedy was

to follow the example of other large cities and go underground. To the horror of Proper Bostonians, a parking garage was built beneath Boston Common, matching the one built on the other side of the country beneath Pershing Square in Los Angeles. Enlarged parking facilities, however, had precisely the same effect as improved traffic arteries: they encouraged more people to drive into the downtown section and were overcrowded almost as soon as they opened.

Freeway construction in metropolitan centers also presented problems similar to those encountered in the building of express highways in rural areas. Highway departments had the same regrettable propensity to regard the bulldozer as the appropriate means for settling disputes over rights-of-way and the preservation of historic or artistic sites. They had their defense; their job was to build highways as economically as possible. There were signs that public opinion was beginning to react against indiscriminate destruction for the sake of building superhighways. San Franciscans, for example, revolted in the early 1960's against the desecration of their cherished Embarcadero. The result is that the motorist who drives into San Francisco by the route that was at one time unflatteringly nicknamed Bloody Bayshore finds that after passing an impressive six-level interchange at the civic center and then the exit to the Bay Bridge, the magnificent freeway suddenly comes to a dead end. The growing strength of this attitude was reflected in a supplemental piece of federal highway legislation passed in 1962. This act required among other things that planning for federally-aided urban expressways should provide for the preservation of "social and community values."

Finally the automobile posed for Metropolis an acute and intensifying problem of atmospheric pollution. It was not the first offender in this matter. Industrial operations and domestic heating plants were blanketing cities with smoke and waste gases long before automotive exhausts added their contribution. Pittsburgh's reputation as the Smoky City was established in the nineteenth century. What the motor vehicle did was make a bad matter worse by intensifying the formation of "smog," a word coined to combine smoke and fog. Although it has other components, by far the greatest part of the smog that now plagues many American cities consists of hydrocarbons and nitrous oxides emitted from motor-vehicle exhausts. Smog from this source first appeared in critical volume in metropolitan Los Angeles during the 1940's and was for long considered to be a peculiarity of the Los Angeles area, because conditions there are unusually conducive to atmospheric pollution. The Los Angeles basin is enclosed on the land side by high mountain ranges. Since the prevailing winds blow off the Pacific Ocean with an average velocity of less than ten miles an hour, the smog-laden air does not get dispersed laterally, and it is often prevented from rising vertically by a distribution of atmospheric layers known as temperature inversion, whereby a layer of warm air at high levels keeps the low-level air masses down. The situation has nothing to do with the automobile. The Los Angeles basin was identified as the "valley of the smokes" by the first Spanish explorers to visit it. When, however, the world's most intense concentration of motor vehicles began pouring exhaust gases into this atmospheric dead end, the result was critical.

Los Angeles met the difficulty by creating an Atmospheric Pollution Control Board, which had a fair amount of success in curtailing pollution from non-automotive sources such as industrial gases and backyard incinerators. Against automobile exhausts, however, the best the APCB could do was fight a stubborn rear-guard action. All non-essential motor vehicle traffic was supposed to stop during major smog alerts, but this regulation was an unenforceable pious wish. Pressure was exerted on the manufacturers to install smog-control devices on their cars, and in the early 1960's these were required by law on new cars. The results were not satisfactory. The manufacturers were criticized for procrastinating, but they were in reality victims of the traditional American assumption that any technical problem can be solved just by inventing a gadget. Actually only two methods of controlling exhaust emissions gave promise of working, and neither was wholly effective. One went in the crankcase and the other on the exhaust manifold. Their purpose was to consume more of the hydrocarbons in the fuel, but they did not consume all; they had no effect whatever on nitrous oxides, and they required frequent expert servicing. If they were improperly installed and maintained, they were likely to cause serious motor damage. It was worth accepting the limitations of these devices in order to alleviate the smog situation, but it was clear that no easy technical remedy was in sight.

Although the Los Angeles experience was the most extreme and difficult case of atmospheric pollution traceable to the automobile, most other metropolitan areas found themselves wrestling with similar conditions. The massing of large numbers of motor vehicles in a limited area created smog, and barring some new breakthrough either in automotive fuels or in exhaust control, the only guaranteed way to get rid of the smog was to get rid of the motor vehicles. Some cities made encouraging progress in reducing atmospheric pollution, Pittsburgh being an outstanding example, but Pittsburgh was almost as much a special case as Los Angeles. An unusually heavy proportion of its atmospheric troubles consisted of industrial gases, and industrial smokestacks are far more easily controlled than automobile exhaust pipes.

It would be possible, and extremely obvious, to summarize the whole situation by stating that Metropolis can live neither with the motor vehicle nor without it. It is not that simple, although urban planners probably wish that they had this choice. Under present-day conditions Metropolis must live with the automobile and somehow in the process reduce traffic congestion and atmospheric pollution. Without automotive transportation for people and goods by private car, bus, and truck, Suburbia would disintegrate; there is no alternative. The inner city problem is more complicated, but although a reduction of highway traffic may be conceivable and desirable, its elimination is wholly impractical. What the urban center needs to achieve is a balance between utilizing the automobile and being smothered by it.

CHAPTER 14

Retrospect and Prospect

The story of the automobile in the United States begins effectively with appearance of the Duryea car in 1893; the first seventy years of the tale was therefore completed in 1963. The anniversary went generally unnoticed, but it was appropriately marked by further evidence of phenomenal growth. In 1963 the total number of motor vehicles built in the United States since the days of the Duryea brothers reached and passed 200,000,000. About as phenomenal was the fact that 80,000,000 of these were in active use. It took until 1948, fifty-five years, to produce the first 100,000,000; the second took just fifteen years. The figures are impressive enough by themselves, but they contain only a fragment of the epic of the American automobile.

Behind the tables of statistics is a production achievement unparalleled in the history of the world, from which came drastic transformations in the economy and the society of the United States. Whether these changes were beneficial or not remains undetermined. Some were and some were not; it is arguable that on balance the advantages have outweighed the disadvantages, but the final verdict has still to be returned. These effects have extended beyond the United States to give the motor vehicle a vital part in the shaping of contemporary civilization. Admittedly the automobile was neither originally nor exclusively an American creation. It

237

TABLE 6

U.S. PRODUCTION SINCE 1900

CAL-ENDAR YEAR	PASSENGER CARS		MOTOR TRUCKS AND BUSES		TOTAL	
	Number	Value (000)	Number	Value (000)	Number	Value (000)
1900..	4,192	$ 4,899	. . .	. . .	4,192	$ 4,899
1905..	24,250	38,670	750	1,330	25,000	40,000
1910..	181,000	215,340	6,000	9,660	187,000	225,000
1915..	895,930	575,978	74,000	125,800	969,930	701,778
1920..	1,905,560	1,809,171	321,789	423,249	2,227,349	2,232,420
1925..	3,735,171	2,458,370	530,659	458,400	4,265,830	2,916,770
1930..	2,787,456	1,644,083	575,364	390,752	3,362,820	2,034,835
1935..	3,273,874	1,707,836	697,367	380,997	3,971,241	2,088,834
1940..	3,717,385	2,370,654	754,901	567,820	4,472,286	2,938,474
1945..	69,532	57,255	655,683	1,181,956	725,215	1,239,210
1950..	6,665,863	8,468,137	1,337,193	1,707,748	8,003,056	10,175,885
1955..	7,920,186	12,452,871	1,249,106	2,020,973	9,169,292	14,473,844
1960..	6,674,796	12,164,234	1,194,475	2,350,680	7,869,271	14,514,914
1963..	7,637,728	14,427,077	1,462,708	3,076,184	9,100,436	17,503,261

NOTE: A substantial proportion of the trucks and buses consists of chassis only; therefore the value of the bodies for these chassis is not included. Value is based on vehicles with standard equipment. Federal excise taxes are excluded.
SOURCE: Automobile Manufacturers Association.

TABLE 7

REGISTRATIONS SINCE 1900

YEAR DECEMBER 31	PASSENGER CARS	BUSES	TRUCKS		TOTAL
			Number	Percent of Total	
1900..............	8,000	—	—	—	8,000
1910..............	458,377	—	10,123	2.2	468,500
1920..............	8,131,522	—	1,107,639	12.0	9,239,161
1930..............	22,972,745	40,507	3,518,747	13.3	26,531,999
1940..............	27,372,397	72,641	4,590,386	14.3	32,035,424
1950..............	40,333,591	223,652	8,604,448	17.5	49,161,691
1960..............	61,558,847	272,129	11,937,589	16.2	73,768,565
1963.............. (Prelim.)	68,452,000		13,606,000		82,058,000

NOTE: Registrations shown here are not synonymous with vehicles in use since the latter implies a count of vehicles in operation on a specific date or an average for a period of time, while registrations are a count of trans-actions (with transfers eliminated) during a specified period. Buses are not segregated from passenger cars or trucks in earlier years. Also included are municipally owned buses engaged in public transit. Due to new method of counting buses in 1959, the bus data for earlier years are not strictly comparable. The addition of Alaska and Hawaii to the registration counts in 1959 accounted for increases in the U.S. totals. Data for the years 1950 to date have been revised to exclude farm trucks registered at a nominal fee in certain states and restricted to use in the vicinity of the owners' farms. Figures for 1950 and following years exclude military vehicles.
SOURCE: U.S. Bureau of Public Roads.

was not, however, the automobile by itself that exerted these profound social and economic influences, but the automobile linked with mass production.

The growth of the American automobile industry is therefore

the heart of the entire story. The industry found the secret of producing complicated mechanisms like motor vehicles in quantity, at low unit cost, and in variety—as expressed in the General Motors slogan of "a car for every purse and every purpose"—and from this discovery flowed all the far-reaching economic and social consequences of the automobile. The breakdown of rural isolation, the explosion of Suburbia, the construction of superhighways, the traffic congestion, the smog, the revision of social habit patterns, and the geometrical increase in productivity resulting from the adoption of the assembly-line technique all came about because the automobile in the United States was seen as a commodity for general and multipurpose use, rather than as an item of luxury. The term "carriage trade" had economic significance when carriages were drawn by horses and only the wealthy could afford them; the mass-produced automobile made it a meaningless expression.

This transformation was brought about by a group of identifiable personalities: Ford, Durant, Leland, Sloan, Olds, Chrysler, Chapin, Knudsen, Nash, Kettering, Packard, Winton, Willys. This list is neither complete nor in an intentional order of priority, although Henry Ford has to come first in any rating of automotive leaders, but it will do as a sample. As individuals they varied widely, but as a group they were forceful, hard-driving, and willing to accept the rough-and-tumble of energetic business competition, and above all completely dedicated to the automobile. This quality can be seen vividly in the less successful men like W. C. Durant or Benjamin Briscoe, whom no amount of discouragement could keep from coming back to the automobile business.

It has been pointed out that the automobile industry in its early days approached the classical concept of free competition. Similarly the men who founded and directed the automobile companies can be taken as case studies in entrepreneurship. They were individuals who saw an opportunity in a technological innovation and accepted the risk of attempting to exploit this opportunity, usually with their own scanty resources or with funds that were very definitely venture capital. If the rewards for successful entrepreneurship were high, they were commensurate with the risks. The incidence of failure as very heavy—not necessarily the spectacular failures like Durant but the forgotten men like David D. Buick and hundreds of others who appeared briefly on the scene and then vanished. One qualification should be made. The automobile men deviate from the theoretical model of the entrepreneur in that they do not seem to have been exclusively profit-motivated. They had a firm respect and desire for profits to be sure, but with Durant and Briscoe again as examples, most of them appear to have been so constituted that they would be happier losing money trying to manufacture and sell automobiles than making it anywhere else. Some of the losers gave up immediately; the commoner procedure, however, was for the defeated party to nurse his wounds briefly and charge back into the competition at the earliest opportunity.

The era of unrestricted competition ended with the establishment of large-company domination during the 1930's, a condition that developed as an inevitable consequence of mass production and mass marketing. Any assumption, however, that the industry went to the other extreme and became non-competitive would be erroneous. There was a tendency to stabilize prices, a propensity common to large-scale industrial enterprises with a heavy fixed investment to protect. The rise of the UAW accentuated this trend by introducing an element of inflexibility into wages. Nevertheless there was energetic and continuing competition on other grounds—new models, styling, technical features. There was ample leeway. The automobile manufacturers were producing for a market consisting of millions of unidentified customers, who had complete freedom of choice and whose tastes and preferences were unpredictable and uncontrollable, no matter how persuasive the advertising might be. The experience in the 1950's of the market turning from big cars to foreign imports and compacts showed that even the big companies had to be constantly alert for changes in consumer attitudes.

An important consequence of the struggle for markets was that the product was steadily improved. From the clumsy horseless carriage of the 1890's to the modern automobile there has been a constant advance in quality, although the fundamental engineering principles have remained essentially unchanged. Through the years engines, transmissions, fuels, brakes, lights, and tires have all been made more efficient and more dependable—basically because the surest way to sell more cars was to keep making them better. The mass use of the motor vehicle in the United States could not have developed on the scale it did, with all the attendant consequences, if the cars had not achieved progressively higher standards of reliability.

Moreover, contrary to general impression, travel by automobile became safer. Statistics of highway accidents on holiday weekends might seem to belie this claim, but it can be substantiated. Deaths from traffic accidents rose by 12,000 in thirty years, from 31,000 in 1933 to 43,000 in 1963, a factor of about 40 per cent. Meanwhile motor-vehicle registrations went from 24,000,000 to 80,000,000, an increase of 233 per cent. The rate of highway fatalities for this period declined from 15.6 to 5.4 for every 100,000,000 vehicle-miles traveled, or, calculating it another way, from 13.2 to 5.2 for every 100,000 motor vehicles. The meaning of these figures is that as far as automotive and highway engineering can achieve it, the possibility of accident from causes other than human error has been reduced to a minimum, and the likelihood of death or injury in the event of accident has also been lessened.

No one was happy about traffic accidents, least of all the insurance companies who found themselves in a race between premiums and damage claims. If the possibility of personal injury was statistically less, the costs of medical and hospital care were higher, and repair bills went up geometrically as automobiles became bigger and more complicated. The financial and legal consequences of highway accidents were an increasingly burdensome problem. Court dockets were badly overloaded with accident claims. Some states tried to resolve the question of liability by compulsory insurance laws, others by requiring financial responsibility. None of them could claim to have found a fully satisfactory solution.

RESEARCH AND DIVERSIFICATION

Charles F. Kettering is supposed to have dismissed the study of history on one occasion by remarking that no one could make progress by looking in his rear-view mirror. The historian's obvious retort is that the motorist who never looks in the rear-view mirror is inviting trouble, but that is beside the point. It is understandable that so young an industry should be more concerned with its future than its past. As a matter of fact, concern even with the future is a fairly recent phenomenon. Until midcentury the automobile industry lived very much in the present. Development consisted of working on next year's model, and research was thinking of what to do for the year after that.

There were exceptions. The Sloan reorganization of General Motors included a General Motors Research Corporation. Its purpose at first was principally to make a place in the structure for Charles F. Kettering, where he could pursue his own individualistic way. Subsequently it grew into a full-scale research organization, renamed General Motors Research Laboratories. In addition, in the 1920's the more important automobile companies began to equip themselves with elaborate proving grounds to test their products. This in itself was testimony to the advancement of the automotive art. The motor vehicle had become too sophisticated a mechanism to be tested adequately on a convenient stretch of vacant road, to say nothing of the fact that stretches of vacant road were becoming harder to find, and the notion that the racetrack could function as a proving ground had been discarded.

The greatest growth of research activity occurred after the Second World War, which brought into being or into prospect of realization several technological changes that had hitherto been remote. The automobile industry was deeply enough involved in the development of these technologies to be aware that the motor vehicle of the not distant future could be very different from the automobile as it then existed, and it behooved the manufacturers to study carefully the likely directions of change. There was much talk at the end of the war about nuclear power for motor vehicles, based mostly on ignorance of the problems of utilizing nuclear energy. The potentialities of the gas-turbine engine came closer to immediate practicality. It was obvious at the end of the war that the piston engine for aircraft was on the way out, although in commercial as distinct from military use the piston engine displayed a greater tenacity than might have been expected. Nevertheless, the automobile companies needed to keep abreast of gas-turbine technology.

There was scope for consideration of the future of the motor vehicle itself. The great expansion of aviation during the war revived speculation about the replacement of the family automobile by some kind of aircraft, perhaps a helicopter, but once again this prospect failed to materialize, despite a substantial increase in private flying. The technical and production problems were difficult but not impossible if the market existed; the insuperable obstacle was just that flying any kind of aircraft requires a much higher degree of skill and training than is required to drive an automobile. Thus the motor vehicle was likely to survive, but it could still face radical changes. It might, for instance, give up its wheels and ride on a cushion of air; both Ford and Curtiss-Wright demonstrated experimental models of such a vehicle in 1959.

In the early 1960's several of these possibilities, and others, were under serious investigation in automotive research laboratories, and some were approaching the testing stage. The Chrysler Corporation actually built and sold a limited number of prototype cars with gas-turbine engines in 1963. Another radical change that appeared to be within reach was an electric automobile with current supplied by fuel cells, or possibly by a completely novel type of battery. Either of these developments held prospects of major social and economic consequences. First, there would be repercussions in the petroleum industry, since the gas turbine uses simpler fuels than the piston engine, and the electric motor needs no petroleum products except lubricants. Second, the problem of atmospheric pollution would be markedly reduced, because a gas-turbine engine effects more complete combustion than a piston engine, and the electric motor discharges no waste products into the atmosphere.

The advance of electronics offered other prospects. By 1960 experiments were being made on a device whereby a car could be steered automatically by a current in the highway and on radar systems that in conditions of poor visibility would show where the edge of the pavement was or if there were obstacles in the vehicle's path. As with most new technologies, time was needed to sort out these various ideas and determine which of them might be really practical. It is one thing to test under laboratory conditions but quite another to put the results into a form that is both economical and feasible for day-to-day operation by the millions of people who drive automobiles. A radically new power plant may have conspicuous technical superiority over the standard gasoline engine, but it cannot be put into general use if it is too complicated for the ordinary motorist to operate or for the local garage to service and repair.

An alternative method of hedging against future change was to diversify, but in view of the mixed experience of automobile firms in venturing out of their field, it was pursued with understandable caution. General Motors, which had to function with the uncomfortable sensation that the Department of Justice was constantly peering over its shoulder looking for monopoly, stayed close to automotive operations, among which it included diesel locomotives, aircraft engines, and earth-moving equipment, this last added by the purchase of the Euclid Road Machinery Company in 1953. In addition, the electrical equipment divisions were drawn by military contracts into missiles and electronics. Through its acquisition of Frigidaire the corporation eventually moved into the manufacture of other household appliances such as electric ranges, washing machines, dryers, and dishwashers. American Motors inherited the Kelvinator Division from Nash and remained in the refrigerator business also.

The Ford Motor Company made the boldest step toward diversification early in the 1960's by moving into electronics and astronautics. The principal move in this direction was the purchase in 1961 of the Philco Corporation, manufacturer of television, radio, and other electronic equipment. Philco also enabled Ford to join General Motors and American Motors as a producer of household appliances. The company moved into missile and space work through its Aeronutronics Division, which was consolidated with Philco in 1963. In addition, Ford, despite its unhappy experience with the Ferguson tractor patents in the 1950's, remained securely established as one of the world's largest manufacturers of wheeled tractors. The White Motor Company also entered the farm machinery business through the acquisition of the Oliver Corporation (1961) and Motec Industries (1963).

There were therefore some indications that the automobile and the automobile industry might be on the threshold of major changes, but that these changes would be made slowly and cautiously. There were valid reasons for avoiding precipitancy, quite apart from the enormous investment represented by the facilities for building, servicing, and supplying existing types of motor vehicles. During its first three-quarters of a century the American automobile had evolved into something much more than a convenient medium for getting from here to there. It is transportation, it is prestige, it is recreation. In one way or another it supports one-sixth of all the business enterprises and one-seventh of all the wage earners in the United States. It has become almost indispensable as an adjunct to courtship. It has enabled people by the million to move about more freely than has ever before been possible, with both good effects and bad. In short, the American automobile has become a way of life, and whatever happens to it must profoundly affect the economy and the whole culture of the United States.

Important Dates

1769   First self-propelled highway vehicle built in France by Nicholas Joseph Cugnot.

1805   Oliver Evans ran the *Orukter Amphibolos* through Philadelphia.

1879   George B. Selden applied for U.S. patent on "road engine."

1893   Duryea car ran in Springfield, Massachusetts.

1895   Selden patent issued.

1896   Henry Ford built his quadricycle.

1897   Commercial production of motor vehicles begun by Pope Manufacturing Co. in Hartford, Connecticut, and Winton Motor Carriage Co. in Cleveland, Ohio.

1901   Curved-dash Oldsmobile introduced.

1902   American Automobile Association organized.

1903   Ford Motor Company founded.
Selden patent suit started against Ford and others.

1905   Society of Automobile (later Automotive) Engineers founded.

1908   Model T Ford put on market.
General Motors Company organized by W. C. Durant.

1911   Final decision in Selden patent case: "valid but not infringed."

1912   Electric starter introduced on Cadillac by Charles F. Kettering.

1914   Complete moving-assembly-line production begun by Ford Motor Company.
Ford instituted five-dollar day.

1915   Agreement for cross-licensing of patents adopted.

1916   Federal Road Aid Act passed.

1921   W. C. Durant left General Motors; founded Durant Motors.
        Federal Highway Act provided for "primary" routes.

1923   Ethyl gasoline developed by Charles F. Kettering and
        Thomas Midgley.
        Alfred P. Sloan, Jr., made president of General Motors.

1925   Chrysler Corporation founded.

1927   Manufacture of Model T Ford discontinued.

1935   United Automobile Workers chartered.
        Federal Motor Carriers Act passed.

1937   General Motors accepted UAW as bargaining agent.

1940   First section of Pennsylvania Turnpike opened.
        Prototype of jeep demonstrated.

1942   Production of civilian vehicles halted.
        Gasoline rationing instituted.

1945   Civilian production resumed.
        Gasoline rationing ended.

1947   Henry Ford and William C. Durant died.
        Fiftieth anniversary of commercial automobile production
        celebrated in Hartford.

1950   Tubeless tires introduced.

1954   Nash and Hudson combined as American Motors.
        Studebaker and Packard merged.

1955   Record production year—more than 9,000,000 motor ve-
        hicles.

1956   Interstate Highway Act passed.
        Ford Motor Company stock offered to public.
        Tollroad system from New York to Chicago completed.

1959   Foreign cars accounted for more than 10 per cent of sales on
        American market.

1963   Gas-turbine cars put on market by Chrysler.

1964   Studebaker transferred all automobile production to Hamil-
        ton, Ontario.

Suggested Reading

There is an extensive body of literature on the American automobile. The following list is intended to be selective rather than inclusive, indicating where the interested reader might profitably start on some of the varied aspects of the history of the automobile.

GENERAL WORKS

R. E. Anderson, *The Story of the American Automobile* (1950) is a good survey of early development. R. M. Cleveland and S. T. Williamson, *The Road Is Yours* (1951), D. L. Cohn, *Combustion on Wheels* (1944), and M. M. Musselman, *Get a Horse!* (1950) are all written in popular style but are sound historically. Merrill Denison, *The Power to Go* (1956) is frequently superficial but also has shrewd insights; it is especially good on the history of trucks. J. B. Rae, *American Automobile Manufacturers: The First Forty Years* (1959) concentrates on the history of the industry.

Several older works remain well worth reading: R. C. Epstein, *The Automobile Industry* (1928); C. B. Glasscock, *The Gasoline Age* (1937); E. D. Kennedy, *The Automobile Industry* (1940); T. F. MacManus and Norman Beasley, *Men, Money, and Motors* (1929); and L. H. Seltzer, *The Financial History of the American Automobile Industry* (1928).

On the chatty, personal reminiscence side are E. W. Lewis, *Motor Memories* (1947), by an official of the Timken Roller Bearing Company, and C. G. Sinsabaugh, *Who, Me?: Forty Years of Automobile History* (1940), by an editor of automotive magazines.

Automobiles of America (1962), compiled by the Automobile Manufacturers Association, is an indispensable reference.

HISTORIES OF COMPANIES

The great classic in this field is Allan Nevins' and F. E. Hill's three
volumes: *Ford: The Times, the Man, the Company* (1954); *Ford:
Expansion and Challenge 1915–1932* (1957); and *Ford: Decline and
Rebirth 1933–1962* (1963). They are detailed and authoritative. The
only history of General Motors is Arthur Pound, *The Turning Wheel*
(1934). The Studebaker centennial produced Stephen Longstreet, *A
Century on Wheels: The Story of Studebaker* (1952). K. S. Smallzreid
and D. J. Roberts, *More Than You Promise* (1942) is more detailed on
the Studebaker family. *The Pope Manufacturing Company: An Industrial Achievement* (1907), compiled by the company, is now rare,
but it is almost the only detailed account of this important pioneer automobile manufacturer.

BIOGRAPHICAL

Henry Ford has naturally been given detailed attention by biog-
raphers. His own autobiography, *My Life and Work* (1922) written
with Samuel Crowther, is a useful book, presenting Henry Ford as
he wanted to appear rather than as he was. The Nevins and Hill
volumes give a complete life story and a sympathetic but scholarly
appraisal. Roger Burlingame, *Henry Ford: A Great Life in Brief* (1955)
is a really excellent short study. Keith Sward, *The Legend of Henry
Ford* (1955) is an unfriendly study by a former UAW organizer, useful
as an antidote to the aura of hero-worship surrounding Ford. Harry
Bennett, *We Never Called Him Henry* (1951) has little to offer. J. K.
Galbraith's essay "Was Ford a Fraud" in *The Liberal Hour* (1964 ed.),
117–37, gives well-deserved credit to James S. Couzens as a builder of
the Ford Motor Company, but the denigration of Ford in order to
glorify Couzens is overdone.

Walter P. Chrysler and Boyden Sparks, *Life of an American Work-
man* (1937) is a lively account of Chrysler's career. There is a similar
volume on Alfred P. Sloan, also in collaboration with Sparks, *Adventures of a White Collar Man* (1941). Sloan's later autobiography,
My Years with General Motors (1964) has useful information but the
presentation is formal and pedestrian. J. C. Long, *Roy D. Chapin* (1945)

is unfortunately a limited edition. Norman Beasley, *Knudsen: A Biography* (1947) is worth reading as is T. A. Boyd, *Professional Amateur: The Biography of Charles F. Kettering* (1957), written by a close associate of Kettering.

No one should miss Hiram Percy Maxim's delightful *Horseless Carriage Days* (1937), now in paperback. F. L. Smith, *Motoring Down a Quarter Century* (1928) is also an enjoyable tale by an early president of the Olds Motor Works. Charles E. Sorensen, with S. T. Williamson, *My Forty Years with Ford* (1956) is a revealing story, probably more so than its author realized or intended. There are no good biographies of Nash or Durant. Margery Durant, *My Father* (1929) is a work of filial piety. R. E. Olds, after a long period of neglect, has been given an adequate biography in G. A. Niemeyer, *The Automotive Career of Ransom E. Olds* (1963).

INDUSTRIAL ORGANIZATION

There are two good, well-written surveys of mass production. Christy Borth, *Masters of Mass Production* (1945) focuses on the automobile industry and the personalities who were responsible for mass production there; Roger Burlingame, *Backgrounds of Power* (1949) is a broader survey by an outstanding student of the history of technology.

The authority on the Selden patent case is William Greenleaf, *Monopoly on Wheels* (1961), although there is a tendency in this book to exaggerate the threat of monopoly.

For the development of business organization in the automobile industry, especially the General Motors contribution, the conclusive studies are A. D. Chandler, Jr., *Giant Enterprise: Ford, General Motors, and the Automobile Industry* (1964) and *Strategy and Structure: Chapters in the History of the Industrial Enterprise* (1962). Paul F. Douglass, *Six upon the World* (1954) and Peter Drucker, *The Concept of the Corporation* (1946) explore the same topic with a different but equally effective approach. H. C. Vatter, "Closure of Entry in the American Automobile Industry," *Oxford Economic Papers, New Series*, IV (1952), 213–34, is a scholarly and penetrating study of the evolution of oligopoly and is especially informative on the Kaiser-Frazer experiment.

The marketing of motor vehicles, particularly the franchised dealer system, is spelled out in detail in Federal Trade Commission, *Report on the Motor Vehicle Industry* (1939). A more analytical approach is

B. P. Pashigian, *The Distribution of Automobiles: An Economic Analysis of the Franchise System* (1961).

The subject of technical standardization is brilliantly analyzed in G. V. Thompson, "Intercompany Technical Standardization in the Early Automobile Industry," *Journal of Economic History*, XIV (Winter, 1954), 1–20.

LABOR RELATIONS

Sidney Fine, *The Automobile under the Blue Eagle* (1963) is a thorough and fascinating account of the tangled labor situation in the automobile industry at the beginning of the New Deal. Selig Perlman, *Labor in the New Deal Decade* (1945) is a useful survey, and Benjamin Stolberg, *The Story of the CIO* (1938) has a good deal of detail on the rise of the UAW. Ely Chinoy, *Automobile Workers and the American Dream* (1955) takes an unusual approach to the problems of the assembly-line worker.

HIGHWAY TRANSPORTATION

Neither highways themselves nor commercial highway vehicles have received the attention their importance warrants. The Public Roads Administration of the Department of Commerce issues much informative material on highways. Special mention can be made of *Highways in the United States* (1954). An economist's view appears in C. L. Dearing, *American Highway Policy* (1941).

The same author also collaborates on a study of highway and other forms of transportation in C. L. Dearing and Wilfred Owen, *National Transportation Policy* (1949). It is less inclusive than Harold Barger, *The Transportation Industries, 1889–1946* (1951).

For the general reader the best sources are two pamphlets written for the Automobile Manufacturers Association by F. M. Reck, *A Car Travelling People* (1958) and *From Horses to Horsepower* (1954). They are concise, well written, and informative.

SOCIAL CONSEQUENCES

The social revolution brought about by the automobile was vividly described for the 1920's in R. S. and H. M. Lynd, *Middletown* (1929). The community selected as "Middletown" was Muncie, Indiana. The best general survey can be found in F. L. Allen, *The Big Change*

(1952). *The Exploding Metropolis* (1958), by the editors of *Fortune*, had a lucid and complete analysis of the role of the motor vehicle in metropolitan growth and its attendant problems. It can be supplemented by Wilfred Owen, *The Metropolitan Transportation Problem* (1956) and *Cities in the Motor Age* (1959). Both these books explore methods of drastically reducing automobile traffic in urban centers. No one has done anything comparable on the effect of the automobile on rural life in the United States. A promising foundation for study of this whole topic has been laid by the Public Roads Administration in *Highways and Economic and Social Changes* (1964). It is an invaluable and somewhat overwhelming compilation of data. There is some interpretation, but much more needs to be done.

Acknowledgments

My indebtedness for assistance in the compilation of this book is substantial. Individuals and organizations have given time, effort, information, and materials freely and generously; without their contributions this book could not have been produced. The responsibility for the way in which their contributions have been used, however, is entirely mine. The selection of information, the views expressed, and the errors are to be charged to me alone.

The Automobile Manufacturers Association has provided much in the way of data and illustrations. I wish particularly to thank Robert C. Lusk, Director of Educational Services, and Miss Louise Rose of the Public Relations Department for their patience and goodwill in complying with endless and frequently unreasonable requests. In addition, willing cooperation in providing illustrations has been extended by Governor George Romney of Michigan; the Community Affairs Department of the Chrysler Corporation; John P. Breeden, Jr., Public Relations Assistant, Office of the Vice President, Product Planning and Styling, Ford Motor Company, through whom I also received permission to use material from *The Ford Book of Styling;* Jack Harned, William M. Adams, and Edward T. Breslin, Public Relations Staff, General Motors Corporation; the Public Relations Department, Studebaker-Packard Corporation; Joseph Walsh, Director of Public Relations, International Union, United Automobile, Aerospace and Agricultural Implement Workers of America—UAW; and the Press Relations Department, Sears, Roebuck and Co. I am indebted to the Indiana Toll Road Commission for the data on tollroad travel in Table 3 and to the United States Bureau of Public Roads for the map of the Interstate highway system.

In the preparation of the manuscript I have also had invaluable assistance. My wife, Florence, prepared the index; my daughter Helen typed my drafts with patient devotion; and my son James gave me the benefit of his extensive knowledge of modern cars. I am especially grateful to Jerome W. Hall, who made two excellent studies of highway development while he was a senior at Harvey Mudd College and who was of major assistance in collecting material on this subject. Arnold Ruskin of the Department of Engineering at Harvey Mudd College gave me some very useful suggestions on sources of information. Finally, Mrs. Glenn E. Thompson, secretary of the Department of Humanities and Social Sciences at Harvey Mudd College, typed the final manuscript with a skill and promptness which greatly facilitated the completion of the work. Some chapters were typed by Mrs. Edith Davies, also of Harvey Mudd College.

My friend Henry E. Edmunds, director of the Ford Archives, has been his usual helpful self in a variety of ways. Chilton Books generously gave permission to use material from my previous work, *American Automobile Manufacturers: The First Forty Years* (Philadelphia: Chilton Co., 1959).

Index

Accidents, 95, 185, 241
Ainsley, Charles, 11
Aircraft industry, 71–72, 108, 148–52, 159
Allison Engineering Co., 119
Alloy steels, 46, 48, 59–60
American Automobile Association (AAA), 29, 30, 194
American Bantam Car Co., 146
American Bicycle Co., 41
American Car and Foundry, 102
American Federation of Labor (AFL), 123, 128–29, 131–34
American Locomotive Works, 44
American Motor Car Manufacturers Association (AMCMA), 37, 38
American Motors Corp., 202, 211–13, 244–45
American Projectile Co., 10
American Standards Association, 41
Anderson, John W., 59
Anglo-American Rapid Vehicle Co., 12
Annual model, 80, 98–99, 126
Antique Automobile Club of America, 217
Apperson, Edgar and Elmer, 9, 10, 24, 31
Assembly line, 60–63, 67–68, 99, 109, 128–29, 199
Association of Licensed Automobile Manufacturers (ALAM), 36–39
Atmospheric pollution, 233–35

Atmospheric Pollution Control Board, 234
Auburn Automobile Co., 101–2, 111
Auto Workers Union (AWU), 130, 133
Autobahnen, 137, 139
Autocar, 102, 203
Automobile, The, 32
Automobile industry, European, 8, 69, 109, 212–13
Automobile industry, American, 1, 38–45, 69–72, 74–75; adopts mass production, 65–68; and aviation, 71–72, 147–52; in 1920's, 85–88, 95–104, 107–9; under New Deal, 110–21, 123–38; in Second World War, 143–59; after Second World War, 160–77, 199–214, 242–45
Automobile insurance, 194, 241
Automobile Labor Board, 132
Automobile Manufacturers Association, 18, 45, 150, 154, 217
Automotive Committee for Air Defense (ACAD), 150
Automotive Council for War Production, 154–55, 158, 202
Autostrade, 139
Avery, Clarence, 60
Aviation Corp. (AVCO), 110–11

Bacon, Roger, 1, 2
Baruch, Bernard, 153
Battle of the Overpass, 135–36

257

"I promised I wouldn't cry," Kate whimpered.

The edge was back in Patrick's voice. "You're crying now, and you promised not to. Kiss the girls for me." He blew her an airy kiss before he strode from the room.

Kate stood in the kitchen doorway watching her husband as he settled his cap firmly on his head and fired off a snappy salute to the reflection in the mirror. She watched him open the front door, step outside, and then kick it closed with his heel. He didn't miss a step and he didn't look back.

Kate slipped to the floor in a huddle, crying heartbrokenly, over and over, "Just promise me there will be a tomorrow for us, Patrick."

Outside in the crisp, early morning air, Patrick walked to the corner bound by apartment complexes to meet Zack Heller. The moment he saw him, he gave him a thumb's-up salute.

"This is it, Heller!" he called.

"You ready for this, Captain Starr?" Heller asked, a slight catch in his voice.

"I've been ready for this since I saw my first airplane. I think I was three years old. The only thing I can't figure out is why God made me a mere mortal instead of a bird. Man, I was meant to fly. I don't ever want to do anything else. How about you?"

"I'm dedicated, Starr. You're fucking obsessed."

"You got that right. It's my life."

"No, it isn't. That family you left back there is your life."

"Yeah, yeah, but after flying. Hey, I'm *readyyyyy*."

Patrick tipped his cunt cap to a rakish angle, jammed his hands in his pockets, and started to whistle.

"Off we go, into the wild blue yonder, climbing high, into the sky . . ."

CHAPTER

1

The sewing machine had a sound all its own, the needle jumping up and down through the bright pink felt square. Two pairs of eyes focused on what was almost a finished product. With her head bent to the intricate stitches the needle was making, Kate Starr could still see the telegram on the little table where she'd dropped it earlier, unopened. Patrick had only been gone ten months. She shouldn't be getting a telegram.

It was supposed to be yellow. Everyone said it was yellow.

"Is this going to be the prettiest dress you ever made me, Mom?" Betsy asked.

"Me too, me too! I want one just like it. Betsy and Ellie looked like Mommy," Ellie babbled around the thumb in her mouth. She pointed to a dress draped over the back of the sofa, her own Christmas dress.

Kate watched as a frown started to build on six-year-old Betsy's face. "Does Daddy want us to all wear the same dress?"

Kate cut the thread and double-knotted it beneath the swirling skirt. "Well . . . yes, I guess so. Daddy . . . always smiled when we paraded in front of him in our mother-daughter outfits. Remember how he always took our picture?" God, her voice sounded so shaky, so . . . fearful. One look into Betsy's eyes told her the child was aware that something she didn't understand was going on.

"I want mine to be different," Betsy said, fighting tears.

"Oh, honey, why?" Kate said, her own eyes misting.

"Want mine different, too," Ellie whined.

Kate stared at the appliqués on the skirt of the dress, refusing even to glance in the direction of the telegram.

Betsy scuffed at the worn carpet. "Daddy isn't here. He won't see us," she said. "I want my dress different."

"Me too. Make it different. Make it like Betsy's," Ellie chortled.

"No! I want mine to be mine. Mommy, don't make hers like mine."

"All right, Betsy. I'll give you a belt buckle and make a bow on the back of Ellie's dress. Do you want pockets?"

Betsy pointed to the telegram. "What's that?"

"It's a telegram," Kate said, her voice sounding desperate. "A telegram is . . . it's a . . . quick way to send . . . news." Bad news, she should have said. Terrible news. She wanted to cry, to shred the telegram.

"Is the news about Daddy?" Betsy asked, the dress momentarily forgotten. "Maybe Daddy is going to be coming home for Christmas. Open it, Mommy, and see if he is." She marched over to the little table, picked up the telegram and thrust it toward her mother. Kate recoiled, almost toppling the chair she was sitting on.

"Put that back. Now! Do as I say, Betsy," she said in a

voice the child had never heard before. Betsy scampered away to obey her mother's orders, then, eyes downcast, scuffed at the carpet.

Kate refused to look at either of her daughters. Instead she bent her head to peer at the stitches she was ripping out. Things were starting to change already, and she hadn't even opened the damn telegram. When a stitch refused to budge with the stitch ripper, Kate yanked at it, ripping the material at the seam. A tear fell on her index finger.

She was losing control, frightening the children. I'm not going to open the telegram, she thought. Not now, not ever. "Oh, God, Patrick, you promised me tomorrow, and now I have a telegram," she muttered under her breath.

Kate looked at the appliquéd Santa Claus on the pocket she'd just ripped off Betsy's dress. She had to say something to the child, look at her and not see Patrick reflected in her little face. Patrick always called her a miniature replica of himself. And he said it so proudly. She rummaged in her sewing box for a buckle that would match Betsy's dress. Needle and thread whipped in and out of the soft fabric.

"Want to try this on now, honey?" Kate said in a voice so choked with emotion, Betsy ran to her and put her arms around her in a tight bear hug. Not to be outdone, Ellie wrapped both her arms around her mother's leg.

She needed to be strong. Tough. Little Miss Homemaker, who didn't have the faintest idea how to be strong and tough. All she knew how to do was be a mother and wife. Patrick took care of everything else.

"I think," Kate said quietly, "we're feeling out of sorts because it's almost Christmas and Daddy won't be here to help us open presents. So tonight we're going to write a very long letter and tell him how much we miss him and how we're going to make Christmas cookies. We have to be brave and . . . and carry on. Daddy will be disappointed if we don't go ahead with things. Now, let's see a big smile from everyone." She stretched her own facial muscles into something resembling a smile, then watched the girls scurry off with their dresses. The moment they were out of sight, she crumpled, her eyes again on the telegram.

It had been delivered an hour ago, just as she was getting ready to sit down at the sewing machine. Soon the notification officer would arrive. A chaplain and accompanying officer would probably knock on her door next. "I damn well won't open it!"

The girls were back, prancing back and forth in front of her in their new Christmas dresses. She made all the right comments, smiled, hugged them, and then ordered them to take off the dresses so she could hem them.

There was a glint in Betsy's eyes when she said, "I don't want to wear the matching panties, Mommy. That's baby stuff. I don't like to show off my undies."

"But honey, the pattern calls for matching panties." Suddenly she felt stupid, ignorant. Was it possible Betsy was right and six-year-olds didn't wear matching panties?

"I want mine to match." Ellie giggled, bending over to show her plain white panties.

"She's a show-off," Betsy grumbled. "Boys laugh at you when they see your underwear."

"All right, plain white for you, Betsy, and matching ones for Ellie. We compromised. That means it's fair for everyone."

"Yippeeeee!" Ellie squealed.

Betsy scowled. "When are you going to open your news letter? We're supposed to share. Daddy said so."

"Later, honey. Change your clothes and bring the dresses back so I can hem them. Then you can play Chinese checkers if you want to."

Betsy wasn't about to be put off. "When you open the news letter later, are we going to share it?"

"Yes," Kate said, because there was no other answer that would satisfy her daughter.

9

Now. She should open it now. But if she did that, she would be breaking a promise to Betsy. There was every possibility the telegram was from Patrick's father or her own parents. But no. She *knew* who'd sent the telegram and she *knew* what it said. THE SECRETARY OF THE AIR FORCE REGRETS TO INFORM YOU . . .

"You wasted your money, Mr. Secretary of the Air Force, because I'm not going to open your hateful telegram," Kate said through clenched teeth.

The girls were squabbling over where to play their game of Chinese checkers. A moment later they were in front of her, demanding that she make the decision for them.

"I have an idea. Why don't you play the first game in Mommy and Daddy's room. Right in the middle of the bed. You can play the second game in the bathtub, and the third game in your own room."

Ellie squealed her delight. Betsy's face indicated it was the stupidest thing she'd ever heard of, but she trotted off behind her sister. Seconds later Kate heard the door to her room close.

She bit down on her lower lip to stop the trembling, and leaned back in the sewing chair she'd upholstered herself. Her position gave her a clear view through the front window.

She thought about her husband then, remembering. As if she could ever forget. Patrick was her life, her reason for being. She knew in her heart that the day God had created her, He'd said to Himself, I'm putting Kate Anders on earth so she can marry Patrick Starr. She'd never told that to anyone, not even Patrick. It was a secret she hugged to herself every day of her life.

She'd known Patrick since grade school, walked behind him and his friends on the way to school, blushing furiously when he turned to look over his shoulder at her. When his friends weren't looking at him, he'd smile and sometimes wink. She'd never told anyone about that, either.

Once in third grade when the teacher had made her head of her relay team, she'd picked Patrick and he'd outright refused to be on her team because his friends heckled him. Later, out in the hallway, he'd hissed at her to never do that again. She'd nodded miserably and then cried like a baby.

On the way home from school that same day, Patrick had rushed to catch up with her and apologized for making her cry. She remembered exactly what he'd said and how he'd said it. "Jeez, Kate, the guys will never let me live that down. Guys don't like that kind of stuff. I don't like to be kidded. I like you. A lot. I'm sorry I made you cry. Don't tell your mother, okay? If you do, she'll tell my dad. Boys aren't supposed to hit girls or make them cry. I'll get a whipping for sure."

Everybody in school knew she *liked* Patrick, and everyone in school, even Patrick's buddies, knew he liked her, too. But it wasn't until they were older, in high school, that they had a real date.

All the girls liked Patrick because he flirted with them, but he smiled at her, his eyes all warm and wet like a puppy's. Once, when she was in seventh grade, he'd touched her hair and said it was like silk. He said she could be his girl if she wanted to, but if she told anyone, then she wasn't his girl. At night she'd added that secret to her growing list, and slept with all of them on a piece of paper under her pillow.

In her teen years every single minute that wasn't used up by school or her family was spent with Patrick. By that time Patrick's friends had paired off with girls, so she was accepted. Patrick was her fella and she was his girl. All the time. If she didn't see him for a day over the weekend, she thought she would die. She knew way back then she could never live without him.

Once she'd been sick in bed with a high fever for three days, which stretched into four and then five. She should have known she was retarding her recovery by being so mis-

11

erable, not eating or drinking fluids. But she didn't need that kind of nourishment; she needed Patrick, to see him, to hold his hand, to have him smile at her.

She'd waited until the family fell asleep and then crept downstairs, put on her mother's ratty fur coat, and in her slipper socks walked around to Patrick's house and threw a small stone at his window. He'd come downstairs in his pajamas and, outside, had hugged her and kissed her eyes and even her ears. He'd said all kinds of really nice things and then made her go home. She was better the next day. All she thought about for weeks after that were Patrick's kisses, sweet as sugar and warm as summer sunshine.

The kisses had stayed sweet and warm, and then they'd become passionate. Always passionate, even when she was pregnant, right up to the last minute before delivery.

If she lived forever, she would never forget the look of rapture on Patrick's face when he held Betsy for the first time. The doctor, smiling, said father and daughter had *bonded*.

Kate's face closed up when she thought of Ellie's birth. Patrick hadn't bonded with Ellie. He didn't pick her up for two whole weeks, and when he did, he said, "She looks just like you, Kate." How pleased she'd been with that compliment. To her dismay, Patrick said over and over that Betsy was his and Ellie was hers. She wasn't sure even now if Patrick loved Ellie. She'd asked so many times, and Patrick would just look at her and say, "Now that's a stupid question if I ever heard one." He'd never given a straight-out yes or no answer.

A sound from outside jolted her. She wiped her tears away, her eyes fastened on the front window.

She knew who he was the moment she saw the Air Force blue sedan with the gold lettering on the door glide to the curb in front of the building.

Every military wife in the world knew who he was.

She leaped from the chair and bolted for the front door.

12

TO HAVE AND TO HOLD

She slammed the door and double-locked it, her face filled with panic. Her hands clenched into tight fists, the knuckles bone-white. Tears streamed down her cheeks.

How shiny the car was, not a speck of dust on it. The car door inched open, and she saw one brilliantly shined shoe, then another. Feet. Black socks. Two legs, and then the whole of him. How sharp the creases were. Almost as sharp as the ones she made in Patrick's trousers.

Kate glanced toward the little table. She should have opened the telegram. Never!

Dress blues. Spiffy. She knuckled her eyes as she tried to stifle the sobs rearing up in her throat. He squared his shoulders, not the way Patrick did it, all slithery motion, but with a quick little snap that looked ominous. Through her tears she watched him settle his cap squarely on his head. Now he was going to come up the walk.

Kate clutched at her heart. How could it be beating so fast when it was broken, shattered into a dozen pieces?

He was moving. Betsy had counted the steps to the front door once when she was having a race with Ellie: twenty-one. She counted each one, her eyes on the black polished shoes. Ten, eleven . . . Betsy's were a child's steps. This man in his dress uniform and shiny shoes made it in eleven. She should have known it would only be eleven. Why hadn't she known that?

The knock on the door was the loudest sound she'd ever heard in her life. Her heart fluttered in her chest. *Don't open the door. Not now, not ever. If you do, your life will change forever.*

The knock sounded again, louder this time. Kate felt herself start to crumple. Her eyes flew to Patrick's chair, to his picture on the little end table. How handsome he was in his flier's gear. Through her tears she could see the excitement in his face, the endearing, lopsided grin. Her husband, and Ellie's and Betsy's father.

13

"Mrs. Starr, are you there?"

Of course she was here; what a stupid question. She had two little girls to take care of, where else would she be a half hour before dinner? *Please, God, make him go away.* The clenched fists kneaded her thighs.

"Mrs. Starr, I *must* talk with you. Please open the door."

"Go away," Kate whimpered. *Please, God, make him go away.*

She sensed movement on the other side of the door.

Kate felt her knees buckle. A second later she was crunched against the front door, her eyes level with the kitchen doorknob. She saw his shadow, saw the brass knob turn, saw his creased trousers, his polished shoes.

"Get out of here!" she whimpered as he entered. "You have no right to come into my house. You broke and entered ... breaking and entering ... you damn well came into my house uninvited. Now, leave now! That's an order, Major. My husband *was* a captain. Is ... still is ... would be ... you're here ... leave me alone!" Kate sobbed.

"I can't do that, Mrs. Starr." He approached her, held out his hand to help her to her feet. Kate knocked his hand away and cowered against the door.

"Mrs. Starr," Major Collier said, dropping to one knee so he was eye level with Kate, "the chaplain is on his way. I'm sorry, I thought he would be here. We do our best to arrive together with Mrs. Willard." Mrs. Willard was the wife of Patrick's commanding officer. "There must have been an emergency. . . ." He let his voice trail off. "I know how difficult this is for you. One is never prepared. . . . It's not as though Captain Starr is dead. We don't know that yet. I'm not here to tell you there's been a change in his status. You know how things are done." His voice sounded even lamer than before.

Kate sprang to life. "What are you talking about?" She wiped at her eyes with the sleeve of her shirt. "If Patrick isn't ... what are you doing here? Why was that telegram delivered?" she said, pointing to the hall table. "I know who you are. You bring messages from the Grim Reaper. Everyone calls you men the big G.R.s How can you do it? *Why* do you do it? Damn you, where is Patrick?"

Nelson Collier flinched. So she hadn't opened the telegram; she didn't know. God damn Air Force.

"Captain Starr's plane was shot down," he told her. "That's all we know. Two of our pilots say they saw him eject. If he ejected, he was alive. He could be anywhere in the jungle, or he could be a prisoner. We just don't know. We try to get the information to the family as soon as we can. Here, let me help you up."

He was taller than she expected, so tall she had to stretch her neck to look up at him. She was aware of everything then, of the radio playing softly in the kitchen, the smell of her meat loaf in the oven, the twinkling lights of the Christmas tree. Patrick wasn't dead. Not confirmed, anyway. Alive somewhere. She had to hang on to that thought. She allowed herself to be led into her tiny kitchen, which sparkled with cleanliness.

"A cup of coffee would taste wonderful, Mrs. Starr."

"All right," Kate said listlessly. She turned off the oven before she measured coffee into the percolator and added water.

"This is a pretty kitchen. My wife would like it," Major Collier said quietly.

"I wallpapered it myself. Patrick . . . said it reminded him of an outdoor garden. It's the ivy pattern on the paper."

"I can see where he would think that, especially with all the plants on the windowsill. Or are they herbs?"

"Both." Placing three green checkered place mats on the table, she watched as Nelson Collier played with the fringe. "I made those, too," she volunteered.

"They're pretty. My wife is partial to green."

"Green was . . . is Patrick's favorite color. Betsy likes green, too. Ellie prefers red. I think I like blue."

"Mrs. Starr, is there anyone you want me to call?"

15

"No. Most of my friends moved off the base. They went back to their families, and I stayed here. There's been no room at my parents' house since my grandparents moved in. They're quite elderly. Patrick's father lives in a retirement village that doesn't accept children. I decided it would be more economical for us to stay here . . . and wait. How long will it be before you have more information?"

"We'll do the best we can. Things like this take time. There's the other side to deal with."

"So, what you're saying is you don't know. It could take months or even years. And what am I supposed to do in the meantime, Major Collier?"

"Wait. It's all any of us can do. Time, Mrs. Starr, will take care of everything."

"That's not good enough, Major. I want details. I want to know everything. I have a right to know, and so do my children. What's to become of us?" she whispered.

"We take care of our own, Mrs. Starr," Nelson Collier said with an edge to his voice. Hearing a knock, the major looked toward the front door. "That would be Chaplain Rollins," he said. The relief in his voice startled Kate.

Major Collier, with Kate's permission, opened the door. An aide ushered in a tall, graying man dressed in regulation blues. When the men joined her in the kitchen, Kate poured coffee with a steady hand as she suffered through the amenities. She knew the chaplain expected her to fall into his arms for comfort, so she deliberately distanced herself from him, preferring to stand by the stove with her rump pressed against the warm enamel of the oven door.

"Do we pray now?" Kate said bitterly.

"She's in shock, forgive her," she heard Major Collier say, sotto voce.

"Only if you want to, my dear," the chaplain said to her, his voice deep and resonant.

"I don't want to."

"God—"

"Don't talk to me about God, Chaplain. Not now. And you, Major, don't tell me the Air Force takes care of its own. When you walk out this door, I'm by myself with my two children. I know *exactly* how the military works. You'll bombard me for a week or even two weeks, and then I get shuffled into some never-never land, at which point I become a liability. No one wants to deal with heartbroken wives and crying children. I *know* how it works. Each phone call is filtered down to people you have to repeat the story to until you reach the maintenance people. I defy you—do you hear me?—I defy you to prove me wrong!" Kate cried, her blue eyes blazing. She fell apart almost immediately, sobbing into her hands.

This couldn't be happening. It was one of those horrible nightmares she had from time to time when the mail was slow and Patrick's letters didn't arrive. They didn't say Patrick was dead; they said they didn't know. Surely not knowing was better than dead. Dead meant Patrick would never walk through the door again. Never hold her in his arms or kiss her good night. Dead meant she would be a widow, her children fatherless.

At last Nelson Collier stood up. This was the part he hated. "Mrs. Starr," he said, not unkindly, "Captain Starr would want you to be the little soldier he knows you are. This has been a terrible shock. You have to be strong, especially for those two little girls inside. You must keep the home fires burning for your husband."

Kate dropped her hands and stared at him, incredulous. "That's bullshit, Major, and you know it. I'm not a soldier. My husband is the soldier, and look what happened to him. I'm a wife and a mother. I don't want to be tough, I don't want to . . . I wish you'd leave. I want to be alone with my children."

"We understand, Mrs. Starr," the chaplain said in the voice

17

he reserved for serious sermons. Nelson Collier nodded. "If you need anything, if you want to talk or . . . pray, call me any time of the day or night."

Kate said nothing as she held the door open for their departure. She didn't say good-bye. The dead bolt seemed to move of its own volition.

There were things to do, things that had to be taken care of. She had to set the table, cook the potatoes, cut up the salad greens, slice bread. All the things she did every day according to her schedule. Later, when it was time for her to sit down and knit, she would think about Patrick and prepare what to say to the girls. Tomorrow. Not today. Her eyes filled again as she peeled potatoes. "You promised me tomorrow, Patrick. You promised. I'm holding you to that promise. You're alive, I know it. I know you'll keep your promise."

She was talking to herself, mumbling under her breath. And why shouldn't she? She'd just had the shock of her life. Anything she did now, no matter how strange or bizarre, shouldn't be held against her. *Oh, Patrick, where are you? Are you alive like they said? I didn't ask when it happened. What was I doing at that precise moment you ejected? There has to be a record. Families need to know things like that. Was it yesterday when I was cranky and out of sorts, or the day before, when I had that awful headache? I should have known, felt something. We were always so in tune with one another. Oh, Patrick, what's happening? Why didn't I feel something?*

She rinsed the potatoes a second time before drying off the pot and clamping on the lid. Her movements were sure, deft from years of practice in the kitchen. Mother Earth, was what Patrick called her. Would he ever call her that again? Yes, God, yes. She would accept nothing else.

Kate sniffed, wiped her eyes on her sleeve, and cut the salad greens into tiny pieces so Betsy would have less trouble chewing with her missing front teeth. Ellie liked little pieces, too, and always lined up the tiny pieces of vegetables to make a ring around the plate. At five she knew her colors and alternated the ring with carrots and peppers, chortling as she arranged the bits of tomatoes in the pyramid in the middle. The shredded lettuce was her moat. Every evening they laughed over it. Or she did, as Patrick seemed to tolerate Ellie's ways.

Her chores done for the moment, Kate glanced around, a wild look in her eyes. Now what was she supposed to do? What if . . . what if . . . Eyes burning, she decided to clean the refrigerator. Busy hands didn't allow time for thinking. God, what if he didn't come back? What if he'd been shot when he landed on the ground? Maybe she should call her mother, one of her sisters, somebody who would say, "Don't worry, Patrick's all right. One day when you're least expecting it, he'll walk through the door. Patrick was too vital to die so young. Patrick was a survivor. Hold on to that."

Kate scrubbed industriously, the stainless steel shelves glistening with her efforts. The enamel blinded her. She wished she knew why she had such a fetish about cleanliness. Maybe someday she'd think about that. Patrick thought about it often, chastising her eat-off-the-floor housekeeping. "We never eat off the floor, so what's the point?" he would say. Sometimes he grinned when he said it, and other times he said it sarcastically.

Finally, satisfied with the condition of the refrigerator, she washed the bottles and jars, making sure the lids were on tight. Her eyes raked the ketchup bottle and the butter dish. Her mother always said you could tell a good housekeeper by the way she kept her ketchup bottle and butter dish. Hers were spotless. Patrick always dribbled the ketchup and got little toast crumbs on the butter and the dish. Tears slipped down her cheeks, and this time she didn't stop them. Maybe she needed a really good cry; better to let it out and then get on with it.

She washed the vegetables, the lemons, the cucumbers, the tomatoes, and then dried them with a dish towel. Patrick said she was balmy for doing it. She hated it when he said things like that, so she tried to wait until he wasn't around. But he always knew.

She'd tried so hard to be perfect for Patrick, the perfect wife, the perfect mother, the perfect housekeeper, the perfect lover, the perfect money manager, the perfect *everything*. Patrick said there was no such thing as perfect, and even if there was, he didn't want it. Her ears and cheeks started to burn when she remembered him saying, "Let's have stand-up sex in the kitchen by the sink." The girls were outside in the sandbox, and the kitchen window was open. She'd refused, and Patrick got testy. "What's the big deal? All I do is push up your dress, pull your panties aside, and bingo!" She'd offered to go in the bedroom and lock the door, but Patrick had said to forget it. Instead he'd gone to the bathroom, alone, and she'd known why. She hated it when he masturbated. It was her fault. Her face and ears continued to burn. Patrick was selfish, but then so was she in her own way. Once he'd even whipped out his . . . *his thing*, and done it right in front of her. She'd cried, told him to stop, but he wouldn't. That time, they were in the hall outside the bathroom and the girls were in the tub.

"The past is prologue," she muttered as she dropped the last polished lemon into the fruit bin.

When dinner was finished, Betsy helped clear the table while Ellie shook out the place mats and put them away. Then both children sat down with their crayons and paper. "Remember now," Kate said, "when the big hand is on the three, you have to finish Daddy's picture and get ready for your bath."

It was a ritual the children performed every evening after dinner. On Fridays Kate folded their drawings and mailed them off to Patrick in a separate envelope.

20

"Mommy, what should I draw tonight?" Betsy asked.

Kate pretended to think. "Draw all of us sitting on your bed. Put a letter in my hand."

"Are you smiling or are you sad?" Betsy asked, her face puckered in a frown.

"I'm smiling. Everyone is smiling."

"What's Ellie doing?"

"Hugging Roseann."

"Can I put a puppy on the bed even if we don't have a puppy? If I put a puppy, will it be a lie?" Betsy asked anxiously.

"No, Betsy, it won't be a lie. It will be a wish. I'll show you how to print the word *wish* on the picture. Daddy will know what it means. A puppy is a good idea."

"Will we ever get a puppy?" Ellie asked wistfully. "If we do, can he sleep on the bed with me? What will we call it, Mommy?"

Kate fought her tears. "That's something for us to think about. Let's all think about a name, and tomorrow after dinner we'll tell each other. The best name gets a lollipop."

"I want a red one. My name will win," Ellie said confidently.

"No sir, I'm the oldest. I know better than you do," Betsy said, petulant.

In order to avoid a squabble she wasn't prepared to deal with at the moment, Kate switched the conversation to the park and the games they would play the following day.

When the girls had finished drawing, Kate beamed her approval at the two pictures and listened patiently as Ellie explained each squiggly line and round circle. She was always amazed at Betsy's drawings. The child had inherited whatever small talent she herself had. She had no difficulty figuring out Betsy's picture. The puppy looked like a puppy, the bed looked like a bed, and even the figures were more than stick lines, rounded out with faces and hair.

"Bath time. Last one in is a smelly fish!"

"Oh, Mommy!" Both girls giggled as they trotted off to the bathroom.

When the girls were in clean pajamas and tucked into bed, Betsy asked the question she'd been dreading all evening. "Who was that man, Mommy?"

"An Air Force major, honey."

"Does he know Daddy?"

"Not really. He knows about him, but he doesn't know him personally."

Satisfied with the answer, Betsy snuggled beneath the covers. "Did we get a letter today?"

"No, sweetie, we didn't, but tonight we're going to read the last two instead of our usual one. I'll read you your last letter and then I'll read you mine, okay?"

"Goody, goody," Ellie said, her eyes closing wearily. A second later she was sound asleep.

"Read mine first, Mommy."

"Okay," Kate said, unfolding the wrinkled letter the little girl handled several times a day.

" 'Dear Betsy and Ellie—' "

"Daddy always puts me first. Does that mean he likes me the best, or is it because I'm the oldest?"

"What do you think?"

"I'm the oldest," Betsy said, wrinkling her pug nose. Her dark eyes glowed as she waited for her mother to read the letter she already knew by heart, just the way she knew some of the nursery rhymes.

" 'I miss you two little rascals. I hope you're being good for Mommy and doing your chores. I love all the pictures you've been sending me. I have some of them in my plane. I show them to the other guys in my squadron and they say you girls are going to be artists someday.

" 'It's going to be Christmas pretty soon. Be sure to make a present for Mommy. Mommies like presents. When I was little like you, I used to make a present for my mother and she would always give me a big hug and a cookie. I think the hug was better than the cookie.

" 'I love both of you very much. I think about you every day and wonder what you're doing. Be good girls and I will be home soon. Remember now, you have to be extra good or Santa won't leave presents in our house. I heard, and maybe this is a secret, but I'm going to tell you anyway. Santa comes all the way over here to Thailand and leaves us fliers a special present. Isn't that wonderful?

" 'Remember to say your prayers every night. You, Ellie, and Mommy are mine to have and to hold, forever and ever. I send you all my love and kisses. Daddy.' "

"Isn't it a wonderful letter, Mommy?" Betsy said sleepily.

"The best letter in the whole world," Kate said. "Maybe tomorrow we'll get a new one." She looked at the date on the envelope: September 23. She could feel herself start to tremble. "I'll read you my letter tomorrow. Sleep now, honey," she said, bending over to kiss both her daughters.

"Okay, Mommy," Betsy said, drifting off to sleep.

She was alone now, more alone than she'd ever been in her life. She knew what came next on her schedule, what she was supposed to do to fill up the hours until it was time to go to bed. If she deviated now, she would be lost. If she called the chaplain now, she could still do everything and only be off by a few minutes. She wasn't going to sleep anyway, so what difference would it make?

She dialed the number he'd left with her and cleared her throat when the chaplain picked up the phone on the third ring. "Chaplain Rollins, this is . . . Kate Starr. Please, tell me what you know and accept my apologies for . . . this afternoon. I'm sorry if I offended you. . . . I didn't mean to."

"I understand, my dear. Major Collier has all the information, but I'll be glad to tell you what I know. I can come over, if you like."

"No. No, I would rather . . . it's better if I'm alone right now. Talking on the phone isn't . . . it doesn't sound so . . . so final."

"I understand, my dear. . . ."

Kate listened carefully for ten full minutes, hating the sound of the man's voice, hating what he was saying.

"Captain Starr was in a right pull-up when his engine stalled on him. He was already on afterburner. As far as we can tell, he had no options. He ejected behind cloud cover. His wing man didn't actually see him eject. We think he's somewhere in enemy territory, Mrs. Starr."

Enemy territory. In a voice she barely recognized, she asked, "Chaplain, is Patrick . . . what I mean is, would it have been better for him to die than be taken prisoner?"

"We don't know that Captain Starr is a prisoner, nor do we know he's dead. He could be hiding in the jungle. Unlikely, but it is a possibility. We just don't know."

"When will we know, Chaplain?" Kate asked in the same small voice.

"I can't answer that, Mrs. Starr. We're doing everything possible to update the situation. As soon as we know, you'll know. Search-and-rescue efforts are under way. You must have faith and you must believe. Put your trust in the Almighty and He won't let you down."

Kate's stomach lurched. She wished she'd practiced her religion more faithfully. She went to church on Easter and Christmas and sent the girls to Bible study, but that was it. Praying was something she rarely did, even though the girls prayed every night before going to bed. "Isn't it a little after the fact now?" she muttered.

"Dear girl, it's never after the fact. God doesn't view it like that. Prayer is never frowned on. I don't say you have to go to church to pray. You can pray anywhere, anytime."

Anytime, anywhere. She knew that. "Thank you for talking to me, Chaplain," she said softly, and cradled the receiver.

24

A moment later she reached for her knitting. Knit one, purl two, *Holy Father* ... She stuck with it, knitting and praying for the forty minutes she allotted for knitting on her schedule.

Then Kate threw caution to the winds and repacked her knitting and sketch pad. The hell with the schedule. She was dying inside, so what would knitting and sketching do for her? With that thought, she burst into tears, burying her face in the sofa cushion so as not to wake the girls. Missing in action. Killed in action. Prisoner of war. When would she know Patrick's fate? *Oh, Patrick, where are you, are you safe?*

It was almost one in the morning when Kate crept off the sofa and walked down the hall to her bedroom. She turned on the light and stared at hers and Patrick's room, seeing it through her husband's eyes. Her face full of misery, she walked around the clutter—and that's what it was, clutter. Her crafts, her busywork. Wooden hearts edged in lace, duck plant holders, geese lined up in a row, picture frames with painted hearts with bows and buttons. Every wall, every corner, was filled with *something*. Panic rushed through her when she tried to see something of Patrick's. Yet she'd left everything just as it had been when he'd left.

She lurched, tripping over the lined-up geese, to Patrick's dresser, yanking open the drawers, knowing what she would find, Victorian lace bags filled with shaved cedar shaving. God, even the tassels on the venetian blinds had hearts and ducks on them. She gagged. How many times had Patrick said, "Honey, do we really need all of this?" How many times had he tripped over the parade of geese the way she just had?

She ran to the bathroom, knowing what she would find. The same homey theme of hearts, ducks, and chickens. She'd appliquéd hearts on the shower curtain with the same trailing ribbons, ending in a bouquet of baby ducklings nestled in a wicker basket. The same patterned decals were stuck to the four corners of the bathroom mirror. The bathroom carpet was oversize, latch-hooked three winters ago. She stared at the huge rooster in the center of the carpet and cried anew.

God, why was this bothering her now? *Because you know Patrick hated all this stuff, but he put up with it because he loved you.*

In the blink of an eye she was back in the bedroom, pulling and tugging at her dresser drawer. Beneath her slips, bras, and panties was the Frederick's nightgown, wrapped in tissue paper. It was so trashy, so . . . *slutty*, a direct contrast to everything else in the house. She opened a second drawer and withdrew a dimity ankle-length nightgown, neatly ironed and smelling of lemon and vanilla. The neckline was high with a prim satin bow she'd added after she bought it. She had three, pale yellow, pale pink, and pale blue. Demure. Old-fashioned. Ridiculous. She folded the Frederick's nightgown and placed it in the drawer, her eyes filled with tears as she left the bedroom.

In the small living room she looked around. If anything, it was even worse. Every inch of available space was filled with *something*. She could fill the back of a pickup truck with all the junk in the house. Once, in a fit of anger, Patrick had called her crafts "junk" and then later apologized. He was right, it was junk. God, where was the picture of him standing next to his plane with Zack? Her hands were feverish, frenzied, as she yanked at one drawer and then another until she found it. The frame didn't fit the Federal blue of all her crafts, so she'd shoved the picture in a drawer. She'd promised to find a place to hang it. Patrick had looked crushed, but he'd never mentioned it again. *Oh, Patrick, I'm sorry.*

Now when it was too late she was . . . What was she doing? Assuming guilt for her husband's situation? Blaming herself for not being more like the wife he wanted? Blaming herself for being selfish, not caring about what he wanted? All she'd tried to do was make a cozy, warm, happy home. What she *really* had was a cluttered, stifling, sort-of happy home.

Kate sank onto the sofa and reached for one of the pillows to hug against her breast. Dear God, had she done *anything* right all these years? "Our sex life was good," she whimpered. But was it? Patrick liked to experiment, but she didn't. Straight missionary position. She was always satisfied, but was Patrick satisfied? He said he was.

"What's so wrong about going down on me?" he'd asked on his last birthday, when she'd promised to do whatever he wanted and then had reneged on the promise. "Then get on top of me," he'd begged. She hadn't done that either, because she didn't like the way her breasts flopped about and Patrick had wanted to leave the light on. He'd stomped into the bathroom, buck naked, and not only slammed the door, but locked it as well. When he'd come out a while later, his penis dripping semen, he'd shouted, "Are you happy now?" She cried all night into her frilly, embroidered pillow after Patrick had set up camp across the room, and fallen asleep singing the birthday song to himself.

Was it too late to do all this soul-searching? Only if he's dead, she answered herself. But he *couldn't* be dead, he was too vital! She would never believe he was dead. Not Patrick. *Please God, let him come back. I swear I'll be the kind of wife he wants. I'll do whatever he wants. I'll wear trashy clothes and I'll have sex swinging from the chandelier with the lights on if that's what he wants.* She paused, then added, *I'll go back to church, too, and take the girls.* She half expected to hear a clap of thunder, but nothing happened.

God didn't make deals, it was that simple.

Armed with a load of brown grocery bags, Kate attacked the bedroom and bathroom, ripping things off the walls, snatching the shower curtain, kicking at the geese. She lost track of the number of bags she used and the trips she made to the little patio outside the apartment. She was stunned when she finished, at four o'clock, to see how spacious the place really was. She could walk anywhere and not have to dodge or weave her way around things. It was going to take her a long time to patch and paint all the holes in the walls.

Yesterday was gone. Today was here, and tomorrow would arrive soon enough.

CHAPTER

At six-thirty, when it was a bright new day, Kate parted the kitchen curtains. Winter. Her favorite time of the year, but then she said that every year. The truth was, autumn was her favorite time of the year. Autumn back East. She closed her eyes and imagined she could smell burning leaves.

A new day. How was she to think of it? Day one after the news? Day one without Patrick? Day one as head of household? Widow? Alone, with little hope for the future?

Kate clutched the edge of the sink with both hands until her knuckles turned white. How could she go on without Patrick? I don't know how to do anything, she thought. I never worked outside my home. "All I know how to do is keep house, and I botched that up," she said to the sound of the percolator. Her eyes strayed to the clock on the stove. She had an hour before the girls woke. Thank God it was Saturday and she didn't have to take Betsy to school.

Patrick was smart; everyone said so. A graduate of Texas A&M. Not too many pilots had a Master of Science degree in aerospace engineering. Would that get him through whatever was happening to him now? He was equipped for an emergency: he had his Geneva card, his emergency radio pilot stored under his right arm in a survival vest pocket, and he was in top physical condition. At his last physical he weighed in at 190, the perfect weight for his six-foot-two frame. He had wonderful stamina and endurance. Patrick would survive, but would she be able to say the same? She was already falling apart, unraveling like the yarn on a knitted sleeve.

Maybe she shouldn't tell the girls, at least not yet. Maybe it would be better to wait until she wasn't so raw inside, until she wouldn't burst into tears and frighten them. For now, she was all they had, and she had to be their rock. Patrick, she thought, would want it that way. Just pick up the pieces and go on. But on to what?

She ruminated about her situation for a while, and after pouring her third cup of coffee, reached for her Betty Crocker cookbook. She kept her checkbook and passbook to the saving account in the manila pocket in back. Their savings were meager, less than six hundred dollars in the savings account and one hundred in the checking account. If Patrick didn't return relatively soon, she was going to have some serious problems. Military paperwork constantly got snafued. The voluntary move off the base she was contemplating so she could get a job would cost more, and she'd have to have money for security and utilities deposits. It was unlikely that she could get by without getting a job. And if she did get a job, who would look after the girls? Sitters cost money and she wouldn't be making much to start—providing she even found a job without experience. She knew in her gut Patrick's pay and benefits status was going to be a problem.

"Enough," she muttered, slamming the bankbooks back into the cookbook.

"Help your sister get dressed, Betsy," Kate said an hour later. "I have to take the trash out." It took four trips to the Dumpster behind the apartment building to get rid of all the crafts from her rampage the night before. She wasn't sure how she felt when she entered the kitchen. Exposed, the way the apartment now looked.

"Take my socks off!" Betsy screeched.

"Will not. Mine have the pink bows," Ellie shrilled.

Kate's head throbbed. This was new. The girls rarely squabbled, and if they did, it was usually over in seconds. "Just a minute, let me see the socks," she said, and took a look. "Ellie, these are Betsy's. Here, these are yours," she said, pulling a pair of rolled-up socks from the little girl's drawer.

"She went in my drawer. She's not supposed to do that. You said it was private. I don't go in her drawers," Betsy grumbled.

"You do so. You went in yesterday looking for my letter."

"Because you told me to." To her mother she said, "We were playing school and I told her she had to do show-and-tell. I came in here to get mine and she said to get hers. That's why I went in her drawer."

"You did it!" Ellie cried.

"Shut up." Betsy yanked at the bows on her socks. "I hate these bows. None of the other kids in school have bows on their socks."

"I thought you liked them. They match your hair ribbons," Kate said. God, was this desperate-sounding voice hers?

"I don't want them anymore," Betsy said petulantly.

"Then give them to me," Ellie cried, snatching the bows Betsy had pulled off. "Now I can have two bows, one on each side. Will you sew them on, Mommy?"

Something was happening here, and she wasn't sure what it was. "All right, later this evening I'll sew them on, if Betsy is sure she doesn't want them."

31

"I don't. They're stupid. Nancy Davis said they're dumb-looking. She said I wear too many bows and ribbons, and they tease me about the colored buttons *you* sewed on the bottom of my skirt."

"But they look so pretty and colorful," Kate said defensively.

"Sew them on my dress, Mommy," Ellie said happily.

Kate nodded as she stared at Betsy's belligerent face. "I guess that means you want plain things, no ruffles or bows," she said quietly.

"I just want to look like the other girls. I don't want to take those little bags to parties, either. I want to buy a present like everyone else does. If I can't take a bought present, I don't want to go."

"All right, Betsy, you made your point. I'll think about it."

"That's what you always say to Daddy, but you don't think about it. He said so. I heard him say that was just to shut him up."

"Betsy, honey, I'm sorry. I'll try and do better. I promise," Kate said, her voice cracking.

"You always say that, too. You aren't sorry. Sorry means you don't do something again. That's what Daddy said. Ask Ellie, and if she's not pretending to be dumb as Chester Manners, she'll say the same thing." Ellie's head bobbed up and down.

Kate hesitated. "It's not the bows and buttons that are bothering you, although that's part of it. What's wrong, Betsy?"

Betsy looked down at her bare feet, her face full of misery. She bit down on her lower lip, a sure sign that she was about to cry.

"Betsy said Daddy is lost and that man can't find him. Daddies don't get lost, do they, Mommy?" Ellie giggled. "She's just being silly and trying to scare me, isn't that right, Mommy?"

32

Kate knelt and put her arms around both her daughters. "No, that isn't right, Ellie," she said in a whispery voice. "This is all my fault. I should have told you about Major Collier's visit yesterday, but I . . . had to . . . get used to what he said. I was going to talk to you about it today when we went to the park. You see, something happened to Daddy's plane and he had to . . . leave it, to jump out. You both know what a parachute is. Daddy was wearing his, so he landed safely on the ground. He used his radio to call for help, so now we have to wait for . . . for someone to go and get him, or wait for him to find his way back himself. It might take a little while, so we have to be brave and not worry. Daddy wouldn't want us to worry. We'll think about it and talk about it, but we won't worry. Can we agree to that, the three of us?"

"Does that mean Daddy isn't going to be writing any more letters? Will we still write to him?" Betsy asked tearfully.

"Of course we're going to write. That isn't going to change. Daddy is probably too busy to write. He'll have to find his way out of the jungle."

"Don't they have mailmen in the jungle?" Ellie asked.

"She's acting dumb again, Mommy."

"Do you know for a fact that there's no mail in the jungle, Betsy?" Kate chided gently.

"She said mailmen. Like our mailman. I know the difference," she said testily, her large brown eyes sparking.

"I'll tell you what. Today, after the park, we'll stop at the library. We'll ask the librarian to give us everything she has on Vietnam, and a map, too. If we study it, maybe we'll get a feel for where Daddy is and a better idea of how he's doing. I vote we do that."

"I do, too," Ellie said, raising her hand.

"Betsy?"

"Okay."

"I'm sorry I didn't tell you this last night. I was upset."

33

"Is that why you threw everything away?" Betsy demanded.

Kate nodded. How wise this little girl was. How like Patrick. "You faked me out last night, didn't you? You weren't really sleeping, were you?"

"I heard you crying. I saw you throw everything in the bags. All that stuff Daddy said was junk. Now he won't know you did it."

"Tonight we'll write him and tell him."

"It's too late. He's lost and they won't deliver his letter," Ellie said, bursting into tears.

"We're going to write it anyway and pray that Daddy receives it. We'll keep writing every day even if we say the same thing over and over. We'll call the Red Cross and ask them for help.

"Now, let's finish dressing, open all the windows, and head for the park. It's going to be a lovely day, the sun is shining, the sky is blue, and we'll have a picnic and play in the park."

"Why can't we buy hot dogs and french fries like everyone else?" Betsy said, pressing her advantage.

"That might be a good idea. It's time we did something different. With relish and mustard, how's that?"

"Oh, goody, real hot dogs. We can write and tell Daddy we had hot dogs. He won't believe us. Will you write it, Mommy, so he truly believes?" Ellie demanded.

"Absolutely," Kate said, forcing a smile to her face. "In fact, we'll have Betsy draw a picture of all of us eating the hot dogs." She tweaked Betsy under the chin. The child grimaced, her facial muscles stretching into something that resembled a smile. She didn't forgive easily. "Happy faces, everyone," Kate said as cheerfully as she could. Finally Betsy grinned, showing the gap between her front teeth.

"Okay, breakfast in ten minutes. Wash your faces, brush your teeth, brush your hair, and bring the rubber bands to the kitchen. Grizzly bear pancakes this morning for Betsy, and puppy dog pancakes for Ellie."

"I'd rather have cornflakes with a banana," Betsy said stubbornly. "You said pancakes are just for grown-ups because they have too much syrup and it rots your teeth. I don't want pancakes."

"Fine, then you can have cornflakes. Ellie and I will have the pancakes," Kate said wearily. *God, what's happening to us?*

An hour later, breakfast finished, Kate led the girls outdoors, jackets in hand. "Listen, instead of going into Bakersfield, let's head for Mojave. It will be something different."

"I'd rather go to the park," Betsy said, nudging her sister.

"Me too," Ellie said.

"Okay. Remember, it was your decision."

"Why do you want to go to the desert? They don't sell hot dogs there," Betsy said, staring straight ahead, her hands folded primly in her lap.

"I'm sure they sell hot dogs there. I wasn't trying to get out of buying them for you. I just thought . . ." She sighed. "Girls, do you think you could be a little more . . . What I mean is, I don't want us to have any bad feelings. I know you feel angry, Betsy, but anger doesn't make things better. Just because I'm a grown-up doesn't mean I don't forget—"

"My teacher says no one knows everything," Betsy volunteered.

"And your teacher is absolutely right. I'm sorry if I . . . I wanted to do everything right. I made a lot of mistakes, I see that now. Families shouldn't squabble. From now on if one of us has something to say, that person should say it. The others will listen. We'll . . . we'll vote. Let's vote now to confirm we're going to vote." Kate giggled in spite of herself. "Aye means yes and nay means no."

"Aye," cried Ellie.

"Aye," Betsy added after a slight pause.

"Okay, the ayes have it. I feel better, how about you?"

"Were the pancakes good?" Betsy asked wistfully.

"See, see, you cut off your nose to spite your face!" Ellie chortled. "Didn't she, Mommy?"

"In a manner of speaking, but you aren't going to say that again. Betsy was making a statement. The next time she'll explain to us if she doesn't want something. Do we agree?"

"Aye," they chorused.

When they reached the park, Kate parked the car and followed the girls to the playground.

"Where's your knitting and your book?" Betsy asked.

"I didn't bring them today. I thought I'd just watch you girls and talk to Della if she's here." Colonel Geary's housekeeper brought the colonel's children to the park every Saturday. The children played well together, considering the Geary children were boys. Kate spotted Della at a far bench and walked over, the girls in tow.

Della Rafella was Mexican, a cherub of a woman whose sweet face was always wreathed in a smile. She loved children, animals, and people. She'd been with the Gearys since the boys were born. Francine Geary, Timmy and Teddy's mother, had left after Teddy's birth "for greener pastures," according to Della. Everyone, she said, knew about Francine Geary and her lust for life, men, and wine. She also said Francine had damaged the colonel's chances of moving up in rank.

Something was wrong today, Kate could feel it as she sat down on the bench next to her friend, her only friend. " 'Morning, Della. It's a lovely day, isn't it?"

"I love sunshine even when it's cold. It's what I miss most about home. Sometimes I think I should go back."

"You could go back for a visit. Goodness, what would the Gearys do without you?" She was stunned to see the woman's eyes fill with tears.

"They don't need me anymore. Colonel Geary is getting

36

married next month, and his . . . his new wife is going to be a mother to the boys. She's going to clean the house and care for them. Colonel Geary is being transferred. I cried myself to sleep last night. I'll have to look for a job now, but I'm forty years old. I can't afford to pay rent and buy food. Housekeeping by the day doesn't pay that well. With room and board, I just manage to get by. I have very little savings, maybe enough to last a month or so."

"Oh, Della, I'm sorry. You can stay with me until you find something. You'll have to sleep on the couch, though. We'd love to have you."

Della's face brightened. "Truly, you would let me stay with you?"

"Truly I would."

"What happens when Captain Starr comes home?" She answered her own question. "By then I should have a job. Did you get a letter this week, Kate?"

"No. I won't be getting any letters for a while." Kate told her about the chaplain and Major Collier's visit, fighting her tears as she spoke.

"This is a terrible thing. Oh, Kate, I'm so sorry," Della said, wrapping Kate in her arms. "Look, let me come and help you. You need me, Kate. At least until Captain Starr comes home."

"Oh, Della, I can't pay you right now. Once Patrick's pay is straightened out it will be different. Besides, I can't bear to stay in base housing. The memories would drive me out of my mind. I'm barely making ends meet now. I'm going to leave base housing and find a job. I really don't know how to do much of anything but keep house. I have no talents, no job qualifications. But I can't go back home. I can't go to my sister, she has three children of her own and a very small house. Patrick's father lives in one of those retirement villages that doesn't allow children. And my parents have their hands full with my grandparents. I've never worked a day in my life. The only money I ever earned was from baby-sitting, and a little from my sewing. My God, I don't even know how to operate a cash register. I've always stayed home to cook, clean, iron, and take care of the children."

"That's what I do, and it's a full-time job. Really, Kate. Homemaking is very important."

"I wanted to be perfect for Patrick. He's so smart, he can fly a plane, do all those upside-down things pilots do. I just barely managed to get out of high school. What if he doesn't come back, Della? What if I'm a widow? I swear I won't want to live if that happens."

"That's foolish talk. Your husband will come back home. I feel it here." Della thumped her ample bosom. "I don't know when, but he will come back to you and those beautiful little girls."

"All I've been doing is crying and thinking. The girls . . . Betsy sensed something was wrong. This morning she was impossible . . . well, for a little while. Ellie doesn't really understand. I'm going to buy some newspapers on my way home. I told the girls we're going to go to the library. I hate to admit this, but I don't know the first thing about Vietnam. I should know. I should have studied up on it, asked Patrick questions. I don't know why I didn't. It doesn't say much for me. God, Della, how am I going to get through this?"

"One day at a time. I will help. If you allow me to sleep on your sofa and give me food, I will be your housekeeper. I do not require much, a few cents for church on Sunday. For now it is a solution for both of us, if you are agreeable."

"I'm more than agreeable," Kate said, brightening. "It's settled, then, we're a team. I'll help you and you'll help me. Do the boys know you're leaving?"

"Colonel Geary told them last night. Look at them, they're so quiet. First they lose their mother, now me, and they're getting a third mother. Teddy cried all night. Timmy said he's going to run away. The colonel whacked his bottom and made him do thirty push-ups. It is sad, is it not? Little children should not have to suffer."

"When is your last day with the Gearys?" Kate asked.

"Next Friday."

Kate nodded. "I'll drive down and pick you up after school. Oh, Della, I'm so glad things worked out this way! When God closes one door, He truly does open another. Now, let's go get the children some hot dogs. It's my treat. Sodas too." She stood up and began walking with Della toward the hot dog vendor, then stopped. "What's her name?"

"Whose name?" Della asked.

"The soon-to-be Mrs. Geary."

"Tiffany Wexelworth," Della said, breaking into her first smile of the day.

Kate burst out laughing. "May they live happily ever after."

Kate spent the following week in a state bordering on hysteria. For hours on end she'd read everything she could on Southeast Asia. She tried making up stories for the girls about the people and the strange land she was coming to despise, but Betsy and Ellie both balked after the third session, at which point she made up stories about a frog and a rabbit, which threw them into fits of giggles. While they colored or played school, she pored over the want ads and apartments for rent. Twice each day she called Della to report on the want ads, and if an apartment appeared promising, Della would check it out and report back on her success or failure.

By the end of the week she knew nothing more about her husband's situation. She bristled when she was told about the "government keep quiet policy" and demanded to know *exactly* what "keeping quiet" meant. Captain Bill Percy, her caseworker, who was cadaver thin with bulging eyes, told her the Air Force felt the communists treated prisoners in a humane and civilized way. "I believe our men are treated well," he said authoritatively. She didn't believe it for a minute and insisted on knowing if her husband was a prisoner. Percy looked her in the eye and said, "I don't know, Mrs. Starr," to which she replied, "Bullshit!" She blushed furiously but held her ground.

In his report, which grew thicker by the day, Percy wrote, "Possible troublemaker."

On Thursday, the day before she was to pick up Della, she called the casualty assistance representative for the fourth time to find out when she could expect to receive her husband's pay. There was no return call. For the last five months her checks had been late. One month she received two at the same time. Another time she'd missed an entire pay period. She was now a month behind and when she spoke repeatedly to the finance officer all he would say was he was looking into the matter. She then called her insurance agent to see if she could borrow on the family's insurance policy. With the paperwork involved, she was told the process would take four to six weeks. "We can starve in four to six weeks!" she screamed into the phone before she broke the connection. No one at the insurance office called her back. She then called the finance officer and complained again.

On Friday, Della's last day at the Gearys', Kate picked up Betsy from school and drove to Bakersfield, where the housekeeper tearfully climbed into the car with a suitcase and two paper bags full of her belongings. She leaned over to peck Kate on the cheek before stretching around to chuck the girls under the chin. "I'm here now to take care of you. I will be a mother hen and you three will be my chicks. It is agreed?" she asked.

"Absolutely. I've always wanted to be a chick. Patrick . . . Patrick always said I was his slick chick," Kate said with half a smile.

"Daddy said we were his chicklets," Betsy gurgled. "Chicklets are chewing gum, did you know that, Della?"

"No!" Della said in mock horror. Betsy and Ellie bobbed their heads up and down. "Well, if your daddy said you were his chicklets, he must have meant you were sweet and tasty."

"Is everything all right, Della?" Kate asked, her eyes on the road.

"It was sad. The boys cried, I cried. I'm starting a new life now. I cannot dwell on sadness, nor should you, Kate. I think I found an apartment. I called the owner last evening and he said we could come to look at it at four o'clock. Are you sure, Kate, that giving up housing on the base is the right thing to do? He said it needs work. It's by the California state college. There are three bedrooms—two, actually, and one oversized closet the man said could double as a tiny bedroom. If you like it and think you can afford it, I will sleep there."

"How much is the rent?" Kate asked anxiously. "Yes, moving is right for us. I need to get a job, a life. There's nothing for me at the base."

"He said it is negotiable, which makes me think it'll be a real dump. But we will do what we must to get by until Captain Starr returns. Soap and water plus a little paint can work miracles."

Kate brushed at the tears filling her eyes. "I can't believe this is happening," she whispered. "I have so much to tell you, but we'll discuss it later. I don't want the girls to get upset."

Della nodded. "I bought the paper this morning thinking you wouldn't have a chance to pick one up. Do you think you could be a receptionist? There are several girl Friday jobs listed."

"I don't know. I've never worked on the outside. But I can learn," Kate added firmly.

Twenty minutes later, after following Della's directions,

Kate stopped the car in front of a run-down building with a FOR RENT sign in a front yard that was more of a trash dump than a yard. She cringed at the sight. "I guess this is it." Neither woman made a move to get out of the car. A man as unkempt as the front yard appeared out of nowhere and sauntered over to them, hitching up his pants as he went along.

"Afternoon, ladies," he said, tipping an imaginary hat. "Come along, it isn't as bad on the inside as it is outside. If you decide to take the apartment, I'll have the trash hauled away." He gave his pants a second hitch as he shrugged his light flannel shirt into place over his skinny shoulders. Despite his youthful manner, Kate could see he wasn't a young man; he might have been sixty. "Donald Abbott," he said, holding the door open for Della. "I do like a woman with meat on her bones," he said, and winked at Kate.

"I do not like scrawny men." Della gave him a sour look.

"You look like a good cook. The stove in the apartment is almost new. The oven works. Everything works. Even the shower."

"That's a relief," Kate said tartly. "Is this neighborhood safe?"

"Of course it's safe," Abbott said testily. "Families live here. Poor families. They all help one another. Being poor doesn't mean the neighborhood isn't safe. Miss Della told me over the phone you had two little girls. If it wasn't safe, I wouldn't have given her the address." He hitched up his pants again as he marched behind Kate up the front walkway.

Fifteen minutes later, her heart thumping in her chest, Kate said, "Providing you clean this place, and providing the rent is right, I'll take the apartment. One hundred and ten dollars," she said firmly.

"One hundred and fifty dollars, and I'll let you have the wringer washer in the cellar. It works. Laundry tubs included. There's no Laundromat close by. I'll pay the water bill."

Kate weighed Abbott's words. Two showers a day for her and Della, a filled tub for the girls each day, and laundry water, not to mention trips to the Laundromat if she could find one … "One hundred and twenty-five with the washer and no water bill. It's all I can afford, so I can't counteroffer again. Oh, the rooms need painting. If you give us the paint, we can do it ourselves. It's your decision, Mr. Abbott."

It was a terrible apartment, Kate thought. She wasn't sure if paint and curtains would improve it. Maybe she could find the same green-and-white wallpaper and redo the ancient kitchen. "New linoleum in the kitchen," Kate blurted. God, she was really considering moving here!

"You strike a hard deal, little lady," Abbott said, extending his hand. "Consider yourself my new tenant. Rent is due the first of the month. I normally ask for a month's security, but you look to me like you're strapped right now. You can pay me ten dollars a month toward the security."

Thank you, God. "That will be just fine, Mr. Abbott. We'll move in the first of February. Do you need a deposit now, or is my word good enough?"

"Five dollars will hold it. It would help if I knew your name. This pretty lady, too," Abbott said smiling at Della.

"I'm Kate Starr and this is Della Rafella. My girls are Betsy and Ellie."

"Is there a Mr. Starr?"

"Is that any of your business?" Della snapped.

"Yes, there is a Mr. Starr, but he—"

"Jumped out of his plane and he's lost," Ellie chirped.

"I see," Abbott said. "Listen, you don't have to give me a deposit now. February first when you move in will be fine with me. My boy was killed in the Korean War." He shuffled off, his shoulders slumped.

"It's going to be fine," Kate said in the car on the ride

back to the desert. "We'll make that apartment a showplace, you wait and see."

Della blessed herself. "They say God watches over fools and foolish women. I don't have any bad feelings about it, Kate. I might even be able to find some baby-sitting jobs to help out, and Ellie will have someone to play with."

"I made some decisions this week, Della. I have to have a . . . I don't know what to call it, an agenda maybe—maybe that's the wrong word—but I honestly believe Patrick will come back. I don't know when. Until he does, I'll cope rationally with the uncertainty. I'm going to stay as busy as I can and do whatever I can for Patrick, even if it's just writing letters every day that pile up someplace I've never heard of. I'll keep Patrick alive for the girls. He is alive, Della, I know he is. For now I have to be patient because I have no other choice, and when my patience wears thin, I'll . . . do whatever I have to do. What do you think?" she said breathlessly, a catch in her voice.

"Are we really going to move into that dump?" Betsy demanded from the backseat.

Kate's heart fluttered. "It just looks like a dump, Betsy. It isn't really. We are going to have such fun fixing it up. You girls can pick out the color paint you want for your room and you can help paint. When it's all done, we'll take pictures and send them to Daddy. He's going to be so proud of you."

"Pink and red," Ellie said.

"If you paint pink and red, the room will be hot-looking and you'll sweat," Betsy said. "I think we should paint it yellow so on a cold rainy day it will seem sunny. My teacher said yellow is a sunny color. Isn't that right, Mommy?"

"Yes, yellow is a sunny color, but pink and red are kind of cozy. Maybe we can think about doing the walls different colors or making new bedspreads. It's something for all of us to think about and plan."

"Okay," Ellie said agreeably.

"What are we having for dinner?" Betsy asked.

Kate could feel the child's eyes boring into the back of her neck. She was about to say macaroni and cheese but changed her mind at the last second. "Hamburgers and french fries."

"Yippee!" Betsy squealed.

"Yeah, yippee!" Ellie seconded her sister.

Oh, Patrick, where are you?

Betsy squeezed her eyes shut. She should have been asleep a long time ago. She opened her eyes to see her sister roll over.

"Ellie," she whispered, "are you asleep?"

"You woke me up," the little girl whined. Her thumb went into her mouth immediately. "Now I'm scared. Can I have the night-light, Betsy? Can I sleep with you?"

Betsy hated the night-light, it made scary pictures on the wall. "Okay, but you have to be real quiet. Mommy gets mad when you sleep with me. And you better not wet the bed," she hissed.

"I promise," Ellie said, snuggling into the narrow bed with her sister. "I know a secret," she whispered.

Betsy wiggled on her side of the bed to make more room for herself. "I know lots of secrets."

"My secret is about Mommy. Is your secret about Mommy?" Ellie asked sleepily.

Betsy's heart thudded in her chest. She wiggled some more. "If you tell me your secret, I'll let Daddy hug you first when he comes home. That will be a promise. I'll even make a big red X on your tablet so you won't forget." Her voice was anxious when she said, "Tell me the secret."

"Mommy said a bad word today. I heard her. You were in school. I'm going to tell Daddy when he isn't lost anymore."

"If you do that, you'll be a tattletale. Daddy doesn't like it when we tell on someone."

45

"He does so."

"He does not. I'm the oldest, I know. He told me so. When you're the oldest, you know more. I go to school. What's the secret, Ellie?"

"Mommy said a bad word. She was looking in the book for her money and she only had three. She said the bad word and then she started to cry. That's the secret. It's a good secret, isn't it, Betsy?"

"Do you mean the cookbook?"

"It's like the checkerboard. In the pocket." Ellie started to cry, sniffling into her blanket. "Mommy doesn't have enough money, that's why she said the bad word. Maybe we won't have any breakfast tomorrow. Will we starve, Betsy?"

"No," Betsy mumbled.

"Daddy's not here. Mommy is doing everything different. We are so going to starve." She was sobbing now, clutching her sister's arm for comfort.

"We can eat berries and roots like the rabbits do. Miss Roland read us a story like that. People don't starve."

"When is Daddy not going to be lost anymore, Betsy? I want him to come home. Everyone but us has a daddy."

"We do so have a daddy. He isn't here, that's all. Don't you ever say that again. If you do, I won't like you."

"Jackie Rosen's dog got lost and they didn't find him. He's lost forever and ever," Ellie said mournfully.

"That's different. Jackie's dog was dumb. Daddy isn't dumb."

"I bet you're the smartest sister in the whole world. I love you lots and lots, Betsy. Tell me a story about Daddy. A nice story. I don't want to hear a sad story. I don't like sad stories. Maybe the Easter bunny will bring Daddy home. Is it stupid to wish for that?"

"No, it's not stupid. I wish it, too. Did Mommy cry hard and have to blow her nose or did she have tears in her eyes?" Betsy asked in a choked voice.

46

"She put her head down on the table and made funny noises. After she said the bad word. Tell me the story, Betsy."

"Once upon a time there was a little baby named Ellie. . . ."

When Betsy was sure her sister was asleep, she crept from the bed. On tiptoes she walked over to the dresser, opened the drawer quietly, and withdrew her bank. She knew exactly how much money she had: $5.12. She had two one-dollar bills and the rest was in change. Ellie had the same amount in her bank. With the handle of her comb she fished inside the bank until she was able to pull out the dollar bills. Then she did the same thing with Ellie's bank. She rocked back on her heels for a moment as she stared at the bills in her hand. She was stealing Ellie's money. That wasn't right.

She crawled over to her desk and reached for her tablet and pencil. She wrote $2.00 and printed her name. She was borrowing the money to give Mommy. When she opened the cookbook tomorrow, she'd think the Good Fairy had left the money. Ellie wouldn't have to worry about starving and eating roots and berries.

Betsy wanted to cry. Everything was different now. When Daddy was home, things were good. Everyone was happy. Now, everyone was grouchy and grumpy and nobody smiled. At that moment, she settled a thought in her mind. Daddies made a big difference. When a daddy didn't live in the house and take care of things, it went wrong. Mommies didn't know how to do things daddies did. There was always money in the back of the cookbook when Daddy was here. He was going to be proud of her when she told him she put money in the pocket to help Mommy. He'd hug and kiss her and say she did the right thing.

Careful not to make any noise, Betsy walked down the hall to the kitchen. She stood on her tiptoes to reach for the Betty Crocker cookbook. She carried it over to the counter under the night-light and looked into the back. Ellie was right. Three one-dollar bills were folded neatly. With chubby hands she smoothed out the four bills in her hand, laid them on top, and then folded them again. Now they wouldn't starve.

When her daddy came home, she'd tell him Mommy tried to do her best. She cried, then, as she made her way back to her room and crawled into Ellie's bed. She popped out a minute and pulled the covers up to her sister's chin. She bent over to kiss her cheek and whispered, "We aren't going to starve. I'll take care of you, Ellie, just like I promised Daddy. If Mommy can't do it, I can do it. I made a promise and I'm going to keep it."

She buried her face in Ellie's pillow and cried. "I want you to come home, Daddy. I love you very much. Please, God, this is Betsy Starr talking. Send my daddy home, don't let him be lost anymore."

She slept then, her pillow damp with tears that continued to seep from her eyes even in sleep.

Ground Hog Day turned out to be a beautiful, warm, sunshiny day just the way Kate had promised the girls it would be. "The day of the big move" was how she'd referred to the date. Tears sliding down her cheeks, she walked through the apartment one last time, reliving memories of she and Patrick together. When Patrick returned, they'd come back together and ask the new tenants if they would permit a walk-through.

She was in what Patrick called her "garden kitchen." Her eyes strayed to the phone, which had been disconnected just an hour ago.

Telephones were the lifeline to the outside world, to the military, to news of Patrick. When her new phone was installed on Monday, she would have to start the calls all over again and leave her new number. She knew in her heart her situation would be set back weeks, maybe even months, by something as innocuous as a changed phone number.

During the night, as she'd struggled for sleep, she'd realized she had to change her personal deadline for her husband's return. It simply wasn't going to happen in a matter of weeks or months, as she'd first thought. At some point during her restless night she'd extended his return to a year, possibly two. She'd cried then, begging God to hear her prayers, to return Patrick to her safe and sound.

Her eyes still on the kitchen wall phone, she remembered in agonizing detail the last conversation she'd had with Bill Percy. She'd badgered him relentlessly to tell her how the military could keep records of Patrick.

"If he isn't listed as a prisoner of war, how can he be returned? If those people shot him, will there be a record? Admit to me that Patrick is on his own. I don't want to hear excuses and lame explanations. How long is this war going to last?" She'd been furious and disgusted when Percy couldn't give her the answers. As a parting salvo, she'd shouted, "If you can't give me answers, then I'll have to find someone who will." And as she was hanging up the phone, she'd heard him say in a rock-hard voice, "Mrs. Starr, you will endanger your husband's well-being if you start trouble. You must remain calm and let us do what we're trained to do." To which she'd replied, "Bullshit!" She'd found that the word no longer embarrassed her as it once had.

Kate wiped at her misty eyes. She couldn't fall apart now. She was on her own and she had to hold things together. It was almost a joke. What did she know about things like this? She was a mother, a housewife. Patrick had always taken care of things.

She needed a plan. Two plans. Plan A would work for Patrick's return and Plan B would be . . . would be a means to live her life without Patrick. "I'll learn. I'll learn," she muttered, locking the door, then sliding the key under the mat for the next tenant.

The girls were settled in the car, and Della was waiting on the sidewalk. Her eyes spewing sparks, Kate exploded, the volley of words startling the housekeeper. "I am *pissed off*, Della! *They* should have moved me. *Paid* for this move. They don't care. No orders. My husband is missing in action and they say they have no orders, so my move is my move, but they won't release Patrick's pay for me to pay the rent here. I can't *believe* it!"

"Never mind, Kate," Della said comfortingly, ushering her behind the steering wheel. "Let's just head for our new home. I can't wait to see if our new landlord worked a few miracles on that ratty house. I'm just glad we'll get there before the furniture. I loaded all the cleaning supplies in the trunk just in case."

"I don't know what I'd do without you," Kate said, leaning over to hug her.

Church bells were tolling the noon hour when Kate stopped the car in front of her new home. She was relieved to see that the pile of trash was gone and the yard was neatly raked. Grass seed had been planted, and fragile threads of green could be seen waving in the slight breeze. Even the beautiful olive tree had been pruned and clipped. Kate could feel her spirits lifting.

Inside, her jaw dropped before she uttered a squeal of pure delight. All the walls were a pristine white. Light fixtures had been replaced, and there was a new floor covering in the kitchen. "Look, Della, it isn't linoleum, it's floor tile. No cracks, and there's even a border. Ohhh, look how clean this refrigerator is, and the stove positively gleams. Shelf paper! Good Lord, there's wax on the venetian blinds. I can smell it."

"The bathroom has been regrouted. It's so clean and sparkling, you need sunglasses," Della said happily. "The parquet floor is beautiful. And look at that fireplace! It will be wonderful on chilly evenings. We can even have dinner in front of it."

"Mommy, our bedroom is white," Ellie whined.

"Two walls are pink," Betsy said.

"I'm sure there's a reason for the pink walls. Mr. Abbott was trying to be nice to us, so he painted the rooms so we wouldn't have to do it. I think for now we should just appreciate it, and later, if he gives his permission, we can repaint it."

Ellie said, "Okay."

Betsy sulked.

"There's nothing for us to do," Della said, examining the oversize closet that was to be her room.

"I think you should share my room, Della. This is too tiny. We can use it for storage."

"No. Your room is your room. When Captain Starr comes home, he might be upset if he knew I shared what should be his space. This is fine for me. All I'll be doing is sleeping in it. Now it's settled, I don't want to hear another word."

Kate gave in, just the way she always gave in when someone else made a decision that affected her. "I wonder if he'll ever see this room," she mused.

"Of course he will. Never, ever think negative. If you don't think and act positive, the girls will sense it."

"But what if he doesn't come back?" Kate whimpered.

"He will come back. I don't know when, but he will. I hear the moving truck," she cried excitedly. "Take charge, Kate."

"All right, girls," Kate said, dabbing at her eyes. "Forward, march!"

It was five o'clock when the last dishes had been washed and placed in the sparkling white cabinets. At six o'clock the sheets were on all the beds. At six-thirty Della served up hamburgers and french fries and then did the dishes. At seven-thirty the last of the girls' clothing had been placed in the drawers and hung in the closets. By eight-thirty the girls had had their baths and were sound asleep in their beds.

When Kate returned to the living room, Della had a small fire going and the coffeepot was full and waiting. "We deserve this," she said happily as she placed Fig Newtons on the saucer along with the cup.

"Oh, Della, this is so nice. Thank you. Thank you so much for everything," Kate said, flopping against the soft cushions of the worn sofa.

"How are the little ones?"

"Sound asleep. Betsy is . . . anxious. We're off our routine. We didn't write Patrick today, so she wanted to know if that meant we were starting to forget him. We had this routine . . . God, Della, I had every minute of the day accounted for. Now when I think back to those ten months Patrick was gone . . . it seems so . . . so cruel. I had those girls jumping through hoops. Now this. I just know Betsy isn't going to like her new school. She adored her teachers."

Della let loose with a string of Spanish, then switched to English. "Today is a new day, a new beginning for all of us. What we do from here on in is what's important. Drink your coffee. Did I tell you I brought some packets of flower seeds with me, a dozen or so? They came in the cereal boxes and I saved them. Tomorrow while you go through the papers, the girls and I will plant them. This little house will look like a rainbow surrounds it when the flowers bloom."

"That's nice," Kate said sleepily. "You know, next month is Patrick's birthday."

"I'll bake a cake," Della said.

"Double chocolate fudge with real frosting, and colored sprinkles for the girls. Candles, all colors. And a present. One with a big red bow. We'll keep it in the closet until . . . he gets back."

"Wonderful! Now why don't you take your shower first.

52

I'll clean up, damper the fire, and get ready for bed. Everything is going to be fine, Kate, I promise."

Kate believed her. Della was wonderful, the next best thing to a mother. Maybe even better. Her mother had rarely hugged her or praised her; she'd always seemed too busy. Della was a hugger, and she always seemed to say the right words. "Thank you, God, for Della," she said aloud.

That night, for the first time since Patrick left, Kate slept deeply and soundly.

She awakened the next morning to the smell of coffee and frying bacon and hurried to the kitchen. There, seated at the table, was Donald Abbott, and in front of him was a plate of scrambled eggs and bacon. She could hear the girls in the backyard. Della was smiling. And Kate herself smiled when she beheld her landlord in a smartly tailored dark suit, a snowy white shirt, and flowered tie. His black shoes gleamed with polish, and his gray hair had been neatly barbered.

"Morning, Mrs. Starr. I just stopped by after church to see if everything was to your satisfaction and to collect the rent."

Kate sat down across from him. "Mr. Abbott, everything is fine. I can't thank you enough for . . . for everything. I am so pleased. We didn't have to do anything but move in. When I get a job and things are better for me, I'll pay you more rent. I promise. The military has everything mixed up right now, and it will probably be a while before things get straightened out. You've been very good to us. I think you're a very nice man."

"Thank you, ma'am, I am. Guess you thought I was a bit disheveled when you saw me last. I was, but I was working on some property a ways from here. I was in my work clothes.

"And listen, if the military is giving you a problem, you go straight to the top. You call Washington, D.C., and get hold of the general in charge of Air Force personnel and tell him what your problem is. I'd recommend you start with your caseworker, and if you don't get any results, call Washington. I had to do that when my son . . . I had to do that."

"Thank you for the advice, Mr. Abbott."

"That was a real good breakfast, Miss Della," Abbott said when he'd finished eating. "I'll be going now."

"Let me get the rent for you," Kate said.

"Do you need a receipt?"

"I guess not," Kate said.

"That's good. I like it when people trust each other. Nice little girls you have there," Abbott said, pointing to Betsy and Ellie. "They told me they're making a rainbow around the house for their daddy so when he gets back he can see it from his airplane."

"They said that?" Kate said in awe.

"That's exactly what they said. Guess I won't be seeing you till next month. If there's any problem, call me. Miss Della has the number."

"Why don't you come for dinner next Saturday, Donald," Della said. "I'll make some real Mexican food and you can tell me how you like it." Kate's eyebrows shot upward, as did Abbott's.

"I'll be here," he said, then left the house. Kate waited for him to hitch up his pants, which he did when he got to the bottom of the back steps. She smiled. Della smiled, a merry glint in her eyes.

"He looks like he could use some fattening up. He's going to lose his pants one of these days. I wouldn't want the girls to see his drawers if that happened. After all, he is our landlord. We have to be nice to him."

"I agree," Kate said. "I take that to mean he's a widower."

"Yes. He likes us, I can tell."

"Can you now?" Kate teased.

"Get on with you, finish unpacking your clothes. I'll wash up here and help the girls. Get the Sunday papers for yourself. Don't worry about a thing. I think, and this is just my opinion, Kate, but I do believe Donald is going to be a surrogate grandfather to those two little girls, and it's going to be the best thing in the world for them."

"That would be really nice. Do they like him?"

"Ellie does for sure. Betsy was a little reserved. I heard him tell her he had a bicycle he was going to spruce up and did she know anyone who needed one. She told him she was someone and would be glad to take it. He kind of chuckled over that. I think he's looking for a family, Kate, and if you have a mind to share yours with him, he'd be eternally grateful."

"We didn't make a mistake coming here, did we, Della?"

Della shook her head. "Some things are meant to be. Just accept them."

"I think Patrick would approve of all this. No, no, no, I know he would. I can almost hear him say, 'good choice, Kate.' "

It was Sunday, a day of rest for Kate.

Tomorrow her life would continue, but down a different road.

CHAPTER

3

It was December 1971, a year since Patrick had ejected from his plane; twenty-one months since he'd left their little apartment in the desert. And still there was no concrete news of her husband's whereabouts. He was still listed as Missing. Kate still called Bill Percy every day, and every day he said the same thing: "Everything is being done that can be done. We haven't forgotten about your husband. Be patient, Mrs. Starr, and for your own sake, don't stir up a hornet's nest that you can't control."

Her language was stronger these days, she'd found, born of anger, frustration, and despair. "Fuck you and don't hand me that fucking bullshit! I want to know. You keep telling me the government is doing things, but you won't tell me what things. I have a right to know. I'm going to call the newspapers and I'm writing a letter to President Nixon."

To which Percy replied with an edge to his voice: "Please don't do that."

The conversation usually ended at that point with Kate slamming down the phone.

She'd prayed for Patrick's return for Christmas, realizing she was praying for the impossible. The government said he wasn't a prisoner, so how could he be returned? Still listed as Missing, he would literally have to call someone to come and get him, or simply walk out of the jungle and say, "Here I am, come and get me."

Kate now belonged to various support groups and had signed on as a member of the League of Families. She continued to read everything she could, stuffed envelopes, and did mailing for her various groups. It was neither rewarding nor fulfilling. She cried more, lost weight, grew gaunt and irritable with the girls, and with Della as well. She still hadn't found a job that paid her a decent amount of money. She suspected her sallow complexion and look of desperation turned off personnel interviewers. Her part-time job in a used-book store allowed her to stay in the back room pricing and cataloging books. There was little interaction with the other employees, who were out front dealing with the public. She found it easy to withdraw into her shell, and sometimes didn't speak to anyone at all during her four-hour shift. She always cried when she deposited her pitiful check each Friday.

She was tired all the time, and at Della's insistence was taking megadoses of vitamins, which did nothing for her energy level. Going to school at night, taking secretarial courses again at Della's and Donald Abbott's insistence, and studying in the morning, left her drained.

Christmas was upon them before Kate realized it. It was Della and Donald who put up the Christmas tree, Della and Donald who wrapped presents for the girls, Della who baked the Christmas cookies while she kept to her bed, refusing to go to work or to class. She was neglecting the girls but seemed unable to help herself. She lost more weight, grew more gaunt. More than once Della had to drag her from bed and push her into the shower.

From somewhere in the apartment she could hear the sound of Christmas carols being played. And the sound of whispers. Or was that in her mind? she wondered. Lately she wasn't sure of anything. Maybe if she lay there long enough, she'd die. She was so tired, so weary. *Patrick, where are you? You promised me tomorrow, and tomorrow is here.* She buried her face in the pillow, sobs racking her thin shoulders.

Outside in the hallway, the two little girls whispered to one another.

"I just want to see her. Maybe if we sneak in, she'll wake up. I won't make a sound, I promise, Betsy," Ellie pleaded.

"She doesn't want to see us. Santa Claus is coming tonight, and she didn't make Christmas cookies. We can't go in, Della said so."

"I don't care," Ellie whined. "Please, Betsy, just a peep. I'll hold your hand. Will she still be in bed when the Easter Bunny comes? That's a long time, isn't it?"

"A lot of days," Betsy said flatly. "Promise you won't tell Della and Donald, okay? We'll just look at her. You have to promise, Ellie."

Ellie danced from one foot to the other. "I promise," she said.

Betsy licked her lips. Daddy had told her that only lazybones lay in bed for no good reason. The little girl's heart fluttered in her chest as she led her sister to her mother's bed. She wished the blinds were open so she could see her mother better. She felt frightened suddenly, wishing she hadn't come in here. Ellie's hand was wet in hers.

They tiptoed to the edge of the bed, and Betsy stared down at the stranger there. Her hand moved on its own volition. The bedside lamp came on, all rosy and pink. Her eyes bulged when she saw her mother up close. She backed up a step and then another, dragging Ellie with her. Her mother wasn't playing lazybones. Lazybones leaped out of the bed when the light came on, and then giggled and laughed. Lazybones was a game. She knew instinctively, as only a child could know, that her well-being and that of her sister was on shaky ground.

"What's wrong with Mommy's hair?" Ellie whispered.

"That's how hair gets when you don't wash it," Betsy said quietly.

"It smells funny in here," Ellie said.

"I know," Betsy said.

"If Mommy stays in here *forever*, does that mean we don't have a mother anymore? We don't have a daddy. If we cry, will she hug us and get up?" Ellie sobbed.

Tears rolled down Betsy's cheeks. She didn't know how to answer her sister. What if her mother died in bed because she didn't wash her hair or take a shower? What if Daddy never came home? She squeezed her eyes shut. She was supposed to be a big girl and not cry unless she was really hurt. Daddy said so. She hurt now, so bad she didn't know what to do.

Her feet moved, closer, until she was at the edge of her mother's bed. She dropped to her knees, one hand on the mattress for support, the other clutching her sister. "Mommy," she whispered. When there was no response, she whispered again, her face inches from her mother.

"Is she dead, Betsy?" Ellie blubbered. "I want her to hug me."

"You promised to be quiet," Betsy hissed.

"I don't care. Make her wake up."

Betsy felt frightened now that she was so close to her mother. Maybe she was dead. When you were dead, you didn't move, and then you went to heaven, where all the dead people were. She wanted her daddy, more than she wanted Christmas presents, more than the big turkey, more than the Christmas tree. Daddy could carry Mommy out of bed. Her daddy could do anything.

Her hand shot out to touch her mother's shoulder. She reared back when Kate's eyes snapped open. "I'm sorry . . . Mommy, I wanted you to wake up," Betsy cried. "Are you going to die? Ellie wants you to hug her. Are you being a lazybones?" She wanted to run, not look at this person who was supposed to be her mother. Daddy wouldn't like it that Mommy looked so terrible.

Kate stared at her cowering daughters, unable to comprehend what they were doing in her room. She had no idea what time it was or even what day it was.

"Santa Claus is coming tonight," Ellie sobbed.

Kate saw Patrick through a haze. A handsome, sturdy little boy with a rusty bike he rode everywhere. "Oh, Patrick," she crooned, "God made you an angel."

"Are you going to die?" Ellie whimpered.

Betsy waited for her mother's answer. Her mother wouldn't lie about dying. She heard her sister repeat the question. She thought her heart would blow out of her chest until, in a funny-sounding voice, her mother said, "I don't think so."

"Oh, goody," Ellie cried happily.

Betsy ran from the room, giddy with relief. God wasn't going to make them orphans. "If You made us orphans, Daddy wouldn't know where to find us," she whispered. "I knew You wouldn't do that on Christmas."

In her room, Kate crushed her face into the pillow. The day before Christmas. She dozed then, dreaming about a little boy with the face of an angel on a rusty bike, his wings flapping in the breeze as he careened past her house.

Patrick.

Kate woke with a pounding headache, knowing it was still the day before Christmas because she could hear the girls singing "Jingle Bells." Ellie was babbling about Santa coming down the chimney. She had to get up, take part in whatever was going on outside her room. She managed to pull on her robe and stagger to the kitchen, where Della, Donald, and the girls looked at her with wide, staring eyes. Della shooed the girls into the living room with fat sugar cookies in the shape of Christmas trees.

"I'm glad you're up, Kate," Della said sternly. "I have something to say to you. I'm sorry it's today, it being Christmas Eve and all. I'm leaving the day after Christmas. Donald here, well, he's asked me to be his bride, and I've . . . accepted."

If Kate had been looking anywhere but at Della, she would have seen the look of shocked surprise on her landlord's face. "But . . . you never said anything about leaving," she cried. "I can't . . . what will the girls do without you?" Her heart was pounding as fiercely as her head.

"I'm just your housekeeper, Kate. You're their mother. Somewhere along the way, you forgot that. They need you, not me. This is Christmas, and you didn't lift a finger to help, didn't care enough for those little girls to make any kind of effort. They're going to remember this. If you can't take care of them, Social Services will place them in foster homes. How will you explain that to your husband when he gets back? He left you in charge of his daughters, trusting you to keep . . . his home for him until he returned. Instead you lie in bed, refuse to eat, and leave it to me to do everything. I can't do it anymore. I'm getting to be an old woman, in case you hadn't noticed. Donald has promised to make life easy for me."

"That's a selfish attitude," Kate mumbled.

"Perhaps you should look in the mirror and see who the selfish one is. You haven't even paid the bills. Do you know the electric company is shutting off our electricity the day after Christmas? There's no more wood for the fireplace, and Donald has been buying our food. And it won't do any good to cry. I've had enough of your tears and your whining. Your husband would be so disappointed in the way you're acting."

Kate's shoulders shook and tears rolled down her cheeks. She wiped her eyes on the sleeve of her robe. "I have a terrible headache," she cried. "I had this dream . . . it was awful . . . I was a child back in Westfield, and Patrick had just moved in around the corner with his family. He . . . he had his old, rusty bike and he was pedaling it past my house. In my dream . . . he was leaning over my bed, but I was me, like I am now. He said he was an orphan or something like that. I wanted to put my arms around him, but I couldn't move. His voice was funny, like he was trying to cry. Patrick never cried. He was so proud of that. I can't comprehend that, Della. Never crying, I mean. I cry all the time. It's such a release. Men . . . men should cry, too. God, my head is killing me."

"You always have a headache, and if it isn't a headache, your stomach is bothering you or you have cramps or you're coming down with a virus. You drink black coffee by the gallon, smoke cigarettes you can't afford to buy, and you don't eat. No wonder you're sick all the time. . . . I'll stay through Christmas because I can't let those little girls be disappointed again. All week they've been making presents for you. What did you do for them?" Della turned back to the stove and winked slyly at Donald, whose eyes were bugging out of his head.

"The first Christmas wasn't so bad," Kate said hesitantly. "We had Patrick's letters and we knew he'd be home for this Christmas. He isn't here. . . ."

"But you are. You have to make the best of it. I'm tired of your whining. Now I know where Ellie gets it. Betsy is like her father. It's not right of you to make Betsy responsible for Ellie. You're messing up their lives," Della said quietly.

Kate squared her shoulders. "It's true. You're right. . . . Has Donald really been buying our food?" She turned to stare at him, and Donald met her questioning gaze with pity in his eyes. "Do you love Della?"

Donald's Adam's apple bobbed up and down in his stringy neck. He hadn't been expecting the question, but now that it was put to him, he answered honestly. "She's a fine woman, and the man who gets her is one lucky man. And to answer your question: yes, I do."

"How could I not know that?" Kate asked, puzzled.

"Because you shut us all out of your life, that's how," Della said, not unkindly.

"I'm sorry. Do the girls hate me?"

"Oh, Kate, of course not, but they don't understand. They need to talk to you, need to have you hug them. They're so vulnerable. Betsy is having some problems in school, and Ellie is . . . Ellie is starting to lie . . . a lot. They need you, Kate."

Kate didn't trust herself to speak, so she merely nodded.

"There's a lot of mail, Kate. You haven't looked at it in over a month."

Kate nodded again.

"I could use some help with this turkey. I wanted to make bread today. I promised Betsy I'd make it for her. Donald is going to string some Christmas lights around the front door. I can still make a late breakfast for you, if you like, before I get started."

"Yes. Yes, I would. Eggs and bacon and some juice, but first I want to take a shower. I'll help with the turkey. The bread, too. I want to be the one to punch down the dough."

Della drew in her breath. Donald's eyes rolled heavenward. "When you wash your hair, why don't you pile it high on your head with a ribbon. Betsy made this for you a few days ago," Della said, taking a messy red string bow with curled edges from one of the kitchen drawers. "Put it in your pocket for now, you can't mess it up any more than it is already. Toward the end she got frustrated and said it didn't matter because you weren't going to get up anyway."

"Oh, God," Kate said. "What's happened to me, Della?"

Della let loose with a long stream of Spanish, switching to English the way she usually did when she got to the punch line. "The devil got hold of you, and you didn't shake him loose, that's what happened." Her voice was triumphant as she helped Kate up from the chair.

Kate turned to Della and said, "The devil my ass, it's the goddamn military and government. Come to think of it, they're probably in cahoots with the devil."

Della clucked her tongue in disapproval at Kate's language. Donald chuckled.

"I think it worked," Della said softly the moment Kate was out of earshot. "I know I'm a fine, wonderful human being, but were you telling the truth when you said you loved me? And why would someone as fine as myself want a skinny old buzzard like you?"

Donald scratched at his straggly beard. "Well, you're fat, and I don't see anyone better than me banging at this here door. I'm a kind, generous man, have money in the bank, and receive a nice pension. I fixed this place up for *you*. I didn't have to do that. I take you to bingo and give you my card when I win and you don't. I go to church and pass the collection plate. I am an upstanding man, Miss Della. When do you want to marry me, now that you compromised me?"

"Why I—"

"Don't be coy with me now. I put a straightforward question to you and I expect the same kind of answer. Admit it, you've never been asked before and you don't know how to respond."

"I suppose I could do worse. Swear to me you'll take care of me and this little family. I don't ever want to be out on the street without a home. I would have been if not for Kate."

64

Donald threw his hands in the air. "Look at me, woman," he blustered. "Who in the goddamn hell has been taking care of all of you since Kate got the miseries? Well then, I rest my case. When's it to be?"

"June," Della said sourly. "We'll tell Kate you got cold feet and postponed it till June. That way we'll all save face and she won't be the wiser. We really shook her out of whatever she was in. You'd best be getting on with your light stringing, Donald. And make sure you string them all the way across the roof and put some of those little twinkling ones on the Joshua tree."

"You nag, Della."

"And don't forget to do the red arrows. Ellie is going to cry all day and night if you don't get those arrows in place. Can you believe that little tyke worrying about Santa knowing she moved? She's terrified he won't know she's in this house. Red arrows, Donald, or it won't be Christmas for that little girl."

"I made them in my workshop yesterday. All I have to do is line them up. Painted them last night."

When the kitchen door closed behind him, Della danced a jig. Kate was coming out of her bad spell, and she had a proposal of marriage from a man who had his own house as well as Social Security. Christmas truly was a time for miracles.

It was dark, but not scary dark, Betsy thought as she crawled out from under the covers. She tiptoed to the doorway, careful not to wake her sister. She poked her head out the door, her breath hot little gasps. Santa had left the tree lights burning the way he always did. She was in the middle of the short hallway when she stopped, thought about it, and decided she didn't believe in Santa Claus. She turned on her heel to return to her room. Quietly, in the dark, she felt along the edge for her father's picture. She hugged it to her breast as she made her way back to the living room.

The tree was so beautiful she wanted to cry. She felt herself taking deep breaths to savor the spicy pine scent.

This was her moment, hers and her dad's. She dropped to her knees in front of the fir and let her eyes rake the presents that circled the tree. "Merry Christmas, Daddy," she whispered. "This one is for you, and so is this one. Ellie's is the one with the green ribbon. I tied red on mine because you like red. This flat one," she murmured, picking up the tablet-size package, "is the one I made in school for you. Ellie's school present is the one with the macaroni glued to the top. I know what it is, but I promised not to tell. I didn't even tell Mommy. I have to look for Mommy's present to you. We're going to put them in the closet and give them to you when you get home. The whole shelf is for you. Our Easter baskets are there, too. Mommy says if the shelf gets full, we'll ask Donald to build another one. I can't find it, Daddy," she whispered. "Mommy wouldn't forget. It must be in the back, behind the others." She rummaged some more but was unable to find a present for her father with her mother's handwriting on the Christmas tag. A tear splashed on her hand. She wiped at her eyes with her pajama sleeve.

Betsy reached for Patrick's picture and hugged it to her chest. "I know I'm not supposed to cry, but I don't feel like a big girl this morning. I miss you. Mommy's sick and looks different. Ellie said she smells *pee-uey*." Words rushed out of her mouth, some of them garbled, all of them full of fear and anger.

"Miss Rolands read us a story before school was out. Everybody in the class cried but me. It was about an orphan who didn't have anyone to love her at Christmas. She was dressed in rags and she was hungry. The only thing she had to keep her warm was a puppy she found who was as hungry as she was. She was little, like Ellie, and she lost her mommy and daddy. This kind man was on his way home and he saw her and the puppy. He had real big arms and he picked up Martha and the puppy and took them home and gave them hot cocoa and a real big jelly sandwich. He put cocoa in a dish for the puppy and meat in a dish. The mommy came into the room and sat down with the little girl, and the puppy climbed on her lap. She hugged and kissed the little girl. The puppy, too. She let the puppy lick her face. She didn't care about germs. She cared about the little girl and her dog. When everyone was nice and warm and not hungry anymore, the lady and the man took them upstairs and gave them a bath and put them to bed. They hugged and kissed them and sat by the bed all night while they slept. Martha wasn't an orphan anymore. When I go back to school, I have to know what the moral of the story is. That was our homework."

Chubby fingers traced the outline of Patrick's face as her tears rolled down. "I love you, Daddy. Merry Christmas."

Kate stood in the kitchen doorway, her eyes glued to her daughter. She had to move, go to her firstborn, kiss her and hug her close and tell her she was loved, but she waited a moment too long. Her father's picture clutched in her hands, the little girl ran to her room. "My God," Kate whispered, "what have I done to this child?"

Kate ran down the hall to her daughter's room and opened the door. Betsy was curled beneath the covers. "Betsy," she whispered in a choked voice. "Betsy, honey . . ." She dropped to her knees and let the tears flow. The little girl didn't move. Kate reached out a hand, drew it back. The moment was gone. Part of Betsy was gone, too; she could feel it.

"Merry Christmas, honey," she whispered.

CHAPTER
4

He didn't know if it was night or day, sunny or rainy. He no longer knew what month it was, much less the day. He did know he was in a space no bigger than a coffin. He could stand or sit, but he couldn't lie down. He couldn't stretch his legs out in front of him, either.

Captain Patrick Starr wiggled his toes. They worked, but he no longer had toenails. Or fingernails. He was no longer sure if his hip was broken or just fractured; not that it made any difference. For a long time he'd had to lean into the coffin corner with the homemade splint some faceless person had strapped on him.

Crippled. Was it better than being dead? A man could live without toenails and fingernails and with a limp. His tongue slid across his broken teeth with their sharp edges. Teeth could be fixed. Movie stars always had their teeth capped.

Kate had beautiful teeth, an ear-to-ear smile that showed them off to perfection. Kate wouldn't care if he had caps on his teeth.

Patrick shifted his position slightly before he urinated all over himself. Once he'd had a slop bucket, but it was gone now. He reeked of himself, but the smell seemed to be less nauseous than before. With his broken nose, he couldn't seem to smell much of anything.

He didn't want to cry, but he did, tears rolling down his cheeks. He didn't bother to wipe them away, they felt good. No one could take tears away unless they punched out his eyes, which was a daily threat. God Almighty, if his sense of smell was gone, as well as the hearing in his left ear, what would he become if they really carried through with their threat to punch out his eyes? He wouldn't be able to see Kate again or hear the girls laugh. He'd never be able to smell Kate's meat loaf or the Thanksgiving turkey. The Christmas tree might as well be artificial. Worst of all, he wouldn't be able to smell Kate's hair, that warm, sweet vanilla-lemon smell that was always with her.

If . . . if he ever got out of here, he was going to be a gawdamn fucking vegetable. What would Kate say and do when they delivered him to her doorstep, a broken, beaten man with no sight, no sense of smell, and very little hearing? The girls would be scared out of their wits. "You bastards! You gawdamn fucking bastards!" For a moment he thought he'd shouted the words, but he hadn't. The words were less than a whimper.

He continued to cry, more from pain than anything else, as he struggled to his feet to lean into his corner. He felt rather than heard movement near his feet. His good leg shot out and then stamped down. With his good ear he heard a weak squeal and knew he'd smashed one of his roommates, a scrawny rat that had less energy than he had.

Patrick tried to grind himself into his corner when he saw

69

the heavy metal door open, throwing blinding light into his coffin. His arms shot up to cover his eyes. At the same time, he felt a metal prod gouge him in the pit of his stomach. He knew what *that* meant. He was to stagger out into the light, where they would question him and then beat him.

For one wild, crazy moment he thought he saw Kate ladling potato salad onto his plate at the Fourth of July picnic. She was smiling at him, knowing how much he liked her potato salad because she sprinkled little bits of crisp bacon over the top, just for him. By God, he wanted that potato salad more than anything in the world. He did his best to square his shoulders, to walk as straight as he could. He stared into the blinding light and jerked away from the metal pole gouging him in the ribs.

He was a weasel, Patrick decided, this man who constantly interrogated him, speaking perfect English. Once he'd said he was a graduate of UCLA. Then he'd rattled off what he knew of Patrick's credentials.

Back then, when he still believed in things like the Geneva Convention rules, he'd stood his ground and given name, rank, and serial number. After his second—or was it his third—beating, he'd realized the rules didn't apply here in this godforsaken country. He'd shown some spirit, though, calling his interrogator a cocksucking UCLA reject.

Patrick looked around, trying to identify the structure he was in. It seemed different from the last one, but he did recognize the crude table with rows of torture equipment. He tried not to look at the syringes and the small vials of clear liquid. He did his best to steel himself against the man standing in front of him, did his best to meet his level stare, and felt that he'd succeeded. The only thing he couldn't match was the man's evil smile. He waited for his nod, said what he'd routinely been saying: "Fuck you, you son of a bitch!" He saw the arm rise, saw the club with the spiked prongs, a second before his mind retreated to Westfield, New Jersey.

The wind was whipping his hair backward as he pedaled his bike down the sidewalk, the red, white, and blue crepe paper he'd intertwined between the spokes making *thwack-*ing, sputtering sounds. He was new in Westfield, but already he had three good friends and a speaking acquaintance with a blond-haired girl named Kate who lived around the corner. He was riding next to her in the Decoration Day parade. His bike number was six and hers was seven. He had to remember not to pedal fast so she could keep up with him.

His heart beat extra fast when he saw her coming down the driveway on her bike. He reared up on his Schwinn, letting the front tire hit the ground with a thud. He was pulling a roll of crepe paper from his hip pocket when she smiled at him. "You need streamers on your handlebars," he said shyly.

He felt himself jolt sideways on his bike when Kate said, "Do you have enough left over to tie some on my handlebars?"

Did he? "I have a whole roll." He fell off the bike, shook his head to clear it. "You have to rip the streamers. If you do, they make more noise. All the guys are doing it."

"It looks pretty," Kate said.

"Yours looks pretty, mine looks . . . nifty."

"Is that because you're eight years old?"

"Yeah. Boys don't do stuff that looks pretty."

He was on the ground again, tripping over his own feet. Kate was off her bike in a second, reaching down to help him up. She smiled shyly before she climbed back on her bike. Her saddle shoes were so blindingly white he couldn't see past them.

"Let's ride fast, real fast," he muttered, confused by the whiteness of Kate's shoes.

"I'll try to keep up," Kate said, hunching over the handlebars.

They rode down the street, around the corner, passing

strolling couples, children, and dogs, all headed to the fair-grounds. They rode through a cloudburst, shrieking with laughter, the crepe paper *thwack*ing and sputtering, the streamers billowing upward and outward.

Patrick braked and was off his bike in a second. "I have a quarter," he said proudly.

"I have ten cents." Kate giggled. "I'm going to spend a nickel on cotton candy and save the other nickel. The hamburgers and weenies are free. I'm going to eat three of each."

"Go on, I can't eat three, and I'm eight," Patrick said.

"Can so," Kate said huffily. "Wanna make a bet?"

"For money?" Patrick said in awe.

"Sure. The nickel I'm saving. Two ears of corn, too, and maybe a slice of watermelon. I like to eat."

"You'll throw up."

"How do you know that?" Kate demanded.

"Because I know. My dad doesn't eat that much. You shouldn't say something like that unless you can really do it. If you say it and don't do it, then it's a lie. It's like a promise. If you break a promise, it's a lie."

"No, it isn't. It's a mistake."

"It's a lie," Patrick said adamantly. "It's a sin to lie."

"I didn't mean all at one time," Kate said, chagrined. "We have all day. So there, Patrick Starr."

"Then it won't be a lie. What time do you have to be home?"

"When the streetlights go on. Seven-thirty, I guess. What time do you have to be home?"

"Eight o'clock. I'll ride home with you."

"Okay."

"If I win the sack race, I'll give you my prize."

"Why?"

"Because you're a girl. Boys don't want stuffed animals and those jiggers on poles and strings. Boys are supposed to give them to girls. You're a girl."

"It will be my first present from a boy," Kate said happily.

"Don't you go saying that, Kate. It's a prize, not a present. That makes it different. Don't you go telling anyone, either."

"Is it supposed to be a secret? I don't know if I can keep a secret."

"Shoot, yes, it's a secret, and you better not tell anyone, either. If you do, I won't be your friend anymore."

"Okay, I won't tell. Do you have any secrets, Patrick?"

"Shoot, yes. Guys always have secrets. Wanna hear one?"

"I thought you said you couldn't tell a secret," Kate said sourly.

"This one I can tell because it's only about me, not another person. Someday," he said, drawing out his words, a dreamy look on his face, "I'm gonna fly an airplane. When I fly over your house, you have to run out in the yard, and I'll tip my wings so you'll know it's me."

"Ooohhhh," Kate said, her eyes round. "That's a great secret."

"Do you have a secret you want to share?"

"Someday I want to be a mother. The best mother in the whole world."

Disgust showed on Patrick's face. "All girls get to be mothers. Don't you want to be *something special*?"

"Being the best mother in the whole world is special. That's all I want to be. Don't you think that's good enough?" Kate said, grinding the toe of her saddle shoe into the fairground dirt.

"That means you don't have any imagination," Patrick said with a grimace.

"Then what do you think I should be?"

"A movie star. That's special. When you grow up, you'll be real pretty. You can be my girl."

"Honest, Patrick?"

"Don't you go telling anyone I said that. Yeah, honest."

"Ooohhh. I promise. How old will we be?"

"Fifteen."

"Will you take me to the prom?"

"Sure."

"Will you give me a corsage?"

"Sure, those little white flowers that grow like bells on a stem. They smell real pretty."

"Ooohhh," Kate said.

Patrick reached for Kate's hand.

When they dragged Patrick back to the cell, his face bloody and torn, all he could see were two children walking hand in hand into the fairgrounds.

His Kate, from that day on.

No matter what they did to him, they could never take Kate away from him.

He cuddled into his corner, his good arm wrapped around his broken left arm, his wife's name on his lips. "I promise you tomorrow, Kate ... somehow, some way. I promise. I never lied to you, Kate," he whimpered.

CHAPTER
5

It was April 1973, nearly two and a half years since Nelson Collier's appearance at her kitchen door, and Kate did not know any more about Patrick than she did on that day.

She wasn't exactly the old Kate, but thought of herself as the new, improved, better version of Kate Starr. She had put some of her weight back on, the shadows beneath her eyes were gone, and her backbone was stiff with resolve. She'd given up her job at the bookstore and applied for a position as a part-time secretary at an architectural firm. She was typing fifty words a minute without mistakes, and taking dictation. On occasion when the architects needed renderings of a building before work commenced, Kate did them for extra money. She loved her job because she had her mornings free to be with Ellie and to keep up her volunteer work with the League of Families and commiserate with other wives in the same position. Gradually she'd weaned the girls and herself from their daily letter writing to Patrick, simply because it was too sad for all of them. They wrote one letter each week on Sunday afternoon.

When April showers gave way to the bright spring flowers of May that the girls had planted around the house, three letters without a return address arrived in Kate's mailbox. Inside each was a check made out to her for four hundred dollars, drawn on the Wells Fargo Bank. She had no idea who they were from or what the checks were for. Her name was spelled correctly, and the envelopes carried the proper address. The single sheets of paper without letterhead read: FOR SERVICES RENDERED. PATRICK STARR $400. The total was twelve hundred dollars. The dates on the envelopes were all the same, which meant they'd been mailed the same day. The dates on the three sheets of paper were March 1, April 1, and May 1.

For one brief moment Kate thought her head would explode. Patrick was alive and doing something top secret for the government. What else could "services rendered" mean? March, April, and May meant the present. Twelve hundred dollars had to be all the money in the world. She could splurge and get a haircut and finally pay Della for having helped her at a crucial time. The girls could get new shoes, and she could buy some art supplies. Or—her thrifty nature intervening—she could invest the money if it was truly hers. Maybe she would keep some of it, pay Della, and invest the rest.

Her address book within easy reach, Kate called several of the women in her group and asked if they'd ever gotten such unexplained checks. Only one of the women, Bethany Warren, admitted she had. Bethany belonged to the group but always opposed "going public" for news of their husbands. That was fine for Bethany, Kate thought, because her husband was listed as POW, not Missing.

"I don't understand," Kate said quietly. "Who's responsible for these checks? Why am I getting them now after all this time? Does it mean he's alive? Please, Bethany, I need to know," Kate pleaded.

"My situation is different from yours, Kate. I have five children and I can't make it on Michael's pay. I think you should call your contact and talk to him. If you like, we can meet for coffee later in the week." This last was said so fearfully, Kate found herself starting to tremble.

"I'd like that. Friday after work, Mabel's Café."

"Kate," Bethany said hesitantly, "don't cash those checks until you're sure it's what you want to do. What I mean is, you're getting by and you have a housekeeper and a job that might lead to something better that pays a decent salary. I'll see you Friday."

More puzzled than ever, Kate called Bill Percy and asked to set up an appointment. He said he'd stop by later in the evening on his way back to the desert. "Ten or so," he said briskly. She tucked the checks, envelope, and papers into the back of her Betty Crocker cookbook.

It was important, but what was really important at the moment was sewing a satin pocket for the tooth fairy. Yesterday she'd gone to the bank and asked for a shiny new quarter, compliments of the tooth fairy. By bedtime Ellie would lose her first tooth. When Kate finished the satin pocket pillow, she stuck it in her drawer. Ellie would be so happy. She had to take pictures of the girl to send Patrick.

Today was Kate's day off because she worked alternate Saturdays. Della and Donald were taking Ellie to the zoo. They'd offered to wait until Betsy got out of school, but the little girl said she hated to smell the animals, which meant Kate was free until it was time to pick her up. She had phone calls to make, letters to write, lists to make.

I'm doing what I can, Patrick. I'm doing my best. I got lost there for a little while, but I'm on track now.

She had a cheap vinyl briefcase that was ripped at the corner from all her clippings, notebooks, and magazines. Her pens, pencils, and writing paper were secure in a separate side pocket. As always, she read through the articles, skimming over the hateful parts, the parts that offered little hope, and going on to whatever was more positive. There wasn't much. She wept, allowed herself a small amount of time to grieve before she tackled her sixth letter to the President of the United States. She ended this one by saying, "President Nixon, my daughters and myself deserve to know what is being done to bring my husband home. We don't understand how Patrick can still be listed as Missing two and a half years after he ejected over enemy territory." She signed the letter "Captain Patrick Starr's wife, Kate Starr." Later that afternoon, when both girls returned home, she'd have them sign the letter, too.

Next she wrote to the Departments of State and Defense, demanding answers that were long overdue. Her third letter was to the Air Force, to every general on the list she'd gotten from the library. In this one she wrote, "Doesn't anyone care about the families left behind? Don't we deserve something better than evasive answers? What am I to tell my daughters? Please, send someone here to talk to me and the support group we've founded. Don't neglect us any longer. Your motto has always been 'The Air Force takes care of its own.' Give me a date and a time when this will occur." Again she signed the letter, "Captain Patrick Starr's wife, Kate Starr." The girls would sign these letters, too.

I know you're going to come back, Patrick. My heart would tell me if you were dead. I know they want me to believe you are, but I won't believe it, not ever. I pray for you every day. A day doesn't go by that we don't speak of you. The girls kiss your picture good-night. I do the same. I know God will keep you safe.

The urge to smash something was so great, Kate clenched her fists. What good would it do? She was doing so much better these days at controlling her anger. Always think positively, turn every disadvantage into an advantage; it was Patrick's personal motto.

The hours rushed by, and before she knew it, the girls were sound asleep, and Bill Percy was due to arrive. She felt positive now; she'd mail her letters later. She wondered why she felt so confident, so *up*. She'd written the same letters before and there had been no answer. What made things different now? It was the checks, she decided, the strange envelopes, and Bethany's response to her questions.

Five minutes into her meeting with Bill Percy, Kate realized that she'd never really liked the man. It wasn't that he had cold eyes—he had evasive eyes. His voice wasn't compassionate, it was irritable. He accepted her plum tea, the fat sugar cookies Della had baked, and suffered through the amenities, and then sat back and waited.

"It's been two and a half years, Bill." They were on a first-name basis now, but she knew it didn't mean a thing. "There must be some small bit of news. How much longer is this war going to go on? If you don't have something positive to tell me, I'm going to go to the newspapers and beg, plead, get down on my knees, whatever it takes to get answers. The other wives feel the same way. We deserve better than this."

"You are receiving Captain Starr's pay, aren't you, Kate?"

"Yes, but it took almost four months. I had to threaten to call Washington, and then I got an answer in three hours. You should have helped me. What have you done for me, Bill? I have this feeling you don't even like me."

"That's not true. I think you're overwrought. I want you to think about something. If we list your husband as dead, you get a pension. It would not be substantial. Leave things alone now. When we have firm evidence of anything, you'll be the first to know. Everything that can be done is being done. Don't make waves, Kate."

"That sounds like a threat." His forced laugh sent chills up Kate's spine. "Then tell me what that 'everything' is. Spell it out for me and the other wives. We have rights, too. It's been two and a half years, for God's sake!" Kate's eyes sent sparks in Percy's direction. She wondered how people like Percy were picked as "contacts" for wives and families. She stared at him, at his slicked-back sandy hair, at his bulging hazel eyes. She just knew he hated the angry red pimple on his right cheekbone. He'd cut himself shaving, too, she noticed. Maybe he was just supposed to be strange-looking, which he was. He had uneven teeth and never smiled. Maybe it was his ears, she thought. They seemed to be too small for his long, narrow face. Whatever it was, she didn't like him or his long skinny fingers drumming on the table impatiently.

"I know it's a long time. I pass every query you make to the right people. Listen to me, Kate, you cannot stir up any trouble. Do you realize that if you start trouble, the communists will get wind of it and the prisoners could be mistreated? You must remain calm and in control. We are doing everything possible. When we know something, you'll know something. Now, tell me why you needed to talk to me in such a hurry."

"I'm not falling for this again, Bill. I'm going to do whatever I can to get news of my husband, and I'm encouraging the wives to do the same thing. Today I wrote a letter to the President, to the State Department, to all the generals I could find in the Air Force directory. And I'm ready to take on the media if I have to. And yes, I called you for a reason." She had the checks and envelopes out of the cookbook before Percy could blink. "Just what in the damn hell are these for? I think I have an idea, but I want to hear you say it."

"I have no idea, Kate."

"Was Patrick involved in some kind of . . . of covert operation, the kind spy novelists write about? This is guilt money, isn't it—hush money. I don't want it, I want my husband, dead or alive. I want to know, I need to know. So, take this—this whatever it is, and give it back. I want you to know, though, I made copies of everything this afternoon, and they're in a safe place. I don't think I'll be calling you again, Bill, so they can assign you to some other poor wife. Take some advice from me and sharpen up your bedside manner."

"Listen, Kate, you're tired, it's late—"

"Yes, it's late, but I'm not tired. What I am is disappointed and disgusted with the system."

"Kate, don't violate the 'keep quiet policy,' as you refer to it."

"Good night, Bill," Kate said, holding the door open for him. The checks and papers were secure in his calfskin brief-case, she noticed. He looked back once, seemed about to say something, and then thought better of it. "I think I just scored a point for my side," Kate muttered to herself.

It was a lovely night, the sky star-spangled. She found the North Star and made a wish, not for herself, but for Patrick. *Keep him safe and out of harm's way.*

Reluctant to go back indoors, Kate strolled down the walkway to the gnarled old Joshua tree. With the help of one of the neighbors, Donald had fixed a swing for the girls from the lowest branch. She sat down gingerly. This was normal. The meeting inside had not been normal. *Oh, Patrick, where are you? I'm doing my best, but I don't think it's enough. God, how I need you.*

Kate was right: her efforts weren't enough. The meeting with Bethany was a farce. The older woman was so fearful, all she did was cry and bemoan her fate the way Kate had done months earlier. "I don't want them to list Michael as dead. If they do that, I'll have to go to his pension, the extra money stops, and I won't be able to survive. If you keep up what you're doing, you're going to endanger all of us. I think you should stop, Kate."

"Stop what?" Kate said in disgust. "No one answers my letters. Don't you understand, no one cares! So what is it that I'm doing that's so wrong? I gave back the money. I'm not obligated to anyone. And who is this *they* you're so worried about? Look, I'm sorry, I know how hard it is. Your husband has been missing longer than mine. I marvel at your stamina. I fell apart there for a while. I'm working now. I'm thinking of going to college. I realize I can't depend on anyone but myself. I want the life Patrick promised my girls. Since he isn't here to provide it, I have to step in and do it for him. I won't let them declare him dead, I can promise you that. Let them take away our benefits. I'll survive, and so will my children."

"I'm not going back to the group," Bethany said quietly.

"That's your choice," Kate said just as quietly.

"You and all the others have to be aware of what you're doing. If just one of our husbands is killed or tortured because of what you're doing, will you be able to live with that?"

"No, of course not. I want to know what happened to *my* husband. I have a right to know. If he's dead, I have the right to bury him. If he's a prisoner, I have the right to know that, too. This whole thing is wrong. It's been wrong from the beginning. Don't judge me or the others, Bethany. Sometimes you have to . . . to stand up and be counted. Thanks for talking with me. If you ever want to come back or just hang out for a while, call."

Kate was in the parking lot when Bethany caught up to her. "Did you really give back the money?"

"Yes. At least I gave it to Bill Percy. What he does with it is his problem. It felt good, too. I don't like him. I think he's . . . an insignificant piece of snot. Actually, I dismissed him. He hasn't done one thing to ease my worry, or said one thing to give me hope of any kind. I have enough negatives in my life, I don't need him adding more. So, he's out of my life."

Bethany's eyebrows shot upward. "Who will you talk to?"

"Anyone who will listen. Take care of yourself."

"You do the same."

Kate pulled out of Big Bob's parking lot, trying to remember what she'd had to eat. Nothing, just coffee. Bethany had eaten two hamburgers and a huge stack of french fries, yet she'd let Kate pay the bill. Kate wondered how that had happened. Years of tidying up, she supposed. She'd just automatically picked it up because it didn't belong on the table. In the scheme of things, it really didn't matter.

And so Kate's life went on. She attended her local support meetings, journeyed once to an important League of Families meeting, and came home with renewed faith. She was working full-time now and going to school at night. Half her business courses at the community college she attended were being taken care of by the architectural firm she worked for. She was making a life for herself, one step at a time. She thought of it as building a house, brick by brick. Each and every night when she said her prayers, she blessed Della and Donald for all their help, and then she prayed for the safe return of her husband and the well-being of her daughters. She never asked for anything for herself.

Time's pace accelerated, and before Kate knew it, another year had passed. It was January 23, 1974, and she had a pounding headache, an exam at six o'clock, and a full day at the office. Three months and she'd be finished with school. Patrick was going to be so pleased. Then again, maybe he wouldn't be proud of her. He might be annoyed. She swallowed three aspirin.

"I was just thinking, Della, that Patrick would be proud of

me when I graduate. I wasn't sure at first. Once I mentioned taking some night classes, and he didn't seem to like the idea. He would have liked me to go out to work, but school . . . for some reason, he wasn't keen on the idea."

Della grimaced. "Maybe he didn't want you to be as smart as he is. Maybe he would have viewed that as a threat."

Kate forced a laugh. "Just because you're an old married woman now doesn't make you *that* intuitive." She felt instantly ashamed because she'd thought the same thing. "I could never hope to be as smart as Patrick, even if I went to school night and day. He's got such a technical mind. He's so smart he amazes me. I used to hear him talking to some of the men, and he sounded like he came from another planet."

"Ah, yes, but does he have common sense? From what you've told me, he lacked that. Don't let his education take away from your own. I'm proud of you, and so is Donald."

"I couldn't have done it without you, Della. If you hadn't threatened to leave that Christmas, I'd still be lying in bed sucking my thumb."

"Since we're in such a complimentary mood, let me say that if it wasn't for you, I never would have met Donald and I wouldn't be married today. He's helped me with my English a lot. I can write it pretty good now. And he's learning a bit of Spanish, too. I owe you more than I can ever repay, Kate. But most important, I've come to love Betsy and Ellie and you and think of all of you as my own. My family. Donald feels the same way. You're our family, and like he says, we pull together."

Kate wrapped the plump woman in her arms. "I will be eternally grateful to you and Donald," she murmured, her eyes misty.

"Get on with you or you'll be late. I have to listen to Ellie's spelling words before I drop her off at school."

"I'll see you tonight. I'll probably be home early, since I

just have to take the exam. Thanks for offering to help out. I might make it by dinner if you don't serve till seven. What's on the menu?"

"Hot Mexican chili."

Kate grinned. "My tongue is burning already. Have a good day, Della."

During the day, Kate took six more aspirin, received several compliments from her boss, and studied for her exam during her lunch hour while she nibbled on an apple. When she left the office at five-fifteen, she took two more aspirin.

On the ride to the college she ran possible test questions over and over in her mind while she listened to the news on the radio. Her headache disappeared like magic the moment she heard the news commentator say, "President Nixon will address the nation this evening." He went on to speculate as to what the President would say. Kate knew in her gut what he was going to say, had prayed for it faithfully.

Her mind sharp and clear, Kate sailed through the exam and finished at exactly six-thirty. She rushed to the parking lot and drove home in a frenzy of excitement. "Did you hear the news?" she cried when she entered the kitchen.

"Kate, don't get your hopes up," Donald cautioned.

"Things are finally going to move!" In her excitement she failed to see the worried look Donald and Della exchanged. The girls were hyper, picking at their salad and chili.

"Can we stay up?" Betsy pleaded.

"Will they talk about Daddy?" Ellie queried. "I'll hold his picture when they talk to us. Is that okay, Mommy?"

"Of course it's okay. Finish your dinner, take your bath, and we'll have a nice fire while we wait for the program. Maybe hot cocoa with marshmallows. I feel so good about this. I mean, I feel really good. You're going to stay to see the program, aren't you?" she asked Donald. Though they were married, the Abbotts often took their meals with Kate and the children. Della cleaned up and Donald took her for a walk. They always ended with an ice cream cone on their walk home, to their own little cottage less than two blocks from Kate's apartment.

"Of course we're staying," Donald said. "I'll take the trash out and bring in some firewood. I'll have a blaze going as soon as the tykes are ready." To Betsy he said, "I think I finally figured out how we can get smoke to come out of your volcano for your school project. I set everything up down in the basement while you were in school. Now move your tushie so you can take a look at it," he said fondly.

Bless your heart, Donald, Kate told him silently, her eyes warm as she watched him with her children. Thank you, God, for allowing these wonderful people to come into our lives. Then, uninvited, a nasty thought crept in. Patrick would call Della and Donald intruders. He'd say he appreciated their help and then turn to her and say something like, What's in it for them? She pushed the thought back into the recesses of her mind.

Ellie started to cry. "I didn't get an A today."

"What did you get, Ellie? Did you spell 'bear' wrong?"

Ellie hung her head, tears dripping down her cheeks. "Uh-huh. I didn't get a star, I got a rainbow."

"Spell 'bear' for me now," Kate said, smiling.

"B-E-A-R. Bear."

"That's good, honey. Now you'll never spell it wrong again. Sometimes you have to do something wrong before you can do it right. A rainbow is good. I love rainbows. Remember the time you and Betsy planted a rainbow of flowers around the house? All the neighbors said how beautiful it was, and we even sent Daddy a picture of it. Scoot now, into the bathroom."

"You fibbed to her, Mommy," Betsy said. "Everyone in school knows rainbow stickers aren't as good as gold stars. You . . ." She thought for just the right word. "You mollified her."

"So I did." Kate's voice was sharper than she intended. "Everyone can't be number one. Everyone can't get an A."

"Daddy said you can do whatever you want to do if you want to do it bad enough. I want to get all A's so he'll be proud of me. Ellie doesn't care. Ellie's sloppy. I never get rainbows," she said loftily. "I don't like rainbows."

"Then it's your loss, Betsy. Do not make fun of your sister. She's doing the best she can."

Betsy always had to have the last word, just like her father. "She's not doing her best, and when Daddy comes home, he'll know it. I'm going to tell him. Ellie's a baby. You even treat her like a baby."

"I don't want to hear any more talk like this, Betsy. You need to be kinder to your sister."

"She needs a good slap," Betsy said, stomping out of the room.

Kate threw her hands in the air. "Now what do I do?"

"Nothing," Donald and Della said in unison. Della added, "She's upset because Friday is the student-father breakfast, and of course she doesn't have a father to take. Donald offered to stand in for Captain Starr, but she refused. Said it was cheating, and he was too old to pretend to be her father. Maybe you shouldn't make her go to school on Friday, Kate."

"She said that?"

"Lately she's been saying a lot of things like that," Donald said. "The children at school talk about their fathers a lot and what they do with them on the weekend, that kind of thing. She does love her father. Ellie just sails along. Actually, even though Ellie is younger, I think she has a better grasp on everything."

"Well, we'll just see about that," Kate said, and headed down the hall to the girls' bedroom. She was angry now because her headache was back. When she closed the bedroom door, she could hear Ellie splashing in the tub.

Betsy's face was sullen. She was sitting stiffly on the side of the bed. "Are we going to have one of *those* talks?"

"Yes, we are. For starters I'd like to say it's been a very long time since I've seen a smile on your face. You're being very fresh to your sister, and I do not care for your belligerent attitude. Worst of all, you've been unkind to Donald and Della. I need to remind you that without them we might be sleeping in the park in a tent. Donald is helping you with your school project, taking time out of his day to make things better for you. He doesn't want to be your father, he just wants to stand in your father's place for you until your daddy gets home. I think that's wonderful. I expect, and will settle for nothing less than, your full cooperation in this matter. You will go to breakfast and you will take Donald and you will have a smile on your face, and from now on your attitude had better change. It has not been easy for any of us, but we're all trying to live normally. I would appreciate your help. Don't make me resort to other measures, measures neither of us will like. Now, let's see a smile."

"My friends will laugh at me. Donald is too old to pretend to be my father," Betsy stormed.

"If your friends laugh at you, then they aren't your friends. I would assume by now you've explained to all of them about your dad. Donald is not going to pretend to be your father. He's going to be his stand-in. Your teacher will explain that to the class. I can call her and have a talk with her if you like."

"No, I don't want you to talk to the teacher, I'm not a baby." Suddenly she was a little girl again, throwing her arms around her mother and sobbing. "What if Daddy doesn't come home and Donald dies because he's old? Then who's going to stand in for *him*?"

"Don't talk like that, Betsy. Your daddy is going to come home. I don't know when, but he will. He promised me. Your dad never broke a promise. He promised you, too. We can't ever give up hope, even when things get dark and it gets harder and harder to believe. We have to keep going. I won't ever give up hope. I can't make you believe, only you can do that. Now, what's your decision?"

"Okay," Betsy said, blowing her nose. "But it was your decision. You said so when you first came in here. I was going to do it anyway. I don't want to hurt Donald's feelings. It scares me, Mommy."

"What scares you, baby?"

"What if I forget Daddy? I like it when Donald hugs me and sings those silly songs. I like it that he's helping me with my project. What if I start to like him more? What if he dies and leaves me with no one to hug me and sing to me?"

"Oh, Betsy, you will never forget your daddy, I won't allow you to forget. It's okay to love Donald, Daddy would approve. And Donald isn't going to die. He has Della to take care of him. You don't think for a minute she's going to let anything happen to him, do you? Not on your life. Now, let me tell you what I *think* you should do. I think you should find Donald. If he's outside, put on your coat and find him. Give him one of those big hugs that make your ribs ache, and tell him you would be *honored* to take him to the father-daughter breakfast. If you don't really feel that way in your heart, then I won't expect you to do it. I'm going in the bathroom to wash Ellie's hair. You sit here and think about it for a few minutes, okay? Let's see that famous Betsy smile Daddy said was as bright as sunshine."

"I don't have to think about it. I'm going to do it. Right now. Thanks, Mommy."

"My pleasure. That's what mommies are for."

Betsy ran down to the basement, words trembling from her mouth like a waterfall. "Donald, Donald, I need you to go to the breakfast with me. Mommy explained how you'd be Daddy's stand-in. Will you go with me?" Behind her back she crossed her fingers, waiting for Donald's reply.

Donald pretended to think. "Do you have to wear a sign that says I'm a stand-in?"

"No. Everyone knows about my daddy. I'm going to say you're sort of my grandfather. How old are you, Donald?" she asked fearfully.

"Old enough to be your grandfather, that's for sure." Donald chuckled. "I like the idea of acting the part of a grandfather. Is there anything special I need to do besides get all spruced up?"

"Nope. Just walk beside me and sit next to me when we eat. You have to get up and say your name after I introduce you. How old do you have to be to die?" she blurted.

Taken aback, Donald shifted the glasses on the bridge of his nose. Something important was being said here, and he needed to pay attention. "Honey, you can die at any age. Babies die sometimes. Youngsters in high school die. Young men in war. It would be nice to think only old people like me die after we lived our life, but it doesn't work that way. Is there a reason you want to know?"

"I don't want to be an orphan. I'm used to you now. I have *real* grandparents, but they don't bother with me and Ellie. Daddy's father is *really* old. Mommy says he can't remember things, and my other grandparents are too busy with my great-grandparents. Everybody forgot about us but you and Della. I don't want anything to happen to you. Sometimes I get scared."

Donald took a deep breath before he picked her up and set her on his knee. "Honey, it's okay to be scared. I get scared sometimes, too. So does Della. Your mom has been scared for a long time. But we have to live our lives, pray and hope for the best. We're a family now, and family members take care of each other."

Betsy snuggled into the crook of Donald's arm. "When my daddy comes home, will you still stay with us? I wouldn't want you to leave. I love you. I love Della. I don't want to miss you and Della the way I miss Daddy. I don't want to do it two times. Promise me you won't die, Donald. Please promise," Betsy said tearfully.

"Honey, I can't promise something like that. No one knows when they're going to die. Only God knows that. But I'm not going to die right now, that's for sure. I'll probably be hanging around until you get out of college. That's a pretty long time, if you ask me. By then," he said cheerfully, "you'll be pretty darn sick and tired of me hanging around."

"No, I won't. I always want you to be here. My daddy is going to love you and Della. I betcha he gives you a present for taking care of us. What kind of present do you think it will be, Donald?"

Donald laughed. "A big red wheelbarrow."

"A shiny one," Betsy chirped.

"With big green tires," Donald said.

"And we'll put a horn on the handle. I'm going to write Daddy a letter this weekend and tell him all about Christmas, and I'll tell him about the wheelbarrow."

"That's a mighty good idea, little lady," Donald said, hugging the little girl.

"Mommy's all better now. Donald, can you keep a secret?"

"I'm the best secret keeper in the whole world," Donald said, his face solemn.

"Alice Baker told me when you die they put you in a box and close it. Then they put the box in a hole in the ground and cover it up with dirt. You can't get out. You can't ever wake up again, and you turn to bones. People plant flowers over the hole and then they put up a statue of an angel that has your name on it. Alice is so smart she gets all A's. She's the teacher's pet, too. She said her grandmother died and that's what happened to her. Is that true?"

Donald's jaw dropped. Then, instead of answering her question, he asked one of his own. "Is that what's been worrying you?"

"Uh-huh. Mommy wouldn't get out of bed. She started to

look funny and she didn't smile or laugh. I don't know how to be an orphan. I don't want to be an orphan. Ellie will cry all the time if that happens. Daddy said I was supposed to look after her. If . . . I wouldn't be able to do that if we were orphans."

"Well, you don't have to worry about that. Your mother is going to be just fine. She wasn't feeling like herself for a while back then, but she's okay now. Now, you have to promise me you aren't going to worry about things like that anymore. The minute you start to worry, you come to me and we'll talk about it. When you talk about things, it helps and it doesn't seem so bad. I bet you even feel better now."

Betsy smiled before she wrapped her arms around his neck and squeezed him as tight as she could. "I love you, Donald. I love you almost as much as I love my daddy. I have to love him more because he's . . . he's . . . personal."

"I understand." Donald chuckled. "Now that we have all that serious stuff out of the way, let's get down to the real important things like getting this volcano to belch smoke."

"Is it going to be the best project in class?"

"Pretty darn close, Betsy, pretty darn close."

"I love you, Donald, I really do."

Later, when they were settled in front of the television, Della said, "That man is walking on air. I couldn't see his face for his smile. I don't want to know what you said to Betsy, but whatever it was, she seems to be her old self. I've never seen Donald so happy. He truly *wants* to go to the breakfast. He polished his shoes and he's getting a haircut to-morrow. He wants me to take his picture when they walk out of the house."

"Betsy's afraid that Donald will die because he's 'old,' " Kate said to her, "and there won't be anyone to hug her or sing to her. That's all it was, Della. She loves him and is afraid she might start to love him more than she loves her daddy. Explain that to Donald later, okay?"

"There'll be no living with him if I do. He's already like some prancing peacock, but I'll do it because he's such a good man. Kate, we are one lucky family."

"I know. Another minute here and we'll both be slobbering. Another crisis has passed. May they all be solved so easily."

"Time for the cocoa," Donald said, joining them. "It's almost nine o'clock."

"Call the girls in and let's toast some marshmallows."

Della pointed to the hearth, where long sticks and bags of marshmallows were waiting. "Donald got them ready."

Kate bowed her head and said a prayer as President Nixon's face flashed on the screen.

"Did you hear that?" she said ten minutes later. "We're going to sign a peace treaty on January twenty-seventh. That's just four days from now. The first group of POWs will be home in two weeks. Two weeks, Della! By March they'll all be home. Patrick will be home then, won't he? God, he has to be with them!"

"Kate, Captain Starr isn't listed as a POW," Donald said quietly. "He's listed as Missing."

"He's missing over there. If he's in hiding in the . . . jungle or something, he'll come out. Are you saying he won't . . . that he won't be with the POWs?"

"I'm saying I don't know," Donald said.

"I'm not going to work or to class tomorrow. I'm going to call everyone in the world if I have to. He's there, he has to come home with the others. He just has to."

Captain Patrick Starr did not come out in the first group, the second group, or the third group. When President Nixon said, "There are no more prisoners in Vietnam," two things happened. Kate collapsed, and eight-year-old Betsy verbally attacked her mother.

"You lied! You said Daddy was coming home!" she screeched. "You lied to me. You're a liar. Daddy hates liars!"

Della and Donald closed in protectively and coddled the little family that was torn apart once again. It was Donald who insisted a therapist be called in for both Kate and Betsy. With gentle pushing and prodding from Della, Donald, and the therapist, Kate was able to finish the semester and graduate with honors. Her job was put on hold until, as her boss put it, she got her shit together.

CHAPTER
6

It was early, that gray time of morning when the night relinquished its hold on the day. Soon the sun would creep to the horizon, and according to the weatherman, the day would be sunny and golden—perfect for an outdoor birthday party.

Kate shuddered beneath her warm flannel robe and sipped her lukewarm coffee. This year she'd hoped to avoid celebrating Patrick's birthday, but the girls wouldn't allow it, so today was going to be like the other nine birthdays they'd celebrated in the past. Of course "celebrated" was hardly the right word. They all cried, Donald and Della, herself and the girls. Tears rolling down their cheeks, they thumbed through the well-worn photo album, reread all the tattered letters, and then toasted Patrick with tall, frosty glasses of root beer. Those last few minutes of the party, signaling an end to the ritual until next year, were the best for Kate.

Ten years. Five hundred twenty weeks. Three thousand, six hundred, and fifty days. When Betsy had given her the numbers last night, she'd stared blankly at the paper, wanting to make some comment that would ease the misery in her oldest daughter's eyes, but the words wouldn't surface. All she'd managed was, "Ten years is a very long time. I don't think Daddy wants us to live on memories. We have to get on with our lives. That doesn't mean I'm giving up or that I will stop believing he'll return someday. It means I'm being realistic, and you must be, too. It's not healthy for us to live in the past."

Then, seeing the stubborn set of Betsy's shoulders, she'd sighed and added, "We'll have the party today, but this is the last one. It is simply too painful for me to go through the anxiety each year as we prepare. It can't be good for you or Ellie, either."

A tear dripped into Kate's coffee mug. From the Joshua tree she heard a bird chirp its morning greeting. "Good morning," she said softly. Suddenly it was important to see the bird that chirped its greeting to her every morning. In her bare feet she ran down the porch steps and around to the front of the house. She knew the nest was high in the tree, and for one crazy moment she thought about climbing up. She might have attempted it, too, if she hadn't heard Della's chattering voice and turned to see her friends coming down the sidewalk. She waited as Della pushed Donald's wheelchair onto the walkway, feeling silly now that she'd almost given in to her impulse.

"Kate, you look like you're thinking about climbing old Josh here," Donald said, gesturing to the tree. "My boy did it on several occasions and broke his collarbone and then his ankle. That nest has been there for years. If there was one thing I could always count on in those lonely days after his death, it was those birds singing to me in the morning. Right cheerful sound, but now Della's voice is all I need.

You need to find another voice, Kate. And the sooner the better."

Kate smiled. Donald and Della could always wash away her anxiety. She bent over to kiss Donald's weathered cheek. "I'm working on it." She winked at Della, then ruffled the springy tufts of white hair that protruded from Donald's Mets baseball cap. "Is today a good day, Donald?"

The old man flexed his hands, trying to unbend his crippled fingers. "The hot wax helps some. The pills help a little. Della's kisses help the most," he said, chuckling.

"The flowers are so pretty this morning. I think we had some rain during the night," Della said cheerfully. "I'm always amazed at this garden or border or whatever it is Betsy calls it. Just the other day I was talking to a lady at the grocery store, and somehow or other this garden came up in conversation. She said she brings people by just to look at it. She said it was a *whole* rainbow. Betsy's sixteen—I would have thought by now she'd have outgrown this garden."

"Never! She works so hard on it. And each year she uses her allowance to add more seeds. I think the colors are more vibrant this year, don't you? All so she can preserve her . . . father's rainbow." Kate sighed. "Still, Dr. Tennison says it's all right for her to be doing this. Enough of this talk—let's go in and have breakfast. I opt for waffles and blueberries. Donald, what's your choice?"

"Whatever this fine woman makes is okay with me. I'd eat sawdust if she put it on my plate." He would, too, Kate thought fondly as she led the way inside.

"Have you made a decision yet about this evening?" Della asked slyly, her back to Kate.

"Yes, I'm going. I . . . I haven't told the girls yet. I can't believe I'm such a coward, but do you know, I actually called Dr. Tennison to ask if it was okay to go to dinner with a man. Betsy is going to throw a fit. I can't believe I forgot it was Patrick's birthday when I made the date," Kate said, her eyes wild. "Charlie is . . . he's very nice . . . but it's not serious or anything like that—" She broke off and clutched Della's arm. "Oh, God, what if Betsy carries on? What will I do? Maybe this wasn't such a good idea after all."

"Keep this up and you'll talk yourself right out of it," Della said sourly. "You need to have a life of your own. And you need to stop going to bed at eight-thirty at night."

"Listen to her, Kate," Donald said. "She always makes good sense. I say you should go. We'll be here to baby-sit and to wait up for you just like parents."

"What are you going to wear?" asked the ever-practical Della. "Where are you having dinner?"

"I thought I'd wear my navy-blue and white, and I said I'd like to go to Stefano's. I did mention the Jade Garden, but Charlie said he was partial to Italian food, so it's Stefano's. It's simply a dinner invitation, nothing more. Charlie isn't my type. We're friends, nothing more."

"Time—"

"No, Della, time will not change anything. Patrick is— was—is the only man I'll ever love. No amount of dinner dates is going to change that."

Della snorted, a very unladylike sound. She turned, hands on her ample hips. "You are much too pretty, much too vital, to tie yourself to a memory. A ghost. That's what Patrick is now, Kate. It's time to give life a chance. If you don't start getting out and about, you're going to die on the vine."

Kate sat down at the table with a fresh cup of coffee. "I know you're right," she said, sighing. "It's just that I feel so disloyal, so . . . sneaky. If Patrick comes back and finds out, what will that make me in his eyes?"

"Kate, it is unlikely Patrick will come back. It's been ten years. You have to face reality. Hoping is one thing, living on that hope is something else. If Patrick does come back, you'll deal with it then. How many waffles?" Della asked briskly.

Kate smiled. "Three."

"Four for me," Donald spoke up.

"All right, Della, I'll tell them at breakfast," Kate said. Della nodded. Donald reached over to pat her hand.

"Morning, Mom," Ellie said, bounding into the kitchen and leaning over to kiss her mother. "Oh, waffles! I'll have six, Della. What are you going to tell us at breakfast?" She took her place at the table next to Donald and without missing a beat said, "And you're looking dapper and sexy this morning, Donald."

"I know," Donald said seriously. "Women just flock to me. But I'm a one-woman man."

"See that it stays that way," Della groused. She slipped four waffles on his plate and drizzled warm butter and syrup on top.

Ellie cut up the waffles for him. "Nobody answered my question," she said.

How pretty she is, Kate thought.

Ellie would be fifteen in another few months. Lively and outgoing, she had laughing blue eyes and a smile that stretched from ear to ear. She wore her hair in a high, pulled-back ponytail that swished when she walked. She claimed to be irresistible to the opposite sex, and Kate had to believe her, given the endless parade of boys who stopped by on a regular basis. Ellie was a B student at school, whereas Betsy was a straight A student. There was very little that Ellie took seriously except Betsy's garden.

"Tell us what?" she said now for the third time.

"I was going to wait till Betsy came down, but if you absolutely must know now," Kate said lightly, "I'll tell you. I have a dinner date this evening."

"Jeez! With who? Is he good-looking? Do we know him? Where'd you meet him? What time will you be home?"

"His name is Charlie Clark. He's a friend. I met him at work. We're going to Stefano's, and I'll be home early. Della and Donald will stay here until I get back. Any more questions?"

"Yeah. Does this mean the party is off?"

"We're going to do it at two o'clock."

"Aw, Mom, the gang is going roller-skating this afternoon. Look, I thought we agreed not to do the party thing anymore. Can I skip it? Please, Mom."

Kate wondered why she hadn't expected this. She shrugged. "It's your decision, Ellie. But Betsy will be disappointed."

"Well, I'm sorry, but I can't help it. It's the way I feel. Look, I hope I'm wrong and he does walk through the door someday. For Betsy's sake. But I can hardly remember what he looks like. I know you're doing the party for Betsy. But you know what? It's time Betsy grew up and became realistic. You coddle her too much. Scratch this party and let's get on with it."

"Betsy needs—"

"No, Mom, Betsy doesn't need this. It's just her way of getting attention. You give in to her on everything. She has no friends. She keeps writing those stupid letters she never mails. All she talks about is when Dad comes home and the things *they're* going to do. It doesn't help to keep having these parties."

"Just this one last—"

"No. Not for me. You said the same thing last year and the year before that. I absolutely refuse to do it anymore. What's the point?"

Kate sighed. "All right, Ellie, I understand how and why you feel the way you do. I want you to go with your friends today and enjoy yourself. After this party there won't be any more. Now eat your breakfast."

"Mom," Ellie said, picking up her fork, "can I have my own room and my own phone if I pay for it with my baby-sitting money?"

Kate smiled. Nothing kept Ellie down for long. "Donald and I have already been discussing how we can make room for you. He's suggested we take out the linen closet and the hall closet and take three feet from Betsy's room. It'll be a small room, though. Very small. And when you show me you have enough money for the phone installation and enough for three months of bills, we'll discuss giving you your own phone."

"Thanks, Mom. Donald, you're the best. You, too, Della," Ellie said, getting up and planting kisses on all three of them. "I don't care how small the room is. All I need is a bed and my dresser. And a door with a lock so nosy Betsy can't sneak up on me. Can you do that, Donald?"

"You drive a hard deal, little girl," Donald said, flashing his widest grin. "A door with a lock. A girl needs her privacy, Della says."

"I wish we had a rec room," Ellie said from the doorway.

"Don't push it, Ellie," Kate said.

"What's she whining about now?" Betsy said, brushing her way past her sister. She was dressed, her hair combed, her teeth brushed. Her bed would be made, her half of the room tidy. She took being a military brat seriously.

"She wants her own room. Donald has agreed to knock out the closets and take three feet from your room. It shouldn't be too much of a job. Would you like some waffles, Betsy?"

"Two will be fine. When are you baking the cake, Mother?"

"I'm not. I have a lot of work to catch up on. I had to bring it home this weekend, so we moved the party up to two o'clock. Ellie won't be here. I bought some cupcakes and the root beer. I won't be here for dinner this evening. I'm having dinner with a friend."

"Did you at least get a card?" Betsy asked snidely.

"No, as a matter of fact, I didn't. I'm not buying cards anymore, or presents. I'm willing to toast your father's birthday this one last time, but it's been ten years, Betsy. Time to let go."

101

Betsy fixed her narrow gaze on Della and Donald. "Do you feel the same way as Mother?" They both nodded. "Is your dinner date with a man?" Betsy said to her mother.

"Yes, but he's a friend, nothing more."

"I can see how this would be a good time for something like that," Betsy said. "Well, you're all wrong. Dad is coming back. He promised, and he's never broken a promise to me."

"Betsy, we haven't heard a thing in ten years. We need to get on with our lives. Do you want to keep going to Dr. Tennison for the rest of your life?"

"I'm not going anymore, and I want to become a Catholic. Catholic people pray to Saint Jude for helpless and hopeless causes. You can't stop me."

"I won't try," Kate said sadly. "However, I wouldn't close the door with Dr. Tennison."

"Well, I am. I only went to please you. All he does is talk about how we have to look at the world realistically. I know what he's going to say before he says it. I think we should forget the party since everyone is so opposed to it. I'll have my own out in the garden. Don't worry about me, Mother, I have things under control."

Kate stared across the table at her daughter. Where Ellie was pretty and wholesome, Betsy was downright beautiful, with big warm brown eyes and thick lashes. Her dark hair, so like Patrick's, was curly, falling in lustrous waves about her shoulders. And she was so much like Patrick, it was scary at times.

"If that's what you want," Kate said quietly.

Betsy pushed her plate away. "The waffles were good, Della." On her feet, she towered over Kate. "I hope you have a miserable time this evening. You're cheating on Daddy, and that makes you a tramp."

"Young lady," Kate said, reaching for her arm, "don't you *ever*, ever talk to me like that again. You apologize to me

102

now or you will find yourself sitting in this kitchen until you do."

Betsy's eyes ricocheted around the kitchen, took in Della's stunned expression, the disappointed look on Donald's face, the anger on her mother's face. "I'm sorry," she said, and ran from the room.

Kate sighed wearily. "I suppose this all is my fault," she said. "In the beginning I tried to keep him alive for all of us with the letters, the gifts, the parties. I let it get out of hand."

"Then why isn't Ellie reacting the same way?" Donald said quietly. "It's not your fault."

"Then how did she get like this? For God's sake, there's only a year and a half between them! Betsy took this all so seriously, yet Ellie . . ."

"It's not your fault, Kate," Della said firmly. "You can't do more than you've already done. The rest is up to Betsy. If you give in to her and keep on with this nonsense, you'll make yourself sick."

"My God, Della, she called me a tramp. Me, her mother."

"She didn't mean it. You have to put it out of your mind. Tomorrow, when she's had time to think things over, she'll come to you and give you a real apology."

"No, she won't. This to her is the ultimate betrayal. And the funny thing is, it's simply a dinner with a friend who just happens to be a male. I guess I'll just have to live with it."

"Guess so." Della smiled.

"She is a smart woman," Donald said cheerfully. "If I wasn't all crippled up with this dad-blang arthritis, I'd waltz you two fine-looking ladies around the room."

"And we'd both be tripping over our feet. Patrick didn't like to dance, so I never learned. In the scheme of things it didn't seem important. One of these days I just might take lessons." She was relieved to see smiles on her friends' faces.

If she was lucky, she could go about her business and not think about Betsy's stinging remark.

Oh, Patrick, I tried so hard. I want to believe, but it seems so hopeless. I can't believe you'd want us to mourn and grieve forever. I'll never marry again, that much I do promise. We both agreed to that, remember? Where are you? Do you think of us? Are you alive, Patrick?

The sun was high in the sky when Betsy, freshly showered for the second time in the day, stepped into the garden, carrying her gift-wrapped present on a tray along with a glass of root beer and a cake she'd picked up at the bakery, topped with ten candles. Her first trip out she'd carried her portable phonograph, writing tablet, and a pen and lap blanket.

Tears pooled in her eyes when she spread the blanket. Her hands were trembling and she felt light-headed. She hadn't expected her mother's declaration. Sooner or later she knew Ellie would balk, but her mother . . .

Tears dripped down her cheeks when she placed her gift, a complete desk set and a card, on the corner of the blanket. She sat down squaw fashion. Her fingers itched to turn on the phonograph to play the birthday song. She wiped her eyes, feeling suddenly silly and childish. Were they right? Was she wrong?

"I don't seem to belong here anymore, Daddy," she murmured. "Dr. Tennison says I'm holding on too tight. He thinks I'm not stable, that I can't handle life without you in the background. He's wrong. I can. I *know* you're going to come home. I know it. When you know something, feel it like I do, you can't buckle under and say what they want you to say. Mom's right, though, ten years is a very long time. Sometimes I feel myself almost giving up, and then I remember your promise.

"I've tried so hard to be the kind of daughter who will

make you proud when you do come home. I make the honor roll each period. I'm a straight A student. I keep my room neat and tidy because I know how neat you like things. I don't know what else to do anymore except to pray and hope. That will never change.

"Mom is . . . Mom has a date this evening. She said it's not a real date, just a friendship thing. She's never really lied to us before. This is . . . I think this is the first step for both Mom and Ellie in letting go. That's what Dr. Tennison calls it, letting go. I'm not ready to do that, Dad, I don't think I'll ever be ready.

"I can't wait to leave here, to be on my own. I think I feel like you did when you left. You told me it was going to be a big wonderful adventure and something you dreamed of all your life. That's how I feel. So, Dad," she said, turning on the phonograph, "happy birthday."

Betsy drank her root beer in two gulps. She blew out the ten candles she'd lighted, licked at the frosting with her finger. When the song was finished, she bundled up the record player, the gift, and the blanket and glass, and carried them into the house. She threw the cake in the trash. "I won't forget," she whispered.

CHAPTER

7

Kate wondered if it was possible for the mirror to lie. She leaned closer to stare at herself with clinical interest. Lately she hadn't paid much attention to her looks, preferring simply to wash her face, cream it, and leave it alone. It was Ellie, who adored makeup, who'd taught her how to enhance her best features. Now she applied eye shadow, dabbed at the tips of her thick lashes, and rubbed a dot of rouge on her cheekbones. She finished with a glistening coral lipstick that somehow, mysteriously, Ellie said, made her eyes sparkle. She wore earrings, too, tiny pearl drops that seemed to bring a warm glow to her cheeks, a glow that had nothing to do with the rouge.

A month ago she'd gotten a fashionable haircut and had preened when the beautician, a man, said, "Do you have any idea how many women would kill for curly hair like yours?" Then he'd gone on to say she looked like a woman of the eighties, whatever that meant.

She was twirling under a spritz of cologne when Betsy entered the room. "Mom, I'm sorry. I don't know what made me carry on like that. I won't do it again. Is that the perfume Ellie and I gave you for Christmas?"

"No, this is something I picked up at Conrad's last month. They were giving out samples and I decided to buy a bottle. I like to alternate." She didn't want to tell Betsy that the scent the girls had bought her reminded her of the vanilla and lemon she used to douse herself with. For one second her husband's face flashed before her.

"Do you like it, Betsy?"

"I can't get over how you look," Betsy said, her eyes narrowing slightly. "Is that a new dress you're wearing?"

"As a matter of fact it is. I'm going to wear it to the company dinner next week. The salesgirl said it looked good on me. Do you think so, honey?" Kate asked anxiously.

Again Betsy avoided answering directly. "If this is just a dinner with a *friend*, why don't you wear your seersucker suit and that white piqué blouse? I think you have too much perfume on, too. You never used to dress this way."

"What way is that?"

"Sexy. You look sexy," Betsy mumbled.

"You sure do," Ellie chirped from the open doorway. She whistled softly. "If Charlie Clark is just a friend, maybe he'll introduce you to someone who . . . you know, will be more than a friend."

"You are absolutely disgusting, Ellie," Betsy snapped. "Mother is married. Married women don't fool around."

"Get off your high horse, Betsy. I was teasing Mom. But you never know. What are you going to do if he wants to kiss you good night? You have my permission," Ellie said, sticking her tongue out at her sister.

"You really do condone this, don't you?" Betsy spat at her sister.

"Can't you send her away to some special school where they have kids just like her, Mom?" Ellie said. "She's not real. She's like a stupid cop. She monitors all of us, and you know what? She *writes* it all down so she can tell Daddy if he ever comes home."

"You sneak, you read my diary. You miserable little sneak!" Betsy shrilled.

"Get off it, sister dear, I did no such thing. Is it my fault you talk in your sleep? You gonna blame that on me, too? Listen, I can't wait to get out of that room and into one of my own. Why don't you go weed your flowers or plant yourself six feet down. You'd make wonderful fertilizer." Ellie turned to her mother. "Don't let her make you feel guilty, Mom. She thrives on that because she's stupid. You look real pretty, and Charlie Clark, whoever he is, is one lucky guy to be taking you to dinner. Be home by twelve," she trilled, to her sister's horror.

"Twelve! If you're leaving at six . . ." Betsy trailed off. Her eyes flashed dangerously.

Kate's heart fluttered. She had to do something about this child of hers. Lord, where had she gone wrong? "Betsy, you have to stop taking everything so seriously. Ellie needles you and you fall for it every single time. Sweetheart, I'm sorry about today, but I just don't want to be depressed anymore. I want sunshine in my life. I don't want to upset you, Betsy, but I must get on with my life. I will always love your father, that will never change. But we can't live in the past, it simply isn't healthy."

"He is coming back, Mother," Betsy said quietly.

"I pray that he does, but until I see him walk through the door, I can't live my life on hope. I plan to involve myself in several groups and organizations, make friends and go out more. I'm even thinking about starting my own business. And I could use a little more support from you."

"I know Dad is coming back. What's he going to think when he finds out how you've changed? When he sees the way Ellie decks herself out and the way she's chasing boys? What is he going to think?"

Kate straightened her shoulders. "I don't know what he would think, and right now I don't care. When and if he appears we'll deal with it, but not before."

"You're not the same anymore," Betsy said coldly.

"No, I guess I'm not, but I would like you to think about something. If your father does come back, he's not going to be the same man you remember. He'll be changed, too. You've changed, so has Ellie. You're seventeen, ready for college. He has no idea what you're like now. If he's alive, he's thinking of you and Ellie as his *little* girls. Please, don't keep blinding yourself to facts."

"You have an answer for everything, don't you?" Betsy snapped.

Kate sighed. She felt like taking off her clothes and crawling into bed. Betsy always managed to make her feel ashamed and guilty. "If I did have the answers to everything, I'd damn well package them and sell them at a discount. Every time I make advances in my life, you somehow try to make me slide backward. I wish ..."

Betsy's eyes flashed. "What, Mother? That it was time for me to leave for college?"

God in heaven, that's exactly what she was thinking. "I don't care to discuss this anymore, Betsy. And the next time we're in each other's company, I damn well better hear a change in your voice and see a smile on your face or you won't be going away to school, you'll be attending the community college. You think about that this evening. You're *dismissed*."

Alone, Kate sank to the edge of the bed. She'd handled Betsy all wrong. Why was Ellie so ... so normal, and Betsy so ... *Patrick, where the hell are you? Why am I being forced to go through this? She's just like you. I don't know what to do for her, what to say to her. We go over the same things, day after day, and we manage to slide backward each time. I hate to say this, but I don't like our daughter very much these days. She was right, I can't wait till she leaves for school. I'm sorry, Patrick, that I'm not doing a better job. I try so hard. This dinner to-night means nothing, I'm not being disloyal. I'm not cheating on you. Our daughter called me a tramp. Oh, Patrick, where are you?*

"Mom, your . . . friend is here. Oooooh, he's a . . . *hunk*," Ellie hissed from the doorway. "He told me to call him Charlie." She rolled her eyes and gave a thumb's-up salute. Kate laughed. "Remember, in by midnight, and don't do any of those awful things you tell me not to do when I go out. C'mon, get going!" She hugged her, a silly smile on her face.

Kate laughed. "Okay, okay!" Her eyes thanked her daughter.

When the front door had closed behind her mother, Ellie stalked down the hall to the bedroom she shared with her sister. She bounded into the room and grabbed hold of Betsy's hair. "You are a miserable, stinking bitch and I hate your stinking guts. You take all the life out of Mom. You just damn well suck it right out of her. Would it have killed you to be nice to her, to have gone downstairs to meet that guy? You know what?" she said, yanking at Betsy's curly hair. "I hope Dad does come back, because I'm going to tell him what you've done to this family. God, I can't wait till you leave. Promise me you won't come back for the holidays." She gave her sister's hair another vicious yank. "Della said to tell you dinner is ready. I for one hope you choke on your food." She stormed out of the room, slamming the door behind her.

Betsy stared at the closed door, her expression blank. From under her pillow she withdrew her diary and a banana. She dated the pages and wrote, "Happy Birthday, Daddy."

CHAPTER

8

"Comrade." The single word speared through Patrick's body. He really was in Russia. How he'd gotten here, he had no idea. He remembered being shoved onto a plane, remembered the prick of a needle. And now this. This, he decided a moment later, was worse than being in Vietnam. He'd always hated the cold.

They were speaking to him in English. He responded by giving his name, rank and serial number. Then he said, "The rules of the Geneva—"

He was on the floor, clutching his ribs and screaming in agony. He thought about punctured lungs, shattered spleens, before he blacked out. When he came to, he felt something hanging over his eyes. Tentatively he reached up and felt a needle-thin icicle hanging from his eyebrow. He started to shake with pain and cold, welcomed the sight of the needle

111

and the oblivion it would bring. They weren't ready for the needle yet; first they would torment and torture him. His battered ribs were just a teaser.

He retreated to a warmer, safer place, a place where he was free to do whatever he wanted, and what he wanted to do this very minute was climb into an airplane and fly into the heavens.

"I have enough," he said happily. "Forty dollars, enough for both of us for an hour. I know it's just a crop duster, but it has wings, and the pilot said he'd let me take the controls. If you don't want to go, Kate, I can fly for two hours."

"Oh, Patrick, you saved so long for this, you go. I'll stay here and watch. I brought a book with me to read. I'll wave to you when you get up in the air."

He didn't mean for his voice to sound so relieved when he said, "Are you sure? This was supposed to be our day. We talked about it for months. Are you just being nice?"

"Sure I'm being nice." Kate giggled. "You'll have two whole hours, Patrick. I brought three dollars with me. After you land, we can go get some hamburgers and french fries and you can tell me all about it, how it felt. I'll like that better. Besides, I might get sick up high. Remember everything so you can tell me about it."

Later, when they were snug in a booth in the Linden soda parlor, he said, "It was everything I thought it would be."

"Did you feel like a bird? Weren't you afraid?" Kate asked.

"Heck no, I wasn't afraid. I felt better than a bird. You know what, Kate? I felt like God. Just like God. Listen, we have to hurry or my father will beat the bejesus out of me. If either one of our parents ever finds out we rode our bikes this far, we'll never be allowed to leave the house again."

He pedaled faster, right down to the swimming hole, where it was warm and sunny; a paper sack full of egg salad sandwiches for him and the guys. Kate might show up, so he'd brought one for her, too. All his buddies knew Kate was his girl. Well, sort of his girl. Bill Duke had a girl, too, and so did Buck Inhabinet.

He was on his bike again, pedaling and finishing the last of his egg salad sandwich, the best sandwich he'd ever eaten. He'd put little seeds in it, the ones his mother used to use. It put zip into the egg salad. He tossed away the wax paper, braked his bike, and pedaled backward to pick up the paper and stuff it into his pocket.

Kate was ahead of him; he could see her saddle shoes sparkling in the sun. Bill and Buck were bringing up the rear.

Without knowing how he got there, he was suddenly at the senior prom, awkwardly trying to lead Kate on the dance floor.

"Oooooh, isn't the gym beautiful, Patrick?"

"Sure is. Boy, do you smell good. You smell like those flowers in front of your house."

Kate giggled. "That's because I stuck some of them down my . . . bra."

"Will you let me look later?"

"No!"

He groaned. "Come on, Kate, you let me feel you sometimes."

"Feeling is different than looking. The answer is no, Patrick."

"Let's get some soda pop and go outside. Bob has some cigarettes. We're all going to smoke."

"Well, I'm not. You shouldn't, either."

"Why not?"

"Don't do what everyone else does. I like you because you aren't a copycat. You're special."

"What makes me special?"

"You're going to be a pilot someday. That makes you special. You're real smart, the smartest boy in the whole school. In the yearbook they said you would be the most successful. I believe that."

He preened. "They said that because it's true. I'm going to fly all over the world, and when I come home, you'll meet me at the door and have a big chocolate cake waiting in the middle of the table. Lots and lots of frosting. You'll always wait for me, won't you, Kate?"

"That's a silly question. Of course I'll wait for you. I'm going to be the best wife and mother in the whole world."

"It's important to be the best. Mothers and wives don't have to be the best. Just men. You know what I mean."

He was pedaling again, faster than ever. He wanted to be the first to arrive at O'Malley's barn for the last hayride of the season. His plan was to hide in the straw in the wagon and whoop and shout when the others arrived to wonder where he was. He wasn't going to be a kid anymore after tonight. He propped up his bike out of sight and headed for the wagon. The fresh straw felt warm and prickly and smelled earthy. He inhaled deeply, lay down in the straw and thought about Kate.

Kate was warm and soft and smelled good. Kate smiled all the time, did what he wanted when he wanted. Except she wouldn't have sex with him.

Kate was part of his life, would always be part of his life. She was his. Everyone said so. For a moment he wondered what would happen if he told the guys he wanted to give her back. Their eyes would bug out of their heads. You didn't give someone like Kate back. And who would he give her back to, Din Radson? No, Kate was his forever and ever. They were going to get married someday and have lots of little Kates and Patricks.

He looked back over his shoulder and then at the sterile corridor he was standing in. He looked around wildly, expecting to see Bill and Buck. Kate, where was Kate? He had to find Kate, ask her what was going on. He shivered. He'd never been so cold in his life.

"Captain Starr, is this your daughter?" He was shaking,

shivering, unable to get warm. He could barely see the paper his interrogator was holding up in front of him. He couldn't even nod, his neck was too cold to move. He was numb. Where was he?

Then he remembered.

The voice sounded as cold as he felt. He listened to the words, tried to make sense of them.

"She's dead. Your family was killed in an auto crash. You have no family anymore. You are going to live and die here. You will never return to your home, so you might as well tell us what we want to know."

Kate had promised she would always wait for him. Kate never broke a promise. They were trying to wear him down. How damn stupid they were. Didn't they know all they had to do was give him one of their needles and he'd spill his guts? He muttered his name, rank, and his serial number.

The blow caught him over the left ear. He felt something pop inside his head. "Fuck you!"

"I hate it when you swear like that, Patrick," Kate said. "Now, are we going to the park or not? It's such a beautiful day, not a cloud in the sky. I packed some sandwiches. . . ."

CHAPTER
9

The months whizzed by, and before Kate knew it, it was time for Betsy to leave for college. Her two trunks had been sent ahead the week before, and all that was left to do now was carry her two large suitcases to the car and drive her to the airport. The good-byes were going to be awful, Kate thought. I'm going to cry like a ninny, the way I did the day I took her to kindergarten.

They were all lined up on the front porch, Della, Donald in his wheelchair, Ellie and two of her friends. "What's taking her so long?" Kate muttered.

"She's probably primping," Donald said, smiling. Kate didn't respond, and a moment later the screen door banged open just as a taxi pulled to the curb, horn blaring.

Kate felt a rush of panic. "Why is that taxi here?"

"I called it, Mother," Betsy said quietly. "I think it's best this way. You're going to get all emotional and embarrass me, and I don't want that. I'll be fine. Don't worry about me."

"But . . . we agreed. . . . I planned on driving. . . . Oh, why did you do this, Betsy?"

"I told you: I think it's best."

There were no hugs, no kisses. With an airy wave, Betsy marched across the porch and down the steps, suitcases in hand. She didn't look back, didn't wave a second time.

"I'll write and phone once a week," Kate called after her.

"Don't hurry back!" Ellie shrilled.

"Ellie!"

"Sorry, Mom. It just slipped out." Ellie grinned. "See you later. I'm going over to the football field and watch all the guys. I have cheerleader practice at three-thirty, so I might be late getting home for dinner."

Kate sank down on the front steps and glanced up at Della, eyes bright with tears. "I don't believe Betsy did that. It was agreed I would take her to the airport. I would have cried, but I wouldn't have made a fool of myself or embarrassed her. And a taxi! It's just the way Patrick left me. My God, what am I doing wrong?"

Della sat down and cradled Kate in her arms. "This is one more thing you have to get through, Kate. Come on, get up now and come into the kitchen with me and Donald. We're going to have coffee and a slice of my pineapple upside-down cake, and then Donald is going to go over your business plan with you. That child is going to be just fine, Kate. This might be the best thing for her, getting off on her own. She'll be in New York, attending a large university, and she'll make friends. When she comes home for Christmas, she'll be totally different. She'll be forced to interact with the other students. And don't forget she'll have a roommate. Trust me, everything is going to be fine," Della crooned.

"Enough!" Donald roared. "I thought we were going to have coffee and cake!"

117

"We are," Kate said shakily. "I'm all right now. And I want an extra large slice of cake. Do you realize, Della, Ellie will be going off to college next September if she takes two courses next summer? I'll be completely alone then."

"I don't want to hear talk like that," Donald said gruffly. "As long as we're here, you won't be alone. We're a family, and don't you ever forget it."

"Oh, Donald, thank you. Every day of my life I thank God for sending you and Della into my life. I owe you so much."

"You don't owe us anything. Without you, I would never have met or married Della. I wouldn't have my new family. I think we're pretty much even. Now, can we have the damn cake?"

"Yes, sir!" Kate said, saluting smartly.

Dinner that evening was a lively affair, but it was a forced liveliness. The tension was broken at last when Ellie said, "So, okay, I miss her sour puss staring across the table from me. I'm going to miss her hogging the bathroom, too. I might even write her a letter and tell her so." Kate smiled, which was what Ellie had been angling for. "Now, Mom, let's get to business. I'll help Della with the dishes so you and Donald can talk. But I'll be listening. Remember now, I know numbers and I'm going to be a CPA one of these days. *If* I pass the exam."

"You'll be the best CPA in the state of California," Donald said loyally.

Kate spread her papers out on the kitchen table. "This is my business plan," she began. "These are all the papers from the Small Business Administration. There are two possible locations I'm interested in renting if the SBA gives me the loan. The rent is reasonable on both offices. One is smaller than the other, but if my business grows, then I might need a larger one. I've checked out three used office furniture places, and their things are reasonably priced. I've also been in touch with a print shop and know where to get mailing lists for a good price. And my boss said he'd refer his associates to me if they want renderings. What do you think, Donald?" Kate asked anxiously.

"What I think, Missy Kate, is you have a good thing going here. You're just the type of person the SBA likes to help, and having Captain Starr in the background won't hurt you at all. The loan payments are going to be tough for the first year, until you build your clientele. You'll have to use some of the loan to make the payments, but you can pay that back to yourself later on. You low-balled everything. Lenders like to see that. It's when you get in over your head that they turn you down."

"I just did what you told me. Ellie worked up the numbers. If you two think this is okay, then I'm mailing everything off Monday morning. Until I hear from the SBA, I'm going to see if I can line up some customers. I have enough money put aside to buy one mailing list. I can have a modest printing done. If they turn me down, I'll work out of the house. When the weather is nice, I can move my drafting table out onto the back porch. Keep your fingers crossed, everyone."

"Architectural Renderings by Kate Starr," Ellie said, dancing around the kitchen. "A crisp black-and-white sign done in script will look soooo nice, Mom. Are you going to write 'Before' and 'After' on the sign?"

"No. The clients know that I do one drawing of their project before it gets started and then I do the finished product. It's understood. Listen, Ellie, we're going to be living on a shoestring for a very long time. I want to build this business so if I do make a profit, I'll be putting it back into the business."

"Don't worry about me, Mom. I start my part-time job at the supermarket the last week in September, but I can handle cheerleading, school, and the job. Dates only on Saturday night. No problem there." She giggled.

"Okay, as long as you have it all straight," Kate said.

"Will there be enough money for tuition?" Ellie asked anxiously.

"There will be enough. That's my problem, not yours. Your dad and I took out endowment policies when you and Betsy were born. It will get you through at least two years if you work for your spending money like Betsy is going to do. By then the business should be making a profit and things will be easier. If the business doesn't work, I'll get a job and take out college loans."

It was mid-December before Kate received word that the SBA had approved her loan. Euphoric, she set about renting office space and furnishing it. She wanted to open her doors January second. "This is going to be such a wonderful Christmas!" she said happily to Della and Donald as all three sat together in the kitchen. "We'll get this tall, fragrant tree and decorate it. We'll bake and cook, buy presents, not costly ones, just little mementos. Betsy will be home, and we'll be a complete family again. I can't believe how blessed I am. I'm just sorry Patrick isn't here to enjoy it with us."

"You could invite that nice Charlie Clark," Donald said out of the corner of his mouth.

"No, I can't. He's getting married in February. I told you he was just a friend. All we ever talked about was his lady and Patrick. Evan Carpenter was the same, and so was Douglas Withers. Just friends."

"Someday," Della said sourly.

"No, Della, not someday. I'm not like that. Until the United States government tells me Patrick is dead, I am still married. He is still MIA. Besides, I haven't met anyone who even remotely interests me. I have two daughters to put through college and a business to get off the ground. There's no room in my life for a man."

"If you say so," Della said.

Kate laughed. "I say so."

Unfortunately, Kate's happiness was short-lived. Later that evening, during dinner, she received a call from Betsy.

"How are you, honey?" she cried, pleased. "I hear you have snow in New York. . . . Yes, everyone is here, we're having dinner. I have wonderful news. . . . Oh, *you* have wonderful news. All right, let's hear it!" Everyone stopped eating to watch Kate.

"She's not coming home for Christmas," Della and Ellie muttered at the same time.

"I knew it," Donald mumbled.

"If you're sure that's what you want to do, Betsy. I'm afraid money is a little tight right now. I can send you fifty dollars, but— No, I'm not a skinflint! I told you money is tight right now. I sent your allowance out the first of the month. It was short because I had to buy your plane ticket. I don't know if you can get your money back for it. Just remember, Betsy, if you do turn it in, that's January and February's allowance. . . . I'm sorry you feel that way. I doubt very much if you'll starve, since I paid for your room and board. . . . Yes, Betsy, Merry Christmas to you, too.

"Betsy won't be home for Christmas," Kate said flatly when she returned to the table. "She's going to Boston to spend the holidays with her roommate's family. She said her roommate's father was a pilot in Vietnam and managed to return in one piece and said he'd met Patrick at one point. It's understandable why she wants to go."

"Oh, well, Easter is just three or four months away," Ellie said, digging into her apple pie. "Then there's spring break." The minute she was finished she excused herself, but not before she gave her mother a big hug. Only Della saw the tears glistening in the girl's eyes.

Kate carried her plate to the sink. She whirled around. "Look, you two, it's okay. I think I knew Betsy wasn't going to be home for Christmas. She won't be home for Easter, either."

"You didn't get a chance to tell her about the loan and—"

"I'll write her a letter after Christmas or in January. She isn't very interested in what I do these days. If you two want to go home, I can clean up here."

"If you carry in the wood, Kate," Donald said, "I'll build you a nice fire before we leave. There's still a few things I can do on my own, and making a fire is one of them."

Kate bent over to kiss his weathered cheek. "I don't think I've told you lately how much I love you and how grateful I am for all your support and help. I'm sorry I don't say it more often, Donald. I wish there were something I could do for you, something meaningful."

"Make a success of that business. We got you to this place in time. The rest is up to you. Give it all you got, Kate. We'll keep things going here for Ellie."

Tears slipped down Kate's cheeks. "He's not coming back, is he, Donald?"

"I'm afraid not, Kate. As much as I hate to say this, I think you should press the government to give you answers one way or the other. Make a stink, a real one, whose smell will go all the way to Washington. If you tell me what to do, I'll do it. You start the ball rolling, and I'll keep it rolling. I think this family has waited long enough for news of Captain Starr."

"You know what? I think you're right," Kate said grimly.

"Atta girl! We'll make them shudder in their boots. And that's a promise."

"Donald, there are days when I can't remember what Patrick looks like. I have to haul out his picture. Then I feel guilty. Other days I don't think about him at all. I feel like I'm letting him down, that I'm not doing my part."

"Would you like us to stay with you this evening, Kate?" Della asked.

"No, you two have done enough for me. I'm fine. Really."

"You make it sound like we live miles away. We're only

around the corner," Della muttered. "You look peaked to me. Maybe you're coming down with something, it is the flu season."

"I'm fine. I wanted this Christmas to be . . . oh, I don't know, special in some way. Starting the new business, you know, doing something on my own. With your help of course," Kate added hastily.

"Hold on here," Donald said briskly. "You did this all on your own. All we did was listen and support you. Don't you go thanking us for something you did yourself. Don't you ever take away from your abilities."

Kate smiled tiredly. "Patrick would be stunned if he knew what I've been doing. I don't think he ever thought I had the brains to do anything but be a wife and mother. That used to bother me. He is . . . was so smart. I always felt inferior. I wanted so desperately to be part of what he did, to at least understand what he was all about, but when I'd ask him to tell me about his day or the missions, he'd start to talk, then remember it was me asking the questions, and he'd kind of smile this . . . quirky smile, and say, 'Kate, you'd never in a million years understand this stuff. Make bread or sew some curtains, that's what you do best.' He was right, I wouldn't have understood, but the next day I would have looked up all the words, tried to find out more so I could talk to him on an intelligent level. But he wouldn't give me a chance. I gave in too easily. I guess it was better for me at the time to bake bread and sew curtains. What really hurt was that he thought I was stupid. He didn't have to say the words out loud, I could tell by the way he acted."

"It doesn't matter what he believed, Kate," Donald said. "You proved you are a woman who can make it on her own. Della and I are so proud of you we could bust, and if the captain was here now, he would be, too. You've climbed a mountain to get to this place. You're going to make a success of this business. Betsy will come back to the fold when she gets all this anger and hurt out of her system. Until she does, you go on with your life and hope for the best." Donald grunted. "Didn't know I was so long-winded."

"I keep telling you you're a windbag," Della said fondly as she tweaked her husband's ear.

"I love you two, you know that," Kate said tearfully.

After Kate and Della had brought in wood and Donald had gotten a cozy fire going in the hearth, Della and Donald said their good-byes and Kate settled herself in front of the cheerful blaze. How much she owed Donald and Della, she mused. Probably her life, and the lives of her children. She paid Della a pittance to cook their meals and keep up with the house. With the low rent Donald charged, she'd been able to put money aside for Betsy's tuition. Still, it wasn't enough. Earlier in the summer she'd been sitting at the kitchen table going over her finances, trying to figure out where she could juggle, whom not to pay so Betsy could go to the school of her choice, when Donald and Della had joined her in the kitchen. Donald had a bankbook in his hand and handed it over. All the deposits were the same, her monthly rent for years. His voice gruff, jerky, he'd said, "Della and I don't have much use for this. It's just sitting here drawing interest. I have my pension and the rental from two other houses, so it would please us if you used this for Betsy's college."

"We want to do this, Kate," Della had added. "We feel like we're the girls' grandparents, and grandparents always help out. It's not a loan, we're giving it to you. If you have trouble with that, we can call it a loan and you can pay us back when you're rich and successful." God, she'd cried that day—no, howled like a banshee would be more like it.

Later she'd thought about her parents back in New Jersey. She'd asked them for a loan and had been turned down cold. Business wasn't good, they had the grandparents to take care of. She'd hung up the phone and cried some more.

They'd seen her only once in ten years. They never wrote, never called. Gradually she'd stopped calling and writing, too.

Kate marched out to the kitchen to look for her address book. She always kept it in the cabinet with the tea bags and coffee. She reached for it and flipped it to Bill Percy's number, not caring that it was ten o'clock at night. She identified herself, went through the amenities, then charged ahead, drawing a deep breath as she did so.

"I'd like an update, Bill, on my husband's situation. It's been eleven years. Surely the government is willing to say *something*. If Patrick is dead, I want to know that so I can hold a service. I need to know. I'm not the same weak-kneed person I was when you and I last met. I've got a backbone now, and it's stiff, Bill. With resolve."

"You sound like Elizabeth, Kate. I think you two are working at cross purposes here."

"Elizabeth who? What are you talking about?" Kate said irritably, certain Percy was going to give her the brush-off, as he had in the past.

"Come now, Kate," he said snidely. "Elizabeth Starr, your daughter. Are you saying you don't know about her involvement in all the groups she's joined since going East?"

"No, I don't know what she's involved in. But if she is, what of it? At least she's *doing* something. Something you and your superiors should be doing, getting me and others like me news of our husbands. Now, I want some answers, and I want them now, damn you!"

"Would you like me to make up something just to make you happy? I can't do that, Kate."

"Then declare my husband dead or tell me he's POW. And don't you ever insult my intelligence by telling me there are no POWs over there anymore. I know there are."

"Kate, it's ten minutes past ten. There's nothing I can do at this hour. We're coming up on to Christmas. A lot of the . . . officers have taken leave for the holidays. I'll get back to you in a day or so."

"I'll give you a day or so, but no longer. And you'd better come back to me with *news . . . information*, something concrete."

"I'll do my best," Percy said quietly.

"Your best isn't going to do it this time, Bill. This time you're going to have to actually *do* something. Good night, Bill, and . . . Merry Christmas."

Kate had no idea if the airman returned her greeting or not as she hung up the phone. Now Betsy's trip to Boston made a little more sense. An overwhelming sense of relief washed over her. The Bill Percys of the world wouldn't be able to slough off Betsy, she simply wouldn't allow it. Which doesn't say much for me, Kate thought.

Grim-faced, she got out her writing paper and a pen and composed a letter to the President of the United States and one to the editor-in-chief of the *New York Times*. Both would be ready to mail when Percy got back to her on Friday.

She had just finished and was settling in on the couch when Ellie came in at eleven o'clock.

"How's it going, Mom?" she asked, curling up on the floor at her mother's feet. Kate told her. "Wow, I bet Betsy gets some results. Nobody shuts that girl up. In this instance it might be good for her, for us, too. Do you believe Dad is still alive, Mom?"

"Part of me believes it, part of me doesn't. If your father was alive, I think we would have heard something by now. I know you don't believe it. You always were the realistic one."

"If he did come back, I wonder what he'd be like? How would he react to us? We're all grown up now. And look at you, Mom, you're a smart dresser these days, you're fashionable and worldly, too. You have a job and are going into business for yourself. You went back to school, got a degree. He wouldn't know what to make of you." Ellie giggled.

"I don't think he'd like this new person I am," Kate said sadly.

"Aw, Mom, now you sound like Betsy. He'd be so proud of you he'd just bust. Are you really going to type up those letters and mail them out?"

"With copies to everyone I can think of. It's damn well time I received an answer I can live with. We need to lay your father to rest. It's that simple."

"We can do that, Mom. We can have a private service, buy a plot in a cemetery, put up a stone and visit. You never did go through Dad's things. Those two metal boxes are still in the cellar. Maybe what we could do—what we *should* do—is bury those. On Sundays we can take flowers, or when you feel the need to talk to Dad, you can have a place to visit. If you think it's a good idea, I'm for it."

"Betsy will never agree."

"But the way I look at it, she's outnumbered. It'll be private, just us. No one else needs to know."

"What if . . . if by some miracle your father does come back? What do we do then?" Kate asked.

"Then we take down the stone, dig up the boxes and . . . and say Betsy made us do it," Ellie said, breaking into a fit of hysterical laughter.

Kate smiled in spite of herself.

"I think Dad would understand," Ellie said. "Look, you don't have to decide now, but the new year would be a good time to . . . to make a new beginning. Maybe . . . maybe we could do it between Christmas and New Year's. We can start fresh then. Think about it, okay?"

"Sure. Now I think you should be in bed, young lady, tomorrow is a school day."

"Would you like me to make you a cup of tea before I go upstairs?"

"No, I'm fine. I'll be up soon. Ellie, did you ever . . . feel like I neglected you, that I didn't do my best? Do you think I should have done more where your father is concerned?"

"No, to all your questions," Ellie said, hugging her mother.

"Betsy does."

"Betsy expected you to be her slave, as well as her mother and father. If she had her way, she would have had you grow a telephone out of the side of your head and single-handedly take on the U.S. government and the entire Air Force. Mom, you did your best. Someday Betsy will understand that. And if that day never comes, we'll live with it. 'Night, Mom."

"Good night, Ellie, sleep tight."

Alone, Kate added another log to the fire, then curled back up on the couch. How many lonely nights she'd sat like this, dreaming and hoping for the impossible. And on most of those nights, she'd cried herself to sleep. Memories were wonderful, but they could also be one's undoing. It was time to lock up those memories. Ellie was right, the new year would be a perfect time for a new start on life.

There was one decision she had to make before she could contemplate Ellie's plan. She had to make the decision to give up Patrick's pay and file for his insurance. She'd need a lawyer for that. It wouldn't do any good to declare Patrick dead and continue to take his monthly pay. Either she was going to do it right or not at all. Numbers swam behind her weary eyelids. The government would fight her, that much she knew. Therefore she couldn't count on her husband's insurance. She'd truly be on her own. If I have to, I can get a job working evenings as a waitress, she told herself. I can do whatever I have to do to make a clean start.

When Kate, Donald, and Della entered the house on Friday evening at six-thirty, the phone was ringing. Kate knew it was Bill Percy before she picked up the receiver.

"What do you have for me, Bill?"

Percy cleared his throat. "There is no news, Kate. Captain Starr cannot be declared dead until we have some sort of evidence from the Vietnamese government. Their position is the same, there are no POWs in Vietnam."

"Patrick isn't a POW, he's an MIA. Where is my husband, Bill? You sent him over there, so it's up to you to find him. For eleven years you've been feeding me the same stale, sorry line, and I'm sick and tired of it. I gave you my husband, and now you're telling me you can't find him, that there are no records. Well, I'm telling you I want something. I'm mailing a letter to the President, to everyone in the world if I have to. I want to know what happened to my children's father, to my husband. All you're concerned with is your top-secret crap and the lies you tell us. It is so hard for me to believe how shabbily you've treated me and the girls. It isn't fair. We're in limbo. You're ruining our lives, can't you see that?"

"Kate, when I have news, I'll call you. Have a nice Christmas."

"You son of a bitch!" Kate's hand flew to her mouth and she turned to face her friends. "I'm sorry, I never swore like that in my life. He makes me so . . . so angry. He thinks he has me over a barrel, that I won't do anything. He actually told me to have a nice Christmas. I'd like to drop a ten-ton rock right on his head!"

"Now, calm down, Kate, you knew he was going to say what he did," Donald said soothingly.

"I hoped, Donald. God, how I hoped," Kate said sadly. "I thought if I threatened, there would be some small kernel of information. But no one cares. Why is that?"

"I don't know. Tomorrow, mail your letters. I called the church, and the service is scheduled for December twenty-seventh at ten o'clock. Della and I picked out a nice plot and ordered the stone. I know a handyman who will come over in the morning and transport the boxes of personal effects to the cemetery. Are you going to open them?"

"I don't think I can do that, Donald. No, no, I'm not. I don't want to make this any harder on Ellie than it is. I called an attorney recommended to me by my old boss and he's going to open the office and see me tomorrow. He's a Vietnam vet. He said he wouldn't charge me, do you believe that? He said . . . he said he'd be honored to attend Patrick's service and speak if I wanted him to. I said yes, knowing I would choke up. Somebody has to say something, not some strange minister Patrick didn't know. I think it's the right thing to do. At least it seemed like it at the time. What do you think?"

"I think you did right," Donald said. Della nodded agreement.

"Then it's settled. Nicholas Mancuso will speak at Patrick's service. He's nice, you'll like him. He said all the right things, said he knew how I felt, said he knew how guys like Percy operated, and he said—and this is a direct quote—'Don't believe their bullshit, some of our guys are still over there.' He was wearing an MIA bracelet like we all wear. He made me feel good, and said the burial will shake them up."

"Ellie's working late," Della said. "I probably shouldn't tell you this, but the child has been putting in extra hours so she can get you something nice for Christmas. Now don't you let on you know or be cross with her for working the extra hours."

"Okay, Della. I don't suppose there's any mail from Betsy. I wonder if she'll send us a card?"

"I'm sorry, Kate, no. Just the usual mail."

Kate mailed her letters the following morning. She had no great hopes or expectations that either the President of the United States or the awesome *New York Times* would respond.

She managed to get through the days until Christmas, although she felt high-strung, irritable, and moody. She cried a lot as she packed up the things Patrick had left behind. She was doing, by her own choice, what millions of people did when a loved one passed on.

"Maybe . . . maybe this is all wrong, Della," she said with a catch in her voice. "Surely it won't hurt if I put all these things in the cellar. I never go down there, I won't have to see them, but I'll know they're there. It won't be over then. I'll still be Kate Starr, wife of Captain Starr MIA. Am I really doing the right thing?"

"If you want to get on with your life, you're doing the right thing. Does it feel right or wrong?" Della asked quietly.

Kate kicked the box sitting at her feet. "It feels right *and* wrong. My God, what if by some miracle Patrick does come back? How will I ever explain? He'll . . . Lord, I don't know what he would think. . . ." Her shoulders squared imperceptibly. "I guess it's too late to worry about that now."

Della patted Kate's shoulder. "You used the right word a minute ago. It would be a miracle if Patrick came back, and miracles are pretty hard to come by these days. Donald and I both think you're being brave and realistic. For you it's right. You go upstairs and get dressed. I'll transfer these things to that old trunk Donald had in the cellar. They're due to be picked up any minute now."

Kate needed no second urging. Upstairs, Ellie was putting the finishing touches to her hair. "How do I look, Mom?"

"You look nice, Ellie. Your father would . . . he would be so . . . Oh, I can't think straight this morning," Kate said distractedly. "Come into my room and talk to me while I get dressed."

Ellie watched as her mother slipped on a deep brown wool dress with a flared skirt. She cinched it at the waist with a gold and brown braided belt that Ellie had braided for her mother at the YWCA day camp when she was ten or so. Kate brushed her hair, added a slash of lipstick and a smear of rouge across her cheekbones. She finished off with a bright orange scarf around her neck. "We have to remember, this is not exactly a funeral, but a service. Or is it a funeral?" Kate asked jerkily.

"I suppose it's a little of both. We are burying something— all that remains of Dad."

Kate removed the orange scarf. "That's how I think of it. Yes, that's a good way for us to think of it. When we come home, it will . . . it will be all over. We can cry for a few days. We're going to cry, Ellie, at least I will. Then on New Year's we'll . . . we'll get up and . . . go on. I don't know how we'll feel that morning . . . probably sad and . . . probably guilty. For some reason I always feel guilty when I think about your father. I don't know why that is. Do you?"

Ellie shook her head. "If I had to take a guess, I'd say it's because you're still alive and Dad isn't. Time to go, Mom." She took her mother's arm.

"Betsy is never going to forgive me for this," Kate said tightly. "Or you for going along with it."

"I know that. Do I look worried? I wrote her a letter last week. Don't get nervous, it was a nice letter. I explained how I felt and how I thought you felt. I did kind of ream her out for not giving us an address or telephone number where we could reach her. Her going away for Christmas was unforgivable."

"Ellie, you do understand that I'm giving up your father's pay by doing this? It's going to be hard for us to manage, and I can't keep taking from Della and Donald."

"Don't worry about it. I can live on baked beans and toast if I have to. I'll be working full-time this summer, and I can go to the community college if I have to. None of that's important to me. What's important is that what we're doing is going to affect the rest of our lives. Now wipe that grim look off your face or Della will start to cry, and when Della cries, we need towels," Ellie said, striving for a light tone.

"I paid cash for the cemetery plot. They wanted me to buy two, you know, for when I . . . I had to say no, I didn't have the money. My God, imagine not having enough money to bury yourself." Kate stopped at the bottom of the steps and looked at her daughter. "That's not important, either, is it?"

"Not in the least. I'm kind of glad you didn't take the plot on time payments."

A smile tugged at the corners of Kate's mouth.

When they reached the cemetery, Kate was stunned to see a crowd of people around the spot she'd chosen for Patrick's service. The minister was there in his clerical garb, along with a host of men dressed in suits and ties. The only person she recognized was Nick Mancuso. The others, she decided, must be friends coming to . . . what? Pay their respects? Gawk at these unorthodox proceedings? No. She raised her eyes and met those of a man standing at the outer rim of the half circle. Even from this distance she could see the tears in his eyes. No, never to gawk, only to pay their respects. She could feel moisture build behind her own eyelids.

Della pushed Donald's chair over the spiky grass, and Ellie walked alongside her, her arm linked with hers. Kate acknowledged each man and thanked them for coming.

The service began.

Fifteen minutes later it was over. As the vets filed past Kate they handed her a white flower. She nodded her thanks, tears streaming down her cheeks. Nick Mancuso was the last to hand her his flower. "I don't think this was wrong, Kate. I know how hard it is for you. I'll talk to you in a few days," he said, and drifted away.

"I should thank the minister," Kate murmured to Della as the crowd dispersed.

"He's already gone, Kate," Della told her. "I think this was uncomfortable for him. It doesn't matter. Who's that man standing over by the angel stone? I saw him taking pictures before."

"I have no idea. I assume he's one of Mr. Mancuso's people. Why don't you three go back to the car. I need a few minutes here alone. I'm okay, don't worry about me, I can handle this. I just need a few moments of private time."

"Mom, I don't think—"

"I need you to help me push Donald's chair," Della said to Ellie. "The ground is too rough here."

"Go along, honey. It's all right," Kate said soothingly.

Kate stared at Donald's old battered trunk and the two gun-metal gray boxes the Air Force had sent on that she'd never opened. She was dry-eyed now, almost angry. She started to shiver, felt her knees weaken when she felt a presence next to her. She raised defiant eyes to stare at the stranger who had been taking pictures. She stared at him for a full minute before she shrugged off his arm. He was young, twenty-eight or so, with summer-blue eyes and a thatch of unruly curls crowning the top of his head. Freckles marched across the bridge of his nose and cheekbones, ending at his dark hairline. She just knew he hated the freckles and his curly hair. She sensed his tallness, his thinness, when her eyes returned to the three trunks in front of her. "I need to say good-bye alone. I appreciate your coming here, but you should have left with the others. Please, I don't want to be rude, I just need to say good—good-bye alone."

His voice was deep, soothing. "I'm sorry, Mrs. Starr, I didn't mean to intrude. I thought you were going . . . to faint." She nodded, sensed him moving backward. And then she forgot him entirely.

Kate moved forward to place the white flowers on top of the gray metal trunks. What should she say, how should she say it? "I love you, Patrick. I'll always love you." But was that true? Would she always love him? She squeezed her eyes shut and willed his face to appear. Satisfied with the vision behind her closed lids, Kate whispered, "Good-bye, Patrick."

She turned, stumbled, and would have fallen if the man

behind her hadn't reached for her arm. "Easy does it, Mrs. Starr."

"Thank you, Mister . . ."

"Stewart. Gustav Stewart. My friends call me Gus. I'm from the *New York Times*, Mrs. Starr. Your letter was turned over to me. I'd like to talk with you and your daughter. I know this probably isn't the best time, but I flew here at my own expense, and I have to get back to work. I'd like to do a human-interest story on Captain Starr and your family." He was leading her back to the car, and she was following him like a lost puppy.

"Human interest!" she yelped when they reached the car.

Stewart held up both hands. "Whoa, it's not what you think. When *I* say human interest, I mean to make the world aware of what happened to Captain Starr and your family. This . . . service is, to my knowledge, the first of its kind. I think people need to know about this. I'm a good reporter, Mrs. Starr. I'd like you to trust me. I'll even show you the article before I turn it in, in case there's anything you object to or want to change. You did write to us. Did you have something else in mind?" There was such compassion in the reporter's eyes, Kate wanted to cry.

"I don't know what I meant, what I expected. I had to do something. No one was helping me, I didn't know what else to do. I don't think I really thought beyond mailing the letter. I guess I assumed your paper would research the MIAs and speak to the wives. Give us recognition. Eleven years is a long time to be told the same thing. We don't know anything. It's not just me, Mr. Stewart, there are other wives out there in the same place. We gave up our husbands, and now we're like pariahs. Look, if you want, come back to the house with me. We can talk where it's warm over a cup of coffee. Follow us."

It was nine o'clock when Gus Stewart left the Starr house. He felt as if he were carrying a hundred-pound burden on his shoulders. In his gut he carried an even heavier weight. He would do the story, but would it get printed? He'd been given this assignment because he was young, a cub reporter, and none of the pros wanted it. He hadn't lied when he'd told Kate he was a good reporter. His eyes and ears were tuned to the world seven days a week. All the way home on the red-eye his stomach churned. If he handled this just right, it might turn out to be something really big. It wasn't going to be something he dashed off to meet a deadline, either. He had names now, other leads, copies of letters, and he'd get more. He might get an entire feature article and really do some good for the MIAs. He'd even work on it on his own time if it would help. It wasn't going to be the Pulitzer he dreamed of, but damn close.

He liked Kate Starr, really liked her. No matter what, he was going to stay in touch with her. Jesus, imagine burying a guy's belongings because there was nothing else left. What was it she'd said? "For now, this is acceptable. We have a place to go, a place to mourn, a place where we're able to say good-bye."

In his opinion, Kate Starr was a hell of a woman. He couldn't help but wonder if she would be able to handle the fallout if the story got printed. His stomach started to churn again. He grinned in the darkened plane. Kate Starr, he thought, was probably capable of handling anything.

Gus scrunched himself into his window seat. Kate's last words were, "I have a right to know." That's what he was going to call his feature story. Only he would change it to read, *"They Have a Right to Know,"* meaning all the wives of the missing MIAs. And he would feature Kate Starr and her family in the article.

Unfortunately, it didn't work out that way for Gus Stewart or Kate Starr. None of the other wives were as brave as Kate;

they feared the loss of their husbands' pay if they went public and broke the "keep quiet" policy they'd adhered to in the past. They did talk freely and willingly, but in confidence, always ending with, "This is off the record, please don't print what I'm saying."

Gus grew frustrated, angry at the military and the government. He finally began to realize how Kate and the other wives felt. Everywhere he turned he was stonewalled. When he finally called Kate on a late June afternoon to tell her the story had been killed for the third time, she showed no surprise.

"I'm sorry, Gus. I know you worked hard. In a way, you can't blame the wives. A lot of them don't have a Della and a Donald like I do. We tried, that's the important thing. If you ever find yourself in my neighborhood, stop by and I'll take you to dinner."

"You can afford dinner out?" Gus joked.

"A hot dog from a street vendor, maybe a bottle of soda pop."

"How's business? Any regrets?"

"Business is great. I'm making my bills and have a little left over every month. I don't have enough hours in the day. I've been thinking of hiring some part-time help. I've had to turn down three jobs in L.A. because I can't be away from the office. Then there are days when I sit here sucking my thumb and hoping a job will come in."

He didn't want to hang up. It didn't sound like she wanted to, either. "How's Della and Donald?"

"Donald is in pain a lot of the time. Della fusses over him something fierce. They still come over every day."

"And Ellie?"

"Ellie's working full-time for the supermarket, doing the bookkeeping. We have her scheduled for West Chester University in Pennsylvania in the fall. They have a very good accounting department. If my business keeps going the way it has been, tuition won't be a problem."

"You're working seven days a week, aren't you?" Gus challenged.

"Now where did you hear that?"

Gus chuckled. "I just guessed."

"It's the only way I can get ahead. Della makes it easy for me. I've had to get glasses, though. Ellie says I look like an owl."

Gus laughed. "Kate, I really am sorry about the article. I'm not quitting on you. If there's ever an opportunity, or if things change, I'll be right there with it. I just wish there was more I could do."

"You tried. That's more than anyone else was willing to do."

"Call me sometime, okay?" Gus said gruffly.

"You bet. We're friends, aren't we?"

"Yes, yes, we are. I'm going to hold you to that dinner, now."

"I'll start saving now." Kate laughed. " 'Bye, Gus."

" 'Bye, Kate."

CHAPTER

10

It was seven years before Kate saw Gus Stewart again, and then it was by pure accident.

The airport was noisy, crowded with hordes of travelers following tour guides with feathers in their hats for easy identification.

As she entered the rest room on the concourse, Kate wondered—and not for the first time—what she was doing back in her home state of New Jersey. She could just as easily have vacationed at home in bed or in the garden with a book. But, no, that was too easy; she had to come back here and torture herself.

She made a face at herself in the mirror as she applied lipstick, washed her hands, and brushed her hair. She looked nice, moderately professional in a crisp blue-and-white seersucker suit that wasn't exactly crisp at this point. She grimaced at herself again, then straightened the strap of her handbag and marched back out to the concourse.

Her plan was to rent a car, drive to Westfield, cruise past the house she'd grown up in, maybe knock on the door to see who now lived in the house since her parents retired to Florida. Then she'd drive by Patrick's old house, maybe knock on that door. She'd drive through town, go past the church, stop at the library, maybe go in the school and look at her high school class picture on the wall, check out Patrick's picture, too. Then she'd get on the parkway and head for Toms River to check out Patrick's father's house, which had been left to her last year when her father-in-law died. She'd wanted to sell that house, but the attorneys had said that without Patrick's death certificate she couldn't. She should think about renting it, though, to help pay the taxes.

Kate glanced around the concourse to get her bearings and then heard her name being called—not over the loudspeaker, but close at hand. She turned.

"Kate! Kate Starr!"

For a moment she couldn't remember his name, and then it came to her. "Gus! How nice to see you again. What are you doing here? It must be, what, seven years? You look well."

"Ten pounds heavier." Gus laughed. "What are *you* doing here? Too much air traffic over Kennedy, so our pilot landed here. I'll take a ground shuttle into the city. God, it's good to see you. Listen, are you making connections or do you have to be somewhere at a certain time? If not, let's head for the nearest bar and get a drink. I could use a sandwich. I couldn't figure out what it was they served for lunch on the plane, so I passed on it."

"My time is my own. I could use a drink. Only one, though, I'm driving."

"They'll hold your bags if you checked them. Car rental companies are good about late arrivals. See," he said, throwing his hands in the air, "it's all taken care of. Let's dine in this . . . this whatever it is." He motioned to a publike room that had a bar with a brass railing along the sides.

Settled, with menus in their hands, Gus leaned across the table. "Kate, it's so good to see you. How's everything going? You look great."

Kate could feel a warm flush creep up her cheeks. He's flirting with me, she thought, stunned. Seven years ago he'd looked boyishly young. Now he looked mature and . . . *sexy*.

"You look pretty good yourself," she blurted. "I'd kill for your eyelashes and those summer-blue eyes—" God, *she* was flirting. Actually flirting! With a *younger* man. A delicious thrill coursed through her.

"Bet you're beating off the architects with a stick, huh?"

"Hardly." Kate laughed ruefully. "I really have no time for a social life. Occasionally I have a business lunch or dinner, but that's it. I'm trying real hard to make a success of my business. What free time I do have, I help Della. Donald isn't well, and he takes a lot of care. He's crippled with arthritis and he's in constant pain, but he still manages to smile. He's eighty-two. I can't believe it. Where have the years gone?" she said breathlessly.

The waitress hovered. "Kate, what will you have?" Gus asked.

"A pastrami on rye with lots of mustard, and a Michelob."

"Make that two," Gus said, handing over the menus. "How's Ellie?"

Kate preened. "She finally passed the last part of the CPA exam in the fall of last year. She's a bona fide CPA, and I was her first client. Well, Architectural Renderings was her first client. I'm so proud of her."

Gus laughed. "I can tell. Are you still living in the same place with that beautiful garden?"

"No, unfortunately. Three years ago a developer wanted to buy most of the area, three or four entire streets. Everyone sold but Donald. He held out to the last minute to drive up the price, and got a fortune—and I mean a fortune—for the house I rented, his house, and that other little rental property he owned. The four of us lived in an apartment for over a year while he had a house built for us. It's so beautiful, all redwood and glass and very modern. He had a guest house built on the lot, which I thought Ellie and I would live in, but he wouldn't hear of it. So we live in the big house and he and Della live in the cottage. We have a swimming pool, a cabana, and a three-car garage." He was so easy to talk to, Kate thought. "Oh, oh, wait, we even have a Sundance hot tub. It's for Donald. We got this . . . contraption that lifts him out of the wheelchair and puts him in the tub, clothes and all. He loves it, and it really helps his arthritis."

"I like hot tubs. They have one at the gym where I work out. Do you ever go in it?"

"Once or twice. By the time we get Donald in and out, we're too tired to go in ourselves."

The waitress poured their beer. Gus held his glass aloft. "What should we drink to?"

Kate pretended to think. "Chance meetings? Friendship? Airports? Or all of the above?"

Gus nodded. Glasses clinked. The sandwiches arrived, warm and full of oozing, spicy, brown mustard.

"Now this is good," Gus said, munching happily.

He's nice, Kate thought. I like him. "Tell me about you," she said, her eyes watering from the tangy mustard.

"Well, I haven't written my Pulitzer yet. I will someday, you know. I've covered some good stories, gotten my share of bylines. The pay isn't going to get me a hot tub on my patio on Forty-ninth Street. My mother said if you can buy one good suit a year, pay your rent, feed yourself, and give in the collection box every Sunday, you have nothing to complain about."

"A wise woman," Kate said, smiling. She wondered what

it would be like to have a male friend, one she could call on the phone at any time and just talk.

"How's your other daughter, Betsy?"

Kate laid down her sandwich. "I rarely talk to her. She went on to get her master's and doctorate. She teaches now at Villanova University. I see her once a year and she calls every so often. She's never forgiven me for that . . . 'funeral' we had. I understand she's very active in several Vietnam organizations. She doesn't talk to me about what she does. What little information I have I get from Ellie, who gets it from a friend of Betsy's." She hesitated. "You know, what really bothered me most about leaving our home was Betsy's garden. Do you remember that glorious rainbow of flowers she planted around the house? I tried to duplicate that garden a hundred times over the past three years, with no luck. Ellie says Betsy planted them with love and a pure heart, and that's why God made them grow for her. I took pictures from a neighbor's roof before we left and had it enlarged. It's hanging over the mantel now. I think that's my only regret at this point in my life." Kate picked up her sandwich and bit into it.

"Where are you going when you leave here?" Gus asked. "How about us having dinner?"

"We're eating now." Kate laughed. "I was going to Westfield and stir up some old memories, but since I met you, I think I'll just get on the parkway and head for Toms River. I'd like to get settled in before dark." She went on to tell him about her father-in-law's house. "Thanks for the invitation, though. This monstrous sandwich will hold me over until tomorrow morning."

"I love the beach, the sun, blue skies," Gus said wistfully.

"Melanomas . . . tsk, tsk," Kate said, clucking her tongue.

"I wear a number-fifteen sun block. I manage to get down to Point Pleasant three or four times during the summer. I've always been a beach person."

Kate knew he was hinting for an invitation. Should she or shouldn't she? *Definitely not. Absolutely not.* "Maybe you could come down this weekend. Saturday morning, Sunday if you prefer. I can make dinner or lunch." *Breakfast. Definitely not. Absolutely not.* "Or if you get an early start, breakfast."

"Hell yes, I'll come. Thanks for inviting me. Hey, have you ever been to Atlantic City?"

"No, never. I'm not a gambler."

"Me, either, I work too hard for my money. But it's a good way to spend a Saturday night."

"With or without a date?" Kate asked, and could have bitten off her tongue.

"A couple of friends. They think they're going to strike it rich. I watch."

"Don't you have a girlfriend?" Kate asked. She felt her ears grow warm. What in the world was the matter with her? He was a puppy, a warm, endearing puppy. Thirty-one at the most. There was at least fourteen years' difference in their ages.

"I have dates from time to time, but there isn't anyone serious in my life. Like you, I have very little spare time. I'm usually working on a story or doing my Big Brother bit at the Y. Is that a frown building on your face? Look, I come with references. I'm not a stranger, we met before. Kids and dogs like me. Old people think I'm nice. I have a decent job. I don't smoke or drink. Well, hardly ever." He grinned when Kate lit one of her stress relievers and offered him one, which he took with no hesitation. "Terrible habit."

"The worst. But if you look at it as a stress reliever, and taking a drink as an attitude adjuster, it doesn't seem so bad. This is the first vacation I've had in five years."

"That's not good," he said. "Everyone needs a break, even if it's to go to a hotel for the weekend. I make sure I take mine every year. I come back full of spit and vinegar. Shame on you," he teased.

"It's not that easy when you're in business for yourself. You have to stay on top of things. I have two assistants now and I moved into a larger office space. I'm still spread pretty thin, though. I wouldn't exactly say I'm in demand, but I've built up a good business reputation and my prices are fair. Believe it or not, I turn down work if I feel I can't give it one hundred percent. I have money in the bank, I repaid Della and Donald, I managed to put Betsy and Ellie both through college and still paid for Betsy's master's and doctorate," Kate said proudly.

"And I knew you when you were sweating Ellie's tuition. You should be proud."

"I am, but I could never have done it on my own. Every day of my life I thank God for those two."

The waitress ambled over with the check in her hand. Gus handed her a twenty-dollar bill. "I think she's trying to tell us she needs this table."

Kate looked up to see a line of people at the entrance. "I think you're right, and I hope you're right about our baggage being safe. I'd hate to think I'm going to be walking on the beach in this suit and high heels."

"Not to worry. I'd lend you a pair of skivvies and a T-shirt," Gus said, picking up her carryall. Kate stumbled, certain her face was as red as the carpet she was walking on.

Kate found her bag sitting with six others at the end of the carousel. "I guess I'll see you on Saturday, Gus. Thanks for lunch, I really enjoyed it."

"My pleasure." Gus grinned. "See you," he said, kissing her lightly on the cheek before loping off to catch his shuttle bus.

Kate smiled the whole time she was checking out the Lincoln Town Car she'd rented. She was still smiling when she signed her name and picked up her keys. Then a whirlwind of motion behind her made her turn. In all her life she'd never seen anyone so frazzled: curly hair standing at attention, shirt dragged halfway down his arm with the weight of his suit bags, eyes full of . . . was it terror?

"What's wrong?" Kate asked anxiously.

"You forgot to give me the damn address!" Gus sputtered, sweat rolling down his face.

"Oh. You didn't ask," Kate said lamely. "I'll write it down."

"Jesus, no, don't write it down. If you write it down, that means I have to put all this stuff down, and I'll never be able to harness myself again. Just tell me what it is."

Kate laughed. "It's Eighty-eight Rosemont Road."

Gus trundled off, his bags flapping against his knees as he muttered over and over, "Eighty-eight Rosemont Road."

Kate alternated between smiling and giggling as she drove the rental car down the service road and out through the toll booth onto the New Jersey Turnpike.

What kind of clothes had she brought? For the life of her she couldn't remember. Well, she could always go to the mall and buy some new things. What did a forty-four-year-old woman wear on the beach with a man who was at least fourteen years younger? She wasn't exactly ugly, but she wasn't going to be any match for the young beach bunnies with their golden tans and string bikinis. She groaned, feeling every one of her forty-four years.

Maybe they'd run on the beach. Running was good. Would her thighs jiggle? Running was not good. Sweatpants, thin cotton ones. A baggy overblouse, again thin cotton. She wouldn't look so white and . . . slightly overweight. Maybe she'd pick up one of those Indian cotton mumu things women wore on the beach. Those things covered *everything*.

God, what if Gus made . . . advances? How would she handle that? Was she jumping the gun here? She did have an active imagination. He was just coming for the day. Just to get out of the city and . . . and just enough for the day. There was nothing wrong with two people walking on the beach, eating together, talking together, having a drink together. So what if he was about thirty and she was forty-four? He knew how old she was. He knew everything there was to know about her. Ellie would say, "Oooh, he issssss delicious." Kate broke into a peal of laughter when she drove the car into the driveway.

Saturday was only a day away.

CHAPTER
11

It was a tidy little four-room house in a retirement village. Patrick's father had always been a tidy man, much like Patrick. The furniture was old, shabby, from a long-ago era. Tears pricked Kate's eyes when she ran her hand over the back of the sofa. How many times she and Patrick had cuddled and necked in the corner. It had to be fifty years old at least, yet it wasn't junk, nor was it an antique. It was just old, shabby, and full of stains.

In many ways the box of a house was a memorial to Patrick. His pictures were everywhere. Kate wished now she'd done more, but the elder Starr had been a private person and not one to show interest or love for anyone. She'd done her best, sending cards, small gifts on Father's Day, his birthday, and Christmas. She'd sent the girls' school pictures faithfully, even though he never responded.

She felt like an intruder as she walked through the house. It was hers now. Maybe she shouldn't rent it. What in the world would she do with all of her father-in-law's belongings? Send them off to California? Store them in the basement or the garage until she died herself and the girls had to go through her things? Better to leave the house empty, pay the taxes and insurance, and thank God she was able to do it.

She busied herself then, unpacking, washing the linens for the bed, and dusting. She ran the dishes she thought she would need through the dishwasher. It was eleven o'clock when she pushed the upright Hoover vacuum cleaner back into the closet.

Kate scanned her appearance in the bathroom mirror. She looked presentable enough to go to Pizza Hut for her dinner and to the 7-Eleven for her breakfast. She ate, showered, and was in bed by twelve-thirty, but she couldn't sleep. The street outside bathed the front bedroom in a yellowish glow even though the white shade was drawn to the sill. Patrick's picture glared at her from the dresser. She got up, turned the photograph facedown, and got back into bed. Still she couldn't sleep. She got up again and slid the picture into the top drawer of the dresser. When she got back into bed, she fell asleep instantly and slept soundly, awakening at six o'clock to the sound of birds chirping.

Good Lord, what was she to do with herself all day? At eight o'clock she could go next door and ask to use the phone to call the telephone company to turn on the phone. She could call Della and Ellie and talk to them, call her office and talk to the receptionist. She could go shopping or walk on the beach, but that meant she'd have to get in the car and drive. "You are lazy, Kate Starr," she muttered as she poured coffee into an earthenware mug.

Patrick had sat at this table for his meals from the time he was old enough to eat with the family until he left for college. The top of the table was badly scarred and gouged. She'd eaten at this same table several times when Patrick had invited her to their old house in Westfield. It was a memory now. How sad that there were no male Starrs to carry on the name. She'd been so sure Ellie was going to be a boy by the way she'd carried her. She'd even managed to convince Patrick of it. How clearly she remembered his look of disappointment at the hospital when he'd learned otherwise. Maybe that was why Betsy was his favorite. Maybe a lot of things, she thought sadly.

"I wonder," she said aloud, "what it would be like to kiss another man." She propped her chin into the palm of her hand as she tried to remember what it felt like when Patrick kissed her. It must have been wonderful because the sex was good, at times. She always enjoyed the pillow talk, but Patrick was usually asleep in seconds, and when she chastised him, he'd say, "Honey, it's a compliment to you. It was great and you wore me out." A memory, nothing more.

"I'm beginning to wonder, Patrick, if I ever liked you. I know I was in love with you, but I don't think I liked you," Kate mumbled as she drained her coffee. "And it's taken me eighteen years to figure that out." It was a mistake to come here; she should have stayed in California, gone to the library for rest and relaxation. She didn't need these trips down Memory Lane. That was all behind her.

In the bathroom she pulled on a pair of jeans that were snug around the waist and a Banana Republic T-shirt. She slid her sockless feet into a pair of Keds. There was something she could do; she could go back to Westfield, buy some flowers, and visit the cemetery where her father-in-law was buried. She'd stop at the first phone booth she came to and call the phone company. This way she wouldn't have to bother the neighbors.

The word *pilgrimage* flew into Kate's mind when she pulled to the curb in front of her old house. She tossed the

150

word away immediately. She was merely a lookie-look, checking out the old neighborhood. The house looked shabby and run-down, grass growing between the cracks in the driveway. The lawn was brown in some spots, bare in others. One of the front windows was cracked, and the paint on the front door was peeling. There didn't seem to be any curtains on the second-floor windows. She didn't feel anything when she drove around the corner to Patrick's old house. She stared at it, thought about Patrick running down the front steps to meet her on the sidewalk under the maple tree. He'd kissed her a hundred times under that maple tree. The sidewalk was cracked now where the roots protruded. She remembered how they used to huddle under the umbrellalike branches where the sidewalk was perfectly flat.

Kate drove away and didn't look back.

For lunch she ordered a double cheeseburger and a large order of fries at a Burger King. She told herself she needed the fat to fortify herself for the trip to the cemetery. Then she smoked two cigarettes, sipped a lukewarm cherry Coke, and tried not to think. It was a futile exercise. At last, tires squealing in the parking lot, she pulled out onto the road.

The cemetery was small, quiet, and peaceful. Meandering brick paths wound through the closely cropped grass. Kate knew where the Starr plot was because she'd come here with Patrick to visit his mother's grave when they were both teenagers. They'd sat together on the grass, and she'd held his hand while he cried. He missed her terribly, he'd said, and his father was too busy with his own grief to pay any attention to him. Patrick Starr, Sr., had not been a demonstrative parent in any way. He'd been a stern man, an unyielding man.

"God rest your soul, Mr. Starr," Kate said, laying the bouquet of pink-and-white Shasta daisies near the headstone. Halfway down the brick path she turned and went back. She bent down and undid the wire holding the flowers together at the stem. She picked out seven of the prettiest flowers and laid them beneath the stone that read CHARLOTTE STARR. WIFE. MOTHER. Suddenly she noticed the extra plot. She'd never seen it before, or had never paid attention to it. Why had the Starrs bought it? she wondered. Did some families always have an extra? Whom were they planning to . . . She stiffened. *Maybe Patrick was supposed to be buried here. Oh, God!*

Kate struggled to her feet, stepping on her shoelace. She ran then, the lace slapping at the brick path.

She crawled into the car, her breathing ragged. A fly buzzed past her nose, exiting the window on the passenger side. With trembling hands she lit a cigarette, choking and sputtering on the smoke when she inhaled. She was shaking. Sweat beaded up on her forehead and rolled down into her eyes. Did she have the guts, the strength, to have Patrick's belongings dug up and brought here? Did it matter? She tossed the half-smoked cigarette out the window and fired up a second one.

Nervously she leaned out the car window and looked upward, certain Patrick's parents were there watching her, waiting for her decision. They belonged together, they were family. How many plots had she bought when she'd decided to bury Patrick's things? One? Two? She couldn't remember. If she'd just bought one, then there wasn't room for her when she . . . when she . . . If she moved her husband's things, who would lie next to her when her time came? *Some damn stranger, that's who. Oh, God, oh God.*

She tossed out the second cigarette. The fly was back, buzzing around her head. She swatted at it, missed. "Shit!"

She stuck her head back out the window and yelled, "Okay, okay, I'll give him back . . . *his things*. Maybe I'll have the two boxes the government sent on dug up and shipped back here for . . . for you. I'll keep the trunk I had buried left there so Ellie and I can . . . have a place to visit. That's fair. Yes, that's fair." A cloud rolled by and then another, until there was nothing to see but the summer-blue sky, as blue as Gus Stewart's eyes.

Kate arrived back at the house a little before four o'clock. She turned on the radio, the television, the stove, the oven, and the toaster oven. A minute later she turned them all off. It was something to do. If there had been anything to eat in the house besides puffed rice, she would have eaten it. She always ate when she was under stress. She made a pot of coffee, and while it perked, she called Ellie at her office.

"Honey, listen to me and don't say anything until I'm finished, okay?"

"Sure, Mom," Ellie agreed in her sweet voice.

Kate explained about her day, ending with, "I don't know if it's the right thing to do, so I'm going with my instincts and doing it. Will you make the calls for me, arrange to ship the trunks so they're here by Monday? I'll see if I can find someone on this end to pick them up. Maybe Gus will do it for me."

"Gus who?" Ellie asked instantly.

Kate explained again, saying, "He's coming down tomorrow. He likes the Jersey shore."

Ellie laughed. "What's that I hear in your voice, Mom?"

"Nervousness. Look, don't be getting ideas, Ellie. How is Donald?"

"The same. Della is so worried. He's not eating. I spent an hour last night coaxing him just to eat a little soup. He hates being fed, Mom. He told me he feels like he's losing his dignity, and he absolutely hates that . . . that *thing* Della put on him. Don't worry, though, we're taking real good care of him."

"I know, I know, I hate being such a worrier, but that's the way I am."

"If you want to worry, then worry about what you're going to wear tomorrow for your date. And it is a date, Mom, no matter what you say."

"Ellie, it's not a date. It's a . . . what it is is . . . it is not a date," Kate said, flustered by her daughter's laughter. "For heaven's sake, Ellie, he's only thirty or so! I'm a forty-four-year-old woman."

"Uh-huh," Ellie drawled. "So what are you going to wear?"

"The same thing I'm wearing right now, jeans and a shirt. It's not a date. I don't want you telling Della and Donald, either," Kate said sourly. "I'll never hear the end of it."

"A chance meeting in an airport. I bet they made a movie like that with Ingrid Bergman or somebody," Ellie said dramatically. " 'Bye, Mom, I'll call you when it's all wrapped up on this end."

"Thanks, honey, I'll talk to you later."

"Mom, remember that movie *From Here to Eternity* with Frank Sinatra? You know, where that couple, I can't remember their names, made love on the beach. Well, don't do that, you know how you hate getting sand in your bathing suit."

"Ellie!" Kate sputtered, her cheeks flaming. "I didn't even bring a bathing suit. . . ." But she was talking to a pinging receiver.

Now, why in the world had she ever mentioned Gus Stewart? *Because*, a niggling voice drawled, *you wanted to . . .* What?

"This is stupid," she muttered. Damn stupid. It's not a date. I don't date. Furthermore, I would never date a man that much younger than I am. Good God, do you think I want people to call me a cradle snatcher? "It's not a date!" she wailed.

CHAPTER
12

Kate was sitting on the front stoop waiting for Gus, coffee cup in hand. Dark glasses shaded her eyes from the sun as she watched couples stroll by in sneakers and pedal pushers, their arms linked either in cozy companionship or to hold one another upright. Kate smiled. The retirement park was a busy one, she reflected as an oldster wearing green-and-white-plaid pants and a nifty white blazer pedaled by on a three-wheel trike, his golf clubs in a wire grocery basket hooked onto the back of his wheels. She couldn't help but wonder if Patrick's dour father had participated in the activities provided for the retirement village. She doubted it.

Kate heard people exiting the house next door and glanced in that direction. Her view was obscured at first by an over-large azalea bush. Then her hands flew to her mouth when she saw her neighbors, three couples, hit the sidewalk dressed

155

in western garb. There was a hoedown at the community center, and obviously they were on their way to participate. How wonderful that these retirees were so active, she mused, thinking about Donald and Della and how they'd devoted their lives to her and her family. How much they missed out on by not joining in things designed for their retirement years. "It's by our choice, Kate," Donald always said. "You go to *those places* when your family doesn't want to be bothered with you. We *have* a family, and we take care of them, and we don't have time for such things."

Family was what made the world go 'round.

The street was suddenly quiet again. Kate wished she knew how her father-in-law had passed his time. The last time she'd been here, she'd checked out the community center and had been amazed at the activities. Every hour of the day could be filled if one was so inclined. It bothered her to think that Patrick's father might have spent all his time indoors with the television set. She had to wonder why he'd never invited her or the girls to visit. She gave up further thought when a dark blue Ford Escort wheeled into her driveway. Her guest had arrived.

Kate's breath exploded in a loud *swoosh* sound when Gus climbed from the car. He wore tattered denim shorts and deck shoes. Hairy legs, just like Patrick's. As muscular, too. His oversize T-shirt, stretched out at the neck and hanging crookedly at the hem, announced HARD ROCK CAFE, the burgundy lettering faded to a dull rust color. On his head he wore a Mets baseball cap, and the zippered bag he slung over his shoulders read NIKE in bold white letters. "You are a regular walking advertisement," she said.

"All true," Gus replied, sweeping off his cap and bowing low. "I like being down-and-out comfortable. You make me feel that way, Kate Starr."

Her cheekbones felt warm, and she laughed self-consciously. "Would you like a cup of coffee?"

"Love it. Or would you like to go out to breakfast? Brunch?"

Kate thought about it, then shook her head, remembering her midnight trip to the Shop Rite. She had eggs, Canadian bacon, raisin English muffins, freshly squeezed orange juice, frozen home fries, just-right canteloupes, and plum jam. "I'll make breakfast," she said.

"Good." Gus smacked his hands together and followed her into the house. "There's something about a kitchen that appeals to the kid in me. My apartment has this counter that's supposed to be my kitchen. I eat standing up, no room for chairs."

Kid. He was hardly more than a kid now. "That sounds terrible," Kate said. "We have a marvelous kitchen back home. Every appliance known to man. A center island, pretty tile, cedar beams, and lots and lots of green plants. It's the nicest room in the house. Our table is long and sort of low, with benches we can move so Donald can sit at the table with us. At least he used to. Now Della feeds him separately and he has to wear a bib and—" Kate began to choke up.

Gus's hands shot into the air. "None of that now. Today is my day, yours too. We are going to have fun, lady, just as soon as you feed me. Then," he said, grinning wickedly, "we are going to scoot out and leave the dishes in the sink. What'ya think of that?" He leered at her.

Kate's tongue felt thick. She slapped the succulent Canadian bacon into the frying pan. "What . . . what are we—are you planning?"

"I thought we'd drive to Point Pleasant, hit the beach for an hour or so, and then take in the boardwalk. I'm game for some rides, but none of those spinning things. I get dizzy. We can gorge on greasy killer food that always smells so good, play a little bingo, I'll win you some stuffed animals . . . you know, all that great kid stuff."

157

Kid stuff. She'd never really done any of those things growing up. She and Patrick. "It does sound like fun."

"Sounds like? Trust me, you'll have the time of your life. I am the oldest kid I know," he said proudly. "It's that very quality that endears me to the opposite sex. Women can't wait to get their hands on me. They want to coddle me and cuddle me."

Kate laughed in spite of herself. "I'll keep it in mind."

"I wish you would."

Kate whirled at the tone of his voice. He wasn't bantering now. Confused, she turned back to the eggs she was whipping to a golden froth. "Do me a favor, Gus, in the garage there's a shelf with paper goods on it. Will you get it for me so I can drain this bacon?"

"Sure."

He was gone so long, Kate walked into the garage to see what he was doing. When she spotted him, her breathing seemed to stop. "No!" she shouted. "No, don't touch *that*!"

Gus recoiled as if bitten by a cobra, his arm stretched out in front of him.

"That's—that's—"

"Patrick's bike," Gus said softly. "His father brought it with him when he moved here, eh?"

"Yes . . . I saw it the first time I came here. I couldn't . . . I wanted to touch it. . . . He rode me on the handlebars. . . . The tires are flat."

"I can fix them, Kate, if you want me to," Gus said. "I can get a patch kit and pump them full of air. Hell, I can sand off the rust, too."

"Patrick loved that bike. He delivered papers on it, rode it all over the place, and later, when he got older, he hooked a basket on the back and delivered groceries. He rode it in every parade the town had. He painted it every year. Every year he changed the color. One year he painted it yellow with black stripes. I told him it looked like a long bumblebee. You should have heard him laugh. He called the bike 'B.B.' after that." She started to cry but waved Gus away when he offered her a strip of the paper towel he was holding in his hand.

"Let's go inside, Gus."

"So," Gus said lightly, when they were back in the kitchen, "what did you do yesterday amid the seniors?"

"This place hops, I can tell you that, but I didn't have time to hop, so I went up to Westfield." She told him about her trip and the decision she'd made. She was okay, Gus was making things feel better.

"Jeez. That must have been tough on you."

Kate nodded. "The trunks arrive tomorrow at four o'clock. We're going to have a twilight service. The caretaker of the cemetery is doing it all. I found a minister the caretaker recommended who agreed to say a few words. I'm leaving Monday morning."

"So soon? I thought you were going to stay the week. You said you were staying a week."

It sounds like he's accusing me of something, Kate thought. "Donald isn't doing well. He doesn't want to eat anymore. Ellie said Della thinks he may have had a small stroke. He's being checked over now. I have to get home."

"Kate, I'm really sorry. My being so flip, that doesn't mean anything. I get like that when I'm around a woman I like. Right away I start to think I have to be witty and charming and . . . and all that stuff so she'll like me. I don't handle women well, or they don't handle me well. Christ, how I hate that bar scene and what you have to do to get out socially. I was probably meant to be a hermit living off the land or some damn thing."

Kate slid the eggs onto the plate, placed the perfectly browned toast alongside the bacon. She set the plate in front of Gus, and one for herself across the table, and sat down.

She was stunned when he said grace. Later she would think about what he'd just said.

"You are a good cook," Gus remarked, wolfing down his food, as Kate began to eat. "I always eat fast," he added apologetically. "I come from a family of eleven kids, and you needed a long arm or you went hungry. I was the youngest. God, I wish my mother could live in a place like this. She has this apartment in Brooklyn that's not too swift. She won't come to live with any of us. We grew up on welfare, and my mother did housework on the side. My old man took off after I was born. You'd like my mother, she's like your Della."

Don't do it, Kate. Don't get involved. Absolutely not. "I'm looking for a tenant for this house," she said, looking up. "It's mine, but it isn't mine. I can't sell it. If your mother is interested and can pay the yearly taxes and utilities, she can live here. As you can see, the furniture isn't much, but neither are the taxes, just a few hundred a year. There seems to be a lot to do here for retirees. Do you think she'd be interested? I'd feel a lot better if I knew someone were living here and taking care of the place."

Gus stopped eating to stare at her. "Are you kidding me, Kate Starr? What I mean is, is that a firm offer or something you just threw out?"

"I'm serious, if that's what you mean. Why is it when you try to do something nice, it immediately becomes suspect?" she said defensively.

"I'm a New Yorker," Gus said by way of explanation. "If you fall down on the street, they walk over you or around you. No one wants to get involved. I wouldn't do that, but I've seen it happen. I didn't mean to offend you."

"I guess I'm touchy these days. I don't know what would have happened to me and the girls without Della and Donald. I do try to give back when I can."

"Want to hear something sad, Kate?" At her nod, he said,

"I never lived in a house. We always lived in an apartment in triple-decker bunk beds, six of us to a room. The girls' room had five, but you know what I mean. If you really mean it, I'd like to use your phone to call my mother."

"Go ahead." God, what was she doing? Something good for someone. Her family would approve. A smile built on her face as she listened to Gus's end of the conversation.

"Ma, you there?" he bellowed. "Ma, listen, have I got a surprise for you. I found a house for you in Toms River. . . . No, no, Ma, it's in New Jersey, down at the shore. It has . . ." Kate held up four fingers. "Four rooms, a front stoop, and a back one. You can put your rocker on the back porch. Grass, Ma, real honest-to-God grass and flowers that grow in the ground, not in pots."

"Bingo and activities," Kate whispered.

"Bingo, Ma. Probably every day. All kinds of things to do. I can come down for the weekend and mow the grass and rake the leaves. There's two trees, big ones, shaped like umbrellas. . . . I don't know what kind, Ma, green, and they have brown trunks. You interested? You can move in next weekend. . . . You can afford the rent, Ma, it's free." Gus's voice changed, softened. "Sometimes, Ma, people, nice people, really do things for other people. It belongs to a friend of mine, a very good friend of mine. All you have to do is pay the light bill. . . . Ma, I said the *place* was free, I didn't say the light bill was free." To Kate he whispered, "I'll pay the taxes and heating bill." Listening, he smiled into the phone. "Yes, you can bring your own pillows and blankets and the Depression glass and your Coney Island lamp. The pictures, too. You can bring whatever you want. There's room for your sewing machine." He looked at Kate, who nodded. "Okay, Ma, you call everyone and start packing."

Kate smiled. It felt good, right.

"It was the bingo that did it," Gus said happily as he hung up. "How do I say thanks?"

"You just did. I don't think my father-in-law was happy here. He was such a private person, and so lonely. I don't think he knew how to get involved, or else he didn't want to make the effort. It's so easy to sit in front of the television set."

"He must have loved his son very much, his pictures are everywhere."

"If he did, he never showed it, never said the words to Patrick."

"I think this might be a good time for us to dump these dishes and get moving," Gus said lightly.

"I think you're right," Kate said. "Listen, why do we have to put the dishes in the sink? Why don't we just ... leave them?"

"That's a hell of a good idea. After you, madame," he said, bowing low.

They laughed and giggled, kibbitzed and joked, all the way to the beach. God, he was so nice, so comfortable to be with.

"I have never seen so much ... *skin* in one place in my life. I think half the suits on this beach should be outlawed. I don't care if that makes me sound like a prude or not," Kate said when a young girl of seventeen or so strolled by in two pieces of string and little else.

"This might surprise you, Kate, but I agree. Personally speaking, I like a full suit. To me, it's sexier."

"Hmmmm," was all Kate said.

A bronze Adonis strolled by in a stop-sign-colored Speedo suit. "Nice buns," Kate said, and giggled. The look on Gus's face chased the giggle back down her throat. "They should be outlawed, too," she said virtuously.

"The guy probably takes steroids and never worked a day in his life. I have pretty nice buns myself."

"Oh, yeah," was all Kate could think of to say.

"I'm in my prime, you know."

Kate said "Oh, yeah" again. "Exactly how old are you?" she asked cautiously.

"How old do you think I am?" Gus asked carefully.

Kate hedged. "If I knew, I wouldn't have asked. At a guess, twenty-nine, maybe thirty." God, he was so young.

"Thirty-one on my last birthday."

"And when was that?"

"Two weeks ago," Gus said sheepishly.

Here it comes, he's going to ask how old I am. She waited. When he didn't ask, she blurted, "I'm forty-four. I'll be forty-five next month."

"Oh, yeah," Gus said. "Well, guess what? I already knew that. You told me your age when I wrote that article that never got published. Does that bother you?" he asked curiously.

Kate avoided his gaze. "Sometimes. Forty-five is just five years from fifty. That's the halfway mark. There are times when I feel like I haven't really lived, just existed. I missed a lot. One of these days Ellie or Betsy is going to make me a grandmother. I don't know how I'll handle that. By the same token, I have experienced things other people only read about. I guess it evens out in the end."

"I can't wait to reach forty," Gus said. "I expect this instant wisdom, instant fame, instant riches, instant everything. My Pulitzer. Hey, do you like horror flicks?"

Kate blinked. "I love them."

"Good, let's rent my favorite, *Invasion of the Body Snatchers*."

"I like that one, too. Della chews her fingernails when we watch it. There's no VCR at the house."

"We can rent one."

"Are you going to get married when you reach forty?"

"If I meet her on my fortieth birthday, I might. Being a bachelor has its good points. According to *Cosmopolitan*, I'm in demand. Still, I'm pretty careful. And I'm all for safe sex. What's your feeling? This AIDS thing is scary. It's enough to make a person want to go for monkhood. I know a girl at the paper who went to a nunnery—you know, one of those places where you give up all your rights, and wear black, and don't even think about sex."

"Oh, yeah," Kate said. "Listen, I think we should talk about something else."

"Why? What'd I say? Oh, you mean because I asked you your opinion. It goes with being a reporter. All I do all day long is ask questions. I guess that means you don't get out and about much."

"Is it important for you to know that?"

"Well, hell yes, it is. I like you, Kate Starr. When you like someone, you want to know everything about them. I've made you uncomfortable again. I'm sorry. Come on, let's pick up and head back. We'll pick up a couple of videos, a VCR, some popcorn, and while you're cooking dinner I'll hook it all up."

Relieved that the conversation was taking a new turn, Kate smiled agreement. "It was a wonderful day, Gus, I'm glad you came to visit."

On the boardwalk, while Kate was tying her sneakers, Gus said, "You're a very pretty woman, Kate. You got just the right amount of sun today. The color becomes you. I'm not being fresh, and this is not a come-on of any kind. This is just a guess on my part, but I don't think you've gotten your share of compliments over the years. Was your husband complimentary?"

"Not really. He criticized real good, though," Kate said briskly.

Gus slipped his feet into his Dock-siders, and they made a last run down the boardwalk to pick up the tacky prizes they'd won earlier.

He was nice, Kate thought. Very nice. Real. A "what you see is what you get" kind of person. She liked that. *But he was only thirty-one.*

She had no idea what time it was when the last horror video ended. Earlier she'd taken off her watch to do the dishes, and there was no clock in the living room. Gus, she noticed, wasn't wearing a watch. She wondered why and was about to ask when he said, "According to the clock on the VCR it's one-thirty. Good thing we don't have to get up with the chickens. Hey, let's go for a walk in our bare feet."

That had to be the silliest thing she'd ever heard of. *Absolutely not.* "Okay," she said airily.

"Atta girl. I knew you were my kind of woman," Gus said, reaching down to pull her to her feet.

His kind of woman. What did that mean, exactly? She wanted to ask. The word *foreplay* rushed to mind, and she cringed. The word *seduction* ripped through her when Gus took her hand in his. She tripped, stubbing her big toe. She bore the pain in silence and hobbled along.

The night was warm, soothingly soft, with only the star-spangled sky for light. The sodium vapor lamp at the end of the street wasn't working. She should tell someone. The seniors needed light; they paid for it.

"This is the kind of night poets write about," Gus said lazily. "Look at that moon. It's a perfect crescent. I like moonlight. You?"

"Oh, yes. Moonlight is so romantic." The moment the words were out of her mouth she winced. Her toe throbbed. Her stomach started to churn, and she wasn't sure why. "Are you paying attention to the way we're walking? We could get lost." What an incredibly stupid thing to say.

"Hardly. I used to be a Boy Scout. All you have to do is look for the North Star, and wallah—"

"Really."

"No. I was teasing. I've been looking at the signposts, and we only turned one corner. Trust me, I'll get you back safe and sound."

Kate wondered if he realized her hand was clammy. "Do you ever wish on a star?" she asked wistfully.

"Every chance I get. In New York we have so much pollution, we don't see too many stars. How about you?"

"When Patrick was shot down I did. I wigged out there for a while. I started reading astrology books, wishing on stars. You name it, I did it. I probably should have prayed, but I thought God was punishing me for something. It was a very bad time for me. I wasn't strong enough. There was no one to guide me, to help me mentally. Donald and Della did what they could, but I was stubborn as a mule. Thank God I got myself together."

"And now?" Gus said quietly.

"Emotionally I'm in a good place. Legally I'm in a terrible place. Nick Mancuso, my lawyer, told me I could divorce Patrick, but I could never bring myself to do that. Holding that . . . funeral service wasn't legal. I did it for me. I need to lay Patrick to rest in my mind. I know he's never coming back. There was no one in my life that . . . What I mean is, a divorce wasn't something I gave any serious thought to."

"Don't you want to remarry, to have a life outside your work?" Gus asked quietly.

"Maybe someday."

"Your girls are grown, it seems such a shame for you to be alone at this point in time. You lost the best years of your life, Kate. I don't mean that literally. But think about it. You could have had a second family . . . ah, you know what I'm trying to say."

"But I do have a family, I have Della and Donald. Ellie is in my life every day. Besides, I have this terrible guilt where Patrick is concerned. I also have this vision of God striking me dead if I do something like getting divorced. I really expected to feel His wrath when I buried Patrick's things. I got a little brave when nothing happened." She paused. "Why are we talking about this?"

"I guess I want to know what kind of guy Captain Starr was."

"I never talk about Patrick," Kate mumbled.

"Why is that?"

166

"Because when I talk about him, I feel guilty that I'm alive and he isn't. He was the vital one, the intelligent one. He was so smart, Gus. I always felt so inferior. He contributed. I existed."

"What kind of thinking is that?" Gus demanded, coming to a standstill.

"Patrick said it often enough, so I believed it. Patrick was selfish. There are givers and takers. I was the giver and Patrick was the taker. I had this narrow little existence. Patrick insulated me, or I insulated myself. I think the proudest moment in my life was when I got my degree. Do you want to hear a secret?"

"Hell yes," Gus said, his eyes round with interest.

"The day I graduated, I kept my cap and gown an extra day. That night, around four in the morning—actually, it was morning—I drove back to the college and out to the commencement field and . . . and I put on the cap and gown and walked the whole length of the field. Then I sat in the chair I sat in during the exercise and . . . went through the business of accepting my diploma all over again, walked back to my chair, sat down, and when it was over in my mind, I threw up my hat and screamed at the top of my lungs, 'Now, Patrick, who's the dumb bunny?' Then I wailed like a banshee. I guess it was a stupid thing to do. God, why did I tell you that?"

"Because you needed to say it aloud. You trust me and feel comfortable with me. We're friends. If you're starting to regret telling me, how about I tell you one of my innermost secrets so we'll be even. Let's sit here on the curb. Want a cigarette?"

Kate was certain she was going to hear something startling, something revealing, something that would endear her even more to this strange young man. She hugged her knees and waited.

Gus blew a perfect smoke ring. "Remember I told you my

old man skipped out on us? Well, I'd been working at the paper for about a year when I decided I was going to find the bastard. My mother never once said a bad word about him. Each of us kids had our own secret story about him, but the bottom line was he walked out on us. With the help of a friend, I used the *Times* resources to track him down. It took two years, but I found the son of a bitch. He changed his name, has a new family. He lives in ... on an estate. You should see the house. It must have forty rooms. He's got a butler, maids, governesses for the kids. A pool in the back, tennis courts, belongs to the country club. The bastard has it all. His wife is half his age, wears diamonds to play tennis, rubs Evian water on her body when she sits in the sun. He's got a six-car garage and it isn't empty. Two Rollses, a Benz, a Jag, a Porsche, and a Lamborghini. He's got a yacht he keeps down here at the shore. Do you want to know the name of it? Well, the goddamn name of it is the *Matilda*. Matilda is my mother's name. He's a building contractor with underworld ties. It's all in the investigator's report."

Kate squeezed his hand and inched closer to him. He was staring across the dark street, barely aware of her. "How awful," she whispered.

"Thousands of dollars were billed to the paper. I felt really bad about that and was going to 'fess up and make arrangements to pay it back somehow. Instead I hit on a better idea. I drove up to Connecticut, to this palatial estate, one evening. The investigative report said Mr. Ronald Wedster—that's his new name—always spent Thursday evenings at home. It took a couple of months to screw up my courage to go there, but I did it. Bold as you please, I walked up to the front door and rang the bell. I wore a suit and a tie. Do you believe that? Anyway, I handed my business card to his snooty butler and was told to sit on this little spindly bench and wait. I waited for thirty goddamn minutes. It took him that long to get over the shock that I was there. When he finally came out to see me, I wanted to kill him. He had the coldest damn eyes I'd ever seen. The funny thing was, he was dressed in a suit and tie, too. I never figured that out. He said, 'What do you want?' "

"Oh, God, Gus, what did you say?" Kate whispered.

"I said," Gus said, clearing his throat, " 'I want what you have.' I didn't mean to say that. I wanted to say something about Mom and my brothers and sisters, but I didn't. I knew in that one split second that he'd used those thirty minutes to make a few calls, check me out. No one fucks with the *New York Times.* I found him, you see, so he had to pay attention. If I found him, other people could find him."

"Then what?"

"Then the son of a bitch said, 'How much?' "

"Oh, my God," Kate said.

"I said, 'Fifty thousand a month. Deposit it on the first day of every month at Chase Manhattan. The up-front payment is five hundred thousand, payable *now.*' He wrote the check on the spot. He did ask a question, though."

"What?" Kate squeezed his hand.

"He said, 'What does this buy me?' "

"And you said . . ."

"I said," Gus said hoarsely, " 'It doesn't buy you a goddamn fucking thing,' and he said, 'That's what I thought, you are your mother's son,' at which point I decked him. What do you think about *that* secret?"

"My goodness," was all Kate could think of to say.

"I never told my brothers or sisters or my mother. I never spent any of the money. It's sitting in the bank. The deposits are made once a month, right on the first day of the month. I did take out enough to pay back the *Times,* but that was it. It's all invested. There's a lot of money in the bank. Close to four million dollars. I don't know what to do with it. This last year I've been dicking around with the idea of parceling it out to the others, but I can't come up with a story about where it came from. I don't want any of them, especially my mother, to know about him. It would kill her. Guess you think I'm not a very nice person, huh?"

"On the contrary. I think you are a very nice person. You did what you had to do. Why don't you look at it as child support, college expenses, birthday, Christmas, and graduation gifts? That would certainly eat a lot of it."

"I've taken money for my silence. What does that make me?"

"The question should be, what does that make your father?"

"I knew I liked you for a reason. You always say the right thing. You're a hell of a lady, Kate Starr. Come on, I think we should be getting back. And I think that's a security car coming in our direction."

A second later Kate was on her feet. Once again her hand was in his. She wasn't sure who reached for whom. How strange that she was the one who felt comforted.

Back home, Kate locked the doors. "There's only one bathroom. You can have the room on the right. I made it up this morning. I'll clean up the kitchen while you use the bathroom."

"I'll help," Gus offered.

"I'm just going to soak the dishes."

"You're sure?"

Kate nodded.

"Kate, does my secret change your opinion of me?"

She smiled. "Not one little bit."

"It kind of makes us conspirators, doesn't it?"

"Yes. Your secret is safe with me."

"And yours with me."

Now what? Kate wondered, her heart fluttering wildly in her chest. Now what, indeed?

Later, in the dim hallway, Gus beckoned her with his index finger. "C'mere," he said.

Trancelike, she moved toward him. When she was standing next to him, she realized how tall he was, towering over her so he had to tilt her chin with the tips of his fingers so he could look into her eyes. He was going to kiss her, and she didn't want to stop him. Her eyes closed of their own accord as she waited. His lips, when they touched hers, were soft, giving as well as taking, persuading her gently to respond. She could feel his arms cradle her against him. He felt strong, and she felt safe and natural in his embrace. His fingers touching her face were tender, trailing whispery shadows over her cheekbones. Having him kiss her felt like the most natural thing in the world. It was a kiss. A tender gesture, tempting an answer but demanding none.

"Good night, Kate Starr. Sleep well," he whispered against her hair. And then he was gone, a door separating them. For one incredible second she wanted to turn the knob on the door, but she didn't.

On the other side of the door Gus waited, sensing her indecision. He felt like applauding her when he heard the door to her room open and then close. Instead he groaned.

How good Kate felt in his arms. The kiss had been just what he'd expected, too. But it wasn't time for anything else. She was still too vulnerable, yet strong in so many ways. He liked it that she had confided in him. They were friends now, open and up front with one another. One step at a time, Stewart, he admonished himself. No game playing here. Games were for children, and more often than not they hurt rather than gave pleasure. Slow and easy, he cautioned himself. You like Kate Starr too much to ever step over the line she's drawn. When and if the time was right, Kate will have to be the one to cross it, because she wanted to.

It was a spartan room, Gus thought as he shed his clothes. Was this considered the spare room, a room for Patrick Starr to sleep in if he ever came to visit? There was just the single bed with a navy-blue spread. Where would Kate and the girls

171

have slept? Out of curiosity he lifted the sheets to check the mattress. It looked new to him, the covering shiny, the threads of the quilting intact. Was Patrick Starr as strange as his father? Kate said he didn't compliment, preferring to criticize. He wished he'd known Kate Starr when she was young, and then he wished he was her age. When he laid his head on the firm pillow, he muttered, "I think I'm falling in love with you, Kate. I really think I am."

Kate was frying bacon and talking on the phone when Gus walked into the kitchen next morning, fresh from the shower. She pointed to the coffeepot and the glass of orange juice she'd poured for him. He listened to her conversation because he had no other choice.

"I'll be leaving at noon tomorrow. Don't worry if you can't pick me up at the airport, I can catch a cab. You're sure now that there's no change in Donald. . . . Ellie, I hate to say this, but doctors don't know everything. What does Della say? Della is with him twenty-four hours a day." She listened carefully as her daughter spoke. "I agree with Della, Donald has had enough poking and prodding. Give him a hug and kiss for me. Gus and I are going to Atlantic City for the afternoon. It's only an hour and twenty minutes from here. . . . Yes, Ellie, I will play one slot for each of you and bring home your winnings in silver dollars. . . . Ellie, they didn't . . . there wasn't anything in the paper today about, you know, digging up the trunk, was there . . . ? That's right, I forgot about the time difference. Well, if there is, there's nothing we can do about it anyway. I'd just prefer . . . God, when is this going to be over?"

"Tomorrow morning," Gus said, mouthing the words silently. Kate favored him with a dazzling smile. He felt lightheaded when he sat down at the table. He wanted to kiss her again. He mouthed the words and grinned when her eyebrows shot upward. He almost laughed aloud when she dropped the spatula. Her face was pink when she bent down to pick it up. His own felt flushed.

" 'Bye, honey," Kate said, and hung up. She turned to him.

"So, how would you like your eggs—over easy, sunnyside up, or scrambled?" she asked briskly. No fooling around this morning, he thought. It must have something to do with talking to her daughter. He felt pleased with his observation.

"Over easy. I like to dunk."

"Me too," Kate said. "I like two cups of coffee when I have eggs. One for dunking the toast with the egg yolk, and a cup for drinking."

"Me too, but I wasn't going to say anything," Gus said happily. "My mother said only slobs eat like that." Kate laughed and poured out four cups of coffee.

They dunked and munched as they grinned at one another over their plates.

"Are we leaving the dishes today, too?" Kate giggled.

"Damn right. Let's get this show on the road. Wait a minute," he said, fishing in his wallet for money. "I'm going to need enough for gas and tolls." He left a ten-dollar bill on the table. "I have forty dollars left. Kick me if I go past thirty-nine bucks."

"Okay," Kate said, and checked her own purse. "I need money for a taxi and buying some magazines, and I like to keep some change in my wallet. That gives me fifty-three dollars." She laid a twenty-dollar bill on the table next to Gus's ten. "Has it occurred to you," she said impishly, "that with all the money you have in that New York bank, and my healthy bank account, we could take A.C. by storm?"

"We are high rollers. Ninety-two bucks between us. Let's make a bet—are we going to be winners or losers today?"

"Winners!" Kate said enthusiastically.

"I agree. How big?"

Kate giggled. "I say we come home with double our money."

"I say we come home with three hundred twelve dollars, and I hope you're the big winner because you owe me dinner. Remember that promise you made, how long ago, seven years?"

"What I said was a hot dog and a soda pop. I didn't forget." God, was it a sin to be happy?

"You can take me to the Lobster Shanty if you win. Deal?"

"Deal." Kate smiled.

"I have to leave here by seven, Kate. There will be miles of traffic for me going home. You look sad," he said, pleased at the crestfallen look on her face.

"I guess I am. I'm missing you already. This has been such a nice weekend. I can't remember when I've enjoyed myself more."

"I can come to California to visit you. Not often, but if you invite me, I'll come."

"I'd like that, Gus, I really would." The smile was back on her face and in her eyes. "Consider yourself invited. You have an open invitation." She reached for his arm, and together they left the house, each wearing a wide smile that rivaled the sun.

CHAPTER
13

The stream of postcards, letters, and Hallmark greeting cards during the following months was constant. Kate's voice sizzled over the long-distance wire to the tune of three to four hundred dollars a month. She and Gus were friends, staying in touch on a daily, sometimes twice-daily, basis. There simply weren't enough hours in the day for either of them to make the three-thousand-mile trip to visit. On recommendations from previous customers, Kate found herself traveling to San Francisco, Sacramento, Los Angeles, and Nevada to quote prices and secure more work than she could handle. A second office in Los Angeles was being considered. On the East Coast, Gus Stewart was up to his hips in a crime investigation that threatened, according to the FBI, to go on forever.

"This friendship is costing me a great deal of money," Kate

muttered as she scanned her latest phone bill. "Good Lord, I couldn't possibly have talked $533.12 worth in one month!" She looked around uneasily, to see if anyone had heard her comment. Della was busy folding laundry and Ellie was swimming her daily laps. Donald was propped up in the hospital bed in the family room so he could see out into the garden.

In the four months since her visit to New Jersey, Donald's health had deteriorated alarmingly. Della steadfastly refused to sign him into a nursing home and insisted on taking care of him herself. At Kate's insistence he had been moved to her house so she and Ellie could spell Della. A home health aide came in at nine in the evening and sat with Donald through the long night.

Della looked up from the pile of sheets she'd just folded. "He knew me for a little while today, Kate. He looked right at me and said, 'You're getting skinny, old girl.' "

"He's right," Kate said worriedly. "We need more help. We're both so tired we can hardly stand up. I know you want to be the one to do for him, I do too, but we have to be realistic. If we wear ourselves down, we won't be any good to Donald. I'm as worried about you as I am about him. None of us has the energy to eat anymore. Look at us! We're skin and bones. I haven't been to the office in three weeks. I'd breathe my own life into Donald if I could, you know that, Della. If it came right down to it, I think I'd give my life for that man. But he wouldn't want this, and we both know it. Decisions are called for here, and you and I have to make them."

"But, Kate, he knew me today," Della said, her dark eyes filling with tears.

"And he knew me two days ago," Kate said quietly. "Look at him, Della, at all those tubes and machines. If he were able to, he would rip them all out. Donald had such dignity. I think we should let him go. We're being selfish. We have to think about Donald, not ourselves," Kate said, wiping her eyes.

"Kate, I wouldn't know what to do without him. How will I get through the days? You and Ellie don't need me, but he does." Della sobbed into a tissue.

"If I ever, ever, hear you say a thing like that again, I'll—I'll smack you. Do you hear me?" Kate shrilled. "I'm going to forget you said that. Now, you . . . go wash your face and make some coffee. We're going to talk when Ellie comes in. We're going to—to do what's best for Donald. Go on, Della."

Tears dripped down Kate's cheeks when she walked over to Donald's bed. Her dearest friend in the whole world couldn't breathe without his oxygen mask, couldn't pee without the catheter, and because he couldn't eat, was receiving glucose and other nutrients through his veins. His hands and feet were so crippled, his fingers and toes were curled backward. When they washed him, they dribbled warm water over his hands and feet. Just yesterday she'd seen Della blow-drying his feet, which were blue with cold. Her eyes fell on the neatly stacked pile of diapers with their sticky tabs.

She reached for Donald's crippled hand, careful not to put any undue pressure on it. "The first time I saw you, Donald, I thought you were a derelict. I'm sorry for that awful thought. I've never known a kinder, more gentle, generous man in my life. For years I've wanted to do something for you, something that would bring a smile to your face, some-thing to make you happy. I wish your son and daughter were here. I know God put you on this earth to take care of us. I believe that with all my heart. So, Donald dear, I think I finally figured out what it is I can do for you. Della won't be able to do it, but I think I can. I'm going to send you to that . . . that place where your son and daughter are waiting for you. I bet your son will be wearing his army uniform, and I bet when he sees you, he's going to snap off a salute that will create a breeze."

"Coffee's ready, Kate," Della said quietly as she entered. "Black and strong, just the way you like it." She fussed with the sheet blanket, brushed at Donald's sparse hair, tweaking a stray away from his ear. She continued to smooth the wrinkles on the blanket until Kate led her into the kitchen.

"Who's watching Donald?" Ellie asked anxiously from the deck.

"He's sleeping," Della said.

"He's comatose, Della."

"I'll sit with him," Ellie said, reaching for a cup. "I'll tell him a story the way he used to tell them to us. Sometimes he smiles. I know—like babies, it's gas. But I don't understand how it can be gas when he doesn't eat. I prefer to think I'm amusing him. I don't care how it sounds."

Della sobbed quietly into the dish towel. Kate blew her nose.

"Della, this is what I think. . . ."

A long time later Della nodded. "You need to get back to the office. Ellie has to get on with her life."

"Della, I don't give a hoot about the office. I can close up shop right now and not look back. Ellie feels the same way. Donald is what's important. You're important. If we lose it all, so what? We were poor once before and we survived."

"Yes, but only because of Donald. Without him we couldn't have made it."

"That's debatable," Kate said briskly. "Now, we're both going to think about what I just said, and tomorrow morning the three of us are going to make a decision, and then we are going to act on that decision. You know I'm right, Della. You sit with Donald and I'll make us something for dinner."

"Not tomato soup again," Della pleaded.

"No, hot dogs with lots of mustard and relish. I'll do them on the grill. And some of that macaroni and cheese that comes in a box." Della shuddered. Kate smiled wanly.

"You look like you could use a friend, Mom, or at the

very least, a massage," Ellie said. "I'm going to clean the bathrooms. Why don't you call your friend Gus?"

"That sounds like a good idea. Are you sure you don't mind doing the bathrooms?"

"Mom, I live here. Della has her hands full. You're going to make dinner. Do you think I'm going to just watch both of you? Leave the salad for me. Everything's going to be okay."

"No, it isn't."

"I meant with us. Go on, call your friend. Did anyone wash towels today?"

"Della has been doing Donald's laundry. I was going to do them after dinner," Kate said wearily.

"I'll do them. Want me to turn on the grill?"

Kate nodded. She reached for the phone to dial Gus's number. He sounded so pleased to hear from her that she felt better almost immediately. They talked for forty minutes, and twice Gus managed to make her laugh. "You're doing the right thing, Kate," he said before he said good-bye. "My turn next time."

"Why did I cook this if no one is going to eat?" Kate grumbled half an hour later as she pushed her plate to the center of the table. "None of us can afford to lose much more weight."

"Who's going to call Betsy?" Ellie asked.

"I will, in a little while. I tried calling her the past several days, but there's been no answer. I'll try again around nine. Now, let's get to it."

Della nodded miserably. Ellie said, "I feel it's the right thing to do. Did you call Donald's doctor? He knows about his living will, doesn't he?"

"Yes to both your questions," Kate said quietly.

"When?" was all Ellie said.

"Dawn. When the sun comes up. Donald always liked to see the sun come up. He said new days were meant for many things, journeys, loving, and just plain old living."

Ellie's eyes were wild. "Are we . . . are we going to . . . keep a vigil? We aren't going to go to bed, are we?"

Kate shook her head.

"I think he knows," Della said. "His breathing's changed. It's like he's fighting something, but he can't wake up fully. He knows. . . ."

At nine o'clock Kate walked into the kitchen to call her daughter. She let the phone ring twelve times before she hung up. She hated her daughter at that moment. She stomped her way back to the family room, her eyes murderous.

At midnight Donald opened his eyes, looked around, and said clearly and distinctly, "It's nasturtiums. That's why we couldn't make a rainbow of flowers. We forgot the nasturtiums." They crowded around the bed, happy smiles on their faces. "Where's my honey button?" he said, again so clearly that Kate blinked.

"I'm here, Donald," Della said. "Did you hear that, Kate? He called me his honey button. Oh, Donald," she said, smothering his face with kisses moist with her tears.

Kate clutched at her daughter, her eyes wild. "My God," she whispered, "we were going to . . . we almost—"

"Shhh, Mom, this isn't what you think. Donald is trying to make things right for us the way he always did, before . . . before he goes. Listen, his voice is weaker, less distinct."

Kate strained to hear what he was saying. "Take some of the money and do good . . . go back to Mexico and help your family. Promise me, Della."

Della threw herself across her husband's wasted body. "I'll do whatever you want, Donald. I promise." When there was no response, she started to shake her husband, but he was in another place, far from the cocoon of sleep he'd crawled from. Kate and Ellie led her over to the chair.

"Even now he thinks of us," Della wept, "never himself."

"That's why we have to do it, Della," Kate said. "Stay with her Ellie, I have to do something."

She was a madwoman when she entered the kitchen and punched out her daughter's telephone number. She didn't care what time of the night it was. Her eyes narrowed when she heard her daughter's sleep-filled voice. "Turn on the light, Betsy, and wake up. Listen to me. Are you listening . . . ?" she asked coldly. "Good. Donald is dying. We plan to remove— Yes, we're going to do it at dawn. He's lapsed into a coma. I want you here. . . . What do you mean you can't make it? You *will* damn well make it! You are a miserable, ungrateful snot, and I'm ashamed to say you're my daughter. Get dressed, Betsy, and be here by morning. I don't care if you have to crawl. You be here! Without Donald you wouldn't be sleeping in that comfortable bed of yours. I will send the state police for you if you don't come under your own power. I mean it!" Kate slammed down the phone, her shoulders shaking.

"Whoah," Ellie said from the doorway. "I didn't think you had it in you, Mom."

"You'd be surprised at what I have in me," Kate said tightly. "I meant it, too. I'll send the state police to bring her here."

"Be real, Mom," Ellie said, not unkindly. "They can't *make* her come."

"She'll come, won't she, Ellie?"

"No, she won't."

"What happened to her? My God, is it my fault? I did my best."

"You know that, I know that, but Betsy . . . Betsy wanted the dream to go on. She was Dad's favorite. Miss Princess Betsy. It was all make-believe. We had to do what we did, go through that fantasy period of believing Dad would come back, in order to go on with our lives. Betsy wanted to stay in that fantasy world. She wanted to keep on playing make-believe, but you wouldn't let her. She isn't a forgiving person. Personally, I think she's warped."

"I will never forgive her if she doesn't come," Kate said.

"Yes, you will. You're a mother. Mothers forgive all their children's sins. Mothers love unconditionally. It's supposed to be that way."

"Not this mother," Kate said grimly.

Ellie stared at her mother, knowing she meant exactly what she said. "On the other hand, there are some mothers who don't . . . who aren't like that."

"Number me among that group, Ellie. I cannot believe that girl is my child. I cannot believe she has 'something more important to do.' Where did she get the nerve, the goddamn *nerve*, to say that to me?"

"I'm going to make some coffee," Ellie said. "Remember how Donald used to say if you drank too much coffee you'd grow hair on your chest? I lived in fear of that. I used to check all the time to be sure. I knew he was making it up, but I checked anyway. I'm really going to miss him, Mom." Ellie threw herself into her mother's arms.

"Me too, honey."

"When the sun comes up and we . . . do it, how long will it be?" Ellie blubbered.

"Not long. Donald's ready to go. Whatever that was—his last words—I believe it was his way of telling us it's okay. I had this talk with him this afternoon. I think he wasn't certain . . . he's counting on us."

"I'll bring the coffee in when it's ready," Ellie said, blowing her nose.

Ellie measured out coffee, filled the pot, and plugged it in. Anger rushed through her, anger at her sister for the way she treated everyone. She tiptoed down the hall to her mother's office, closed the door, and called her sister. Her voice was a growling hiss when she heard Betsy's voice.

"I just wanted to go on record as saying I think you are a first-class bitch—the most selfish, self-centered person I have ever had the misfortune of knowing. All you do is take up air other people need to breathe, people like Donald. Mom's right, you are an ungrateful snot. There's not one good, nice, decent thing about you. As far as I'm concerned, I don't even have a sister. . . . Well, *say* something, you miserable bitch!"

"Good-bye."

Ellie's jaw dropped, and she raised her eyes. "I'm sorry, God, but it needed to be done. Can't you straighten her out? So, sometime in the future I'll write her a note and . . . No, I won't. I meant everything I said. Every word."

Betsy Starr stood in her pristine kitchen and looked around wildly. She clenched and unclenched her hands as she tried to fight the tears she knew were going to drown her if she ever *really* let go.

She started to make coffee, then gave up on the idea when she couldn't remember how much coffee the machine required. She reached for the jar holding the tea bags, dropped it, watched the glass scatter all over her white tile floor. In order to get to the refrigerator for a beer or soda pop, she'd have to walk over the glass slivers or clean them up. Too much effort.

She backed out of the kitchen, found herself in a corner, where she cowered, arms wrapped around her chest. She pressed into the corner, her heart pumping so loudly she could hear it between her sobbing breaths.

This wasn't supposed to happen. Never, ever. Donald was supposed to live forever. No, no, that wasn't true. He'd said he would still be around until she got out of college. The problem was, she hadn't been around. Not because she didn't care, but because she did care. Too much. "That's my problem, I care too much, and I don't want anyone to know, and I don't know why that is!" she said, sobbing.

She thought about her mother's words, her sister's phone

183

call. She sobbed harder. A picture of a shiny red wheelbarrow flashed in front of her eyes. "Oh, Donald, I'm so sorry. I know it wasn't *my* promise to you, but I promised you for my dad. I should have bought it for you. I meant to do that the first Christmas when I went away to college, but I had this opportunity to meet . . . I'm sorry Donald. I love you . . . still love you . . . will always love you. More than I could ever say, more than I could ever show you."

She blew her nose in the hem of her nightgown. She'd so wanted to ask her mother about Donald, but that was another one of her problems: when she needed to talk, to show how she felt, she couldn't. Family was supposed to understand that. Her father, according to her mother, was supposed to have had the same problem.

She wished she were more open, more outgoing, like Ellie. She'd tried when she was younger, but it was such an effort, and people looked at her strangely when she tried to copy her younger sister's ways. She was a serious, solemn, studious person. Just like her father.

What it all came down to was, she felt things too deeply. She loved too much. And she didn't know how to handle those feelings. Ellie was forever calling her an emotional cripple. "I am," she sobbed.

Her life flashed in front of her, all negative. She howled her misery as she stumbled her way back to her bedroom. She dropped to her knees and fumbled under the bed for her suitcase. She threw in clothes any old way, stepped into her slippers, searched for her raincoat, the long military-style one that would cover her nightgown. She found her purse, her car keys, and trudged out to the carport.

She turned on the windshield wipers before she realized her tears were the reason she couldn't see. She drove around for two hours, looking for a store that was open so she could buy a shiny red wheelbarrow. After the fact. *It's too late. It's always too late, Betsy Starr.*

184

She continued to drive until she found herself in front of St. Angela's Church. She ran up the steps and tried to open the door, but it wouldn't budge. Churches shouldn't be locked. People needed to pray. It shouldn't matter what time of the day or night it was. "I need to go in here!" she shouted, kicking at the door again and again. She shouted over and over, "I need to go in here, damn you! Can't you hear? I need to go inside."

She felt a hand on her shoulder and whirled around.

"What is it, child?"

"Oh, Father, I need ... I tried to find this red ... he promised me he'd live till I graduated. ... I need to talk. My father is ... I need help, Father. Please help me. ..."

Kate was dozing on her chair at five o'clock when the front doorbell rang. No one moved. "It must be Betsy," Kate said coolly.

"Maybe the priest decided to come early," Della said.

"Or the doctor," Ellie said.

"I'll get it," Kate said. "There are a few things I want to say to my daughter in private."

She turned on the hall light before she opened the heavy oak door. She wanted to see her daughter's face clearly. She could feel her shoulders tighten with the tension she felt. She saw the whole of him at once, saw the concern, the anguish, in his eyes. She fell into his arms, glad it wasn't her daughter standing in the open door.

"I had to come," was all he said.

"I'm glad you did," she said.

"Are you all right?"

"I am now," she said. "What about your crime story?"

"Let them all kill themselves. The public doesn't need to read about more blood and gore. It wasn't important to me."

"Will they fire you?"

Gus laughed. "There was no contest. Besides, I know this guy in Los Angeles, and he said I could come to work for him anytime. You forget, I'm a rich man. I'll tell you about it later. What's important now is you."

"I'm glad you're here, Gus. You're my best friend. I don't know how that happened," Kate said, puzzled by her own statement.

"You took the time to get to know me. My sterling character started to shine through and you saw it. I knew you'd make a good friend the first moment I saw you. I'm just sorry it took us so long to meet again. Now, what can I do?" he said briskly.

Kate shrugged helplessly. "What color are nasturtiums?"

"Blue? Bluish purple?" He didn't think the question odd at all.

"I wonder if it's one of those flowers that come in all colors? I rather think it does. You know, enough different colors so if planted right they'd look like a rainbow. We have to get some," Kate said simply.

Hell, yes, a whole truckload if she said so. He'd plant them, too. Whatever she wanted.

"It's getting light out," Ellie said, getting up from her chair.

"Ellie, this is Gus Stewart. Gus, this is Ellie, all grown up."

Ellie's hand shot out. They smiled at one another. "Ah," Ellie said, rubbing the back of her neck, "the reason for the high phone bills. They are not tax deductible, you know."

Gus smiled again. He likes her, Kate thought, but then he'd liked her seven years ago. He'd said she was open and a "what you see is what you get" kind of person.

"It's going to be full light in a few minutes," Ellie said.

"I know," Kate replied, moving toward Donald's hospital bed. Tears filled her eyes when she saw Della holding his crippled hand. She was weeping quietly.

"It was so hard for her. She told me once that Donald was

the only man in the whole of her life who ever told her he loved her. She hasn't been able to let go. For weeks now Donald has been drifting in and out of consciousness. Yesterday he lapsed into . . . She knows it's the end, and she's feeling so very guilty because she didn't do what he wanted. He left a living will. He didn't want any of this. His eyes . . . he used to plead with me with his eyes after his last stroke. I couldn't make Della . . . He was her husband. . . ."

Ellie said, "We didn't discuss who was going to—"

"I know," Kate said. "I . . . I'll do it. I should have insisted. I should have done something more. . . ."

"I'll do it," Gus said. Kate sagged against him with relief until she remembered her promise to Donald.

"No. I *have* to do it."

Kate moved then, with an efficiency born of desperation. Ellie and Gus watched her as she moved the oxygen mask, disconnected the catheter, set aside the heart monitor. It was hard, but she pried Della's hand loose. "You have to get his clothes, Della." To Ellie she said, "Get the basin and make sure the water is warm. Ivory soap, Ellie, and a soft towel." Her voice strengthened and grew strong.

All the while she worked, washing and drying Donald's wasted body, Kate talked. "I'm working as fast as I can, Donald. I'm sorry it's taking me so long, but I had to think of Della, too. We're spiffing you up," she said, sprinkling Johnson's baby power on the frail, heaving chest. She quickly pulled on a freshly ironed undershirt and then struggled to get his limp arms through the sparkling white shirt with French cuffs. Her movements were sure, deft, as though she'd been practicing for this very thing. She removed the oversize diaper, washed him. Out of the corner of her eye she saw Della reach for a diaper. "No!" The word exploded from her mouth like a gunshot. "He is not going to meet his son and daughter wearing a diaper. Get his shorts, Della, and get them *now!*"

The boxers shorts were crisp, freshly ironed, pale blue in color. Kate struggled with them and then with the trousers. "I need a belt," she said, tucking the snowy white shirt into the waistband. She was huffing and puffing with her efforts. "Cuff links," she said hoarsely. "Now the paisley tie. Damn you, Della, get the tie! Hurry up," she cried. "Oh, God, I don't know how to tie a tie! Donald likes Windsor knots."

"I'll do it," Gus said, stepping forward. As he struggled with the tie, he could feel the tortured breaths of the man beneath him. His chest heaved, bucked with the effort to breathe without the oxygen mask.

The moment Gus was finished, he stepped aside. Kate straightened the points of the shirt collar, tugged at the jacket, buttoned the vest and then the jacket. Without having to be told, Gus pulled socks onto Donald's crippled feet. His eyes were frantic when he searched the room for shoes, knowing it would be impossible to get them on his feet. He looked at Kate helplessly.

"He's going in his stocking feet," she said. "His son will be so glad to see him, he won't look at his feet."

The room grew so quiet, Kate looked around to see what had caused the sudden silence. Her own chest heaved in grief when she realized Donald's chest was still. "Good-bye, old friend," she whispered. She turned and fell into Gus's arms. "I kept my promise. It was all I could do for him. I hope he understands. . . . I bet he's *up there* already . . . walking around in his stocking feet. He's probably showing Bobby his paisley tie and telling him how much it cost."

"Della is—"

"Sit with her, Ellie. I have calls to make. The service is going to be this afternoon, if I can arrange it. Someone from the funeral home will be here as soon as I call Mr. Muldoon. Donald . . . Donald picked out his own casket a year ago. He knew Della wouldn't be able to do it. You should have seen him picking and choosing, punching at those pillows, fingering the satin coverlet. Della was at the dentist when I took him there. It was the worst hour of my life. He . . . got a big kick out of it, took care of every last detail. He counted on me to . . . to make sure Della did what he wanted, but I couldn't—she wouldn't listen. She thought if she took care of him, cleaned him and sat with him, it was all right to keep him alive even when it wasn't what he wanted." She straightened, blew her nose. "We should have coffee or tea or something. I need to call . . . somebody and take all these things before we get back from the cemetery. I have a . . . a list."

"I could do that for you, Kate. What about the priest or minister?"

"Donald didn't want anything religious at the end. He said he didn't want anyone paving the way for him. God was either going to accept him on his own or reject him. He agreed to *one* prayer at the cemetery. Keep it short and sweet, he said."

"I'm sorry I didn't know him better."

"I'm sorry, too, Gus. He was a wonderful person. He could always make you feel better by saying just the right thing. Della is going to be lost without him."

"Time . . ." Gus said lamely.

"No. Della will grieve the rest of her life. I know her so well. She'll do what Donald wanted, she'll go back to Mexico, help some of the poor families, stay for a while, and then she'll come back here and . . . and wait till it's time to join Donald. And who am I to say she shouldn't do that?"

"I always thought the will to live was so strong," Gus muttered.

"I used to think that, too, back in the beginning, when Patrick was lost to me. I don't think that way anymore."

"Did Donald just have one son?"

"Yes. He had a daughter, but she was killed when she was eighteen. On a bus that was hit by a car. She was going to church. Her name was Lucia."

"Jesus."

"Everything is going to change now. Della is going to leave. When she comes back—*if* she comes back—it won't be the same. I want to hang on to her, but I have to let her go. Ellie is going to move. It's time for her to go out on her own. She's been talking for a while about going to Los Angeles. She needs to have a life of her own, and I accept that. But what in the world will I do with this big, fancy house?"

"You don't have to think about that now, Kate. Why don't you take a shower, put on some clean clothes, and I'll make some coffee and make these calls for you."

Kate nodded. "I'm forgetting something. Damn. There's something I need to do," she said vaguely.

"It'll come to you," Gus said, measuring coffee into the little metal basket. "If you don't dwell on it, it surfaces."

"I suppose you're right. You're a reporter, you should know."

Kate was about to step into the shower when she remembered. She pulled on a bright, lemon-colored terry robe and ran barefoot into the kitchen. "I remembered. I was going to call a greenhouse and ask them to deliver nasturtiums and all those other flowers so we could plant a . . . a flower bed."

"Kate, it's September."

"So?"

"Won't they die at this time of year?"

Kate thought about it. "I don't care. I want to plant them now. They have them in the greenhouse in little plastic things. I don't care what it costs. All colors. Enough to ring the house. See if they can deliver them this afternoon. I want to start planting them when we . . . when we get back. I need to do this, Gus."

"That's fine, Kate, but who are you doing it for? Betsy?"

"What does Betsy have to do with this? Betsy isn't here. She couldn't be bothered. She's never been to this house. I'm doing it for Donald. It was one of the last things he said to

190

me. He came up from that deep, dark place he was in just to . . . It's for Donald. How he loved that other garden. When he looks down, I want him to see it. I don't care, I don't care," Kate said, holding up both arms. "I'm doing it." Her face was so full of determination, Gus could only nod.

"I'll call. How many plants should I order?"

"Enough to plant a ring around the garden. A lot."

"Yes, but what's a lot? Hundreds? Thousands? It's going to cost, Kate."

"Thousands, and I don't care what it costs. Ohhhh, Donald is going to be so pleased."

"Kate . . ."

She heard the worry in his voice. "I'm not *losing it*, Gus. But if you think I am, then humor me," she said with a smile in her voice.

That was exactly what he was thinking, but only for a minute. He waved her away, reaching for the phone at the same time.

When they returned from the cemetery they walked in a huddle, close together as though for warmth, their eyes on the ground.

Gus saw the truck first. Finnegan's Greenhouse. "Thank God," he muttered. "This is what we're going to do, ladies," he said, taking charge, and marching them inside the house. "We are going to change our clothes, have a sandwich and some ice tea, and then we are going to garden." He looked around the huge family room as he spoke. Everything was gone, the carpet vacuumed, the indentations from the hospital bed picked out. It looked like any other room. Even the sickroom smell was gone. The sliding doors to the deck were open, creating a warm, light breeze.

"What is it we're going to do?" Della asked in a daze.

"We're planting flowers," Ellie said lightly. "The way I see it, we might be done two weeks from next Thursday if we

191

get a move on." She led Della from the room without a backward glance.

"I don't know how to thank you, Gus," Kate said, reaching up to kiss him on the cheek.

Suddenly he was embarrassed. He wanted to say, Just love me, just tell me you care about me. But he was afraid to say the words, afraid she would withdraw from him, send him away. "I'll think of something," he said. "Ellie's wrong, we're going to finish this project tonight, if we have to plant by moonlight. I called the placement counselor at the community college, and a dozen or so students will be arriving shortly to help us."

Kate kissed him again, her eyes bright with unshed tears. "I like raw onion on my liverwurst," she said.

"Oh, God! Don't tell me, let me guess, with a dab of tangy mustard?"

"More than a dab. I like to smear the whole slice of onion with it."

"Me too," Gus said in awe.

"Skip the iced tea, I like beer with my liverwurst. So do Ellie and Della."

"Jesus," Gus said.

Kate grinned. "And I like mustard and butter on my bagels."

"I don't believe this. If I searched the whole world over, I couldn't have found anyone with tastes so like mine. I think we were meant for each other." Gus drew a deep breath, expecting her to back off, to run and say something that would squelch any hopes he had of a more meaningful relationship.

"Do you think so?" Kate asked seriously.

"Yeah, I do," was all he could think of to say.

"Imagine that," was all Kate could say.

Gus literally danced a jig in the kitchen as he smeared honey mustard with a bite to it over the large slices of sweet white onion. The rye was only a day old and still fresh, the liverwurst slices stuck together. He made a mess of the meat, then finally gave up and pressed the onion firmly into the liverwurst. Hopefully no one would look beneath the top slice of bread.

It had been a hell of a day so far, yet it was one of the best days of his life. He had so much to tell Kate, things he hadn't wanted to discuss with her over the phone or put on paper. Things that were important to him, and maybe to her, too. He wondered if he was wrong to feel as if he belonged here, to want to be a part of this small family. If it was wrong, someone would enlighten him soon enough.

"Soup's on!" he bellowed.

They ate and drank, two beers apiece. Gus showed his approval by cleaning off the table. "I hate to be the one to mention this, but our planting crew has arrived, I can hear them. Let's order in for dinner. Kentucky Fried. Mashed potatoes, coleslaw. My treat," he said magnanimously.

"You are a kind, generous man, Gus Stewart," Ellie said with a devilish grin on her face.

"Tell that to your mother," Gus grumbled.

"She already knows. She's the one who told me." Ellie winked. "She told Della, too." Kate blushed furiously.

They worked and worked, and then they continued to work, with a ten-minute break on the hour. They took turns handing out iced tea, beer, and cold water. The only ones to complain about aching backs and sore knees were the college kids, who slaved to the tunes of Bruce Springsteen and Rod Stewart, who Gus said was no relation, thank God.

"What time is it?" Kate asked, taking a swig from her beer.

"Three-thirty in the morning," Gus said wearily. "I had no idea gardening was so tiring. My back hurts so bad I don't know if I'll ever be able to stand up again. How about you, Kate?"

"We're all pretty tired. Don't forget, we really didn't get

any sleep to speak of the night before. We can use the hot tub when we're done. That should ease some of the ache."

"I'll drown," Gus groaned.

Kate grinned. "I'll save you."

"Because I'm worthwhile or because you don't want me drowning on your property?"

"Both. I haven't thanked you, have I?"

"Several times." She didn't want him to drown, she'd save him. She'd wrap her arms around his neck and then he'd kiss her and they'd swim off into the sunset or sunrise, whichever happened first.

"Penny for your thoughts," Kate said quietly.

He told her his thoughts.

"We have a wonderful friendship. Anything more would spoil it," Kate said, her bottle drained.

"Will our friendship ever change?" Gus asked seriously.

A lump settled in her throat. "I don't know, Gus. What I do know is I don't want to lose you as a friend. You've become very important to me, very dear to me. I'm not ready for anything else. I can't promise more than that."

He was important to her, dear to her. "For now," he said.

"For now." Kate smiled.

"I can accept that. For now."

Kate's stomach muscles contracted. If this man walked out of her life, she would miss him terribly. I would grieve, she thought.

"A penny for *your* thoughts," Gus said.

She told him.

Gus strutted. She cared about him. She just didn't know how much. Yet.

Before they resumed their planting, Gus pierced her with his summer-blue eyes. "I'm not falling in love with you, Kate, I am *in love* with you." Kate felt her knees start to buckle. Gus reached for and eased her down on the ground.

Across the garden, Ellie nudged Della. "I don't think either one of us has to worry about Mom. That guy is gonna take real good care of her. If she lets him. You don't think she'll do something dumb and let him get away, do you?" Ellie asked anxiously.

Della shook her head. "Your mother's no fool. She may be a little mixed up in her mind when it comes to love and marriage. She may have buried your father's belongings and for a while thought of herself as a widow, but there's another part to your mother, that obsessive loyalty she has to Captain Starr. Then there's your sister. Your mother is going to be forced to make some hard decisions soon."

"You mean do it or get off the pot, that kind of thing?"

"Yes, that kind of thing. Why are we doing this, Ellie?"

"You mean planting the flowers?"

"Yes, why are we doing this?"

"Because Mom has it in her head that Donald is going to wake up in the morning in the Hereafter, look down, and see this ... whatever the damn hell it is. I thought you understood. It's not for Betsy, it's for Donald. She told you, Della, I heard her," Ellie said gently.

"I guess I didn't hear her. I was so wrapped up in my grief, I didn't hear much of anything. I can't even remember what was said at the cemetery. I'm going home, Ellie," the older woman said sadly.

Ellie jabbed at the dark brown earth. "When will you be back?" She could feel her stomach start to churn. Della was like a second mother to her.

"I don't think I'll be coming back."

The plant in Ellie's hand lost its petals as she squashed it with her thumb and index finger. She looked at it, stuck it in the ground, and said, "This one is going to die."

"Everything dies sooner or later," Della said.

"I don't understand. Why don't you think you'll come back? What will Mom do without you? What will you do without Mom? You've been together so long, you're my

195

other mother, Della," Ellie said, wiping the tears forming in her eyes.

Della pointed to Gus. "You said it yourself. He'll look out for her. You're moving to Los Angeles. Donald's gone. He told me to take the money and go home. I have many family members I haven't seen in a long time. I can make their lives easier with the money Donald left me. There's no place at the cemetery for me. I saw it with my own eyes. Donald's first wife is buried there. And it's supposed to be that way. The family, they belong together. That's why Donald said I should go back to Mexico. That's why he . . . he paid me off."

"Oh, no, Della, you mustn't think like that! That wasn't what Donald meant. I don't think Mom knew anything about his first wife. Donald never talked about her, and Mom isn't one to ask questions. You never talk about her, either."

"That's because I didn't know. I thought . . . she left him when the children were young. He never talked about her to me. I didn't know she was dead or buried there with his son and daughter. He should have told me. I had a right to know. I thought I was going to be buried with him."

"Oh, Della," Ellie said, taking the older woman in her arms. "We can buy another plot next to theirs. You can still be buried there."

"No I can't! They're a family. I don't belong there," Della cried. "The last words out of Donald's mouth were to tell me to go back where I came from. So I'm going. One should always grant a dying person's last wish. Your mother is planting these flowers, and I am going back to Mexico."

Out of her depth, Ellie said, "I think you need to talk to Mom about this. Nothing is either black or white, you know." Soothingly, she added, "We won't be able to get along without you."

"I'm seventy-three years old, Ellie, an old woman. I'm not

much good for anything anymore. Your mother thinks she fooled me. At first she had someone come in to do the heavy work, then the work that wasn't too heavy, and finally someone to do the light work. One lady irons and does laundry. A different lady to clean the windows, someone cleans the pool, someone else does everything."

"Mom was trying to make it easy for you, Della. You had all you could do to take care of Donald. It was her way of helping, paying you and Donald back for all the care you've given us over the years. Please don't break her heart. If you want to go back to Mexico for a visit, go, but come back."

"I cannot, my sweet Ellie. I made a mess of things. I didn't do the one thing Donald wanted me to do. I couldn't let him go. I was selfish. I was wrong. I don't want to talk about this anymore. It's going to be light soon, so we must work now to finish, for your mother's sake. I understand what she's trying to do now. And you must understand what it is I must do. Don't cry, Ellie, you'll soak the plants and they will die."

"I don't care," Ellie blubbered.

"I care, so stop," Della said.

Ellie reacted to the authoritative voice she remembered from her younger days. "You're a meanie," she said, as she had when she was little.

"Among other things," Della replied.

"You're going to break Mom's heart," Ellie said stubbornly.

"Enough already. If her heart breaks, that man will mend it for her. Look at them. He loves her very much. I see this. Do not concern yourself with her heart."

The stubbornness stayed in Ellie's voice. "You don't know *everything*, Della."

"This is true, *almost* everything. Dig."

"What about *my* heart?"

"You're young, you'll mend. Dig!"

197

What seemed like a long time later, Kate said, "In another twenty minutes or so it's going to be light. We still have a quarter of the way to go. I was so certain we'd be done. The kids have worked hard. You were right, Gus, it was an impossible, foolish task. What's the use?" She rocked back on her heels. "We might as well quit now. Everyone is dog-tired. Tell everyone to stop, Gus, I simply don't have the energy."

"You're quitting!" Gus said, stupefied.

"Yes."

"Then tell them yourself," he said, continuing with his planting. "I never much liked quitters."

"To each his own," Kate snapped. A moment later she was on her feet, shouting for the others to stop and listen. When she had their attention, she said, "The sun will be coming up shortly, so we're going to stop. I really appreciate your efforts here, working through the night and all. I had hoped by some ... *miracle* we could finish. I just want to thank you all. If you give me a few minutes to wash my hands, I'll pay you. I'll even treat you all to breakfast if you're not too tired to eat."

She watched as one student left the group and stepped forward, a young man with weary eyes, wearing a straggly gray USC sweatshirt. "Ma'am, would you mind telling us why you're doing this?" he asked.

Half a dozen responses flew to Kate's mind, but she knew none of them would satisfy the young man in front of her. They had worked hard and diligently, she told him with tears in her eyes.

The young man looked at the others and then at the grayish dark sky. "If we move the flats according to color, we can finish it. After the sun comes up we can continue planting. The object here is to plant a rainbow. I don't think the plants actually have to be in the ground. From *up there* it will look complete. Move! Move! We have about eight minutes."

In her life Kate never saw such a concentrated effort. She heard shouts of, "More pink, I need a blue, purple, no, no, yellow goes here, the pink there, hurry, faster, more purple, the red goes at the end. Move! Move! Three minutes, more blue, the daisies go there, two minutes, it's almost up, come on, Beasley, you're on the goddamn track team, move it! That's it, one more minute . . . all purple here. Thirty seconds, you got it!"

"Oh, my God!" Kate said, smiling through her tears.

"I'll be damned," Gus said.

"It's beautiful," Ellie said in awe.

"Heavenly," Della said.

"Guys, we do good work," said the kid in the USC shirt. To Kate he said, "Now what?" He looked uncomfortable when he added, "Shouldn't you sort of point, say something, you know, maybe a prayer?"

Kate licked her dry lips. Her tongue felt swollen and thick. She raised her eyes, palms upward. "Hey, Donald," she shouted as loud as she could. "This is for you! For your son, Bobby! For your daughter, Lucia!"

"And now I'm going to make breakfast for everyone," Della said. "Ellie, you will go to the store to buy eggs and bacon."

"Thank you, thank you so much," Kate said, walking among the boys to shake their hands. "If you want to go for a swim, go ahead. We'll make breakfast. This is going to be a long break, and you each get a bonus."

Kate's eyes were moist but full of stars when she looked at Gus. "I never would have thought about lining up the flats, would you?"

"Nope. I'd have kept on digging and planting, though. That kid homed in on it right away. And we're older and supposed to be smarter."

"That's why we send them to college." Kate laughed. "It looks so pretty. I can just see Donald's face. It was worth it, every single backbreaking minute of it. I can use some coffee, how about you?"

"You aren't mad at me for calling you a quitter?"

"Why should I be mad? It was the truth. I would have quit. All my life I've been a quitter. When things get hard or I don't want to deal with them, I crawl into a shell and blank everything out. No, I'm not mad."

Later, coffee cups in hand, the kids' voices echoing up from the pool, Kate said, "What are you going to do, Gus?"

"I have options," he said carefully.

"The *Times* is no shabby paper. Can you rethink . . . Your family is all back there. By the way, did you ever tell them about, you know, the house in Connecticut?"

"Actually, no. I got an attack of conscience and went back to Stamford. I was going to give the goddamn money back, but the house was empty. I checked around and found out the old man sold out his half of the business to his partner and took off. The guy handed me an envelope. He said my old man said I'd show up sooner or later and he was to give it to me. I expected a letter telling me why he left us. Maybe an 'I'm sorry' kind of letter. Maybe he'd asked about Ma or the others. There was no letter, no note. I wanted to bawl. Hell, I did bawl in the car."

"What was in the envelope?"

"The deed to that fancy eight-million-dollar estate. I guess there was a note of sorts. Scrawled across the front of the deed, in pencil, it said, 'You said you want what I have. Here it is. If you're reading this, it means you came here to give back the money, and that makes you a fool.' "

"Why didn't you say something to me? When did this happen?"

Gus shrugged. "A couple of months ago. I did feel like a fool. I didn't know what to do, so I called a family meeting. Jesus, you should have heard them. They called me every name in the damn book. In the end it had nothing to do with the money. They wanted to see him. They said they had as much right as I did and I took that right away. My mother's eyes were so sad. I disappointed her. In time they might forgive me, but I doubt it. I divvied up the money, sent them all checks. But none of 'em cashed them. My mother refused to take a cent. So for all intents and purposes I still have the damn money, and now I have that . . . Mafia-looking estate. Oh, I lied. I didn't get fired. I don't even know why I said that. So, being a quitter isn't half as bad as what I am. I guess I was hoping you'd feel sorry for me and ask me to stay out here. The only thing left back there for me is a few friends. My family hangs up on me if I call. I can't stand to see the hurt in my mother's face, so I don't go there anymore."

"Oh, Gus, I'm sorry. Life is never easy, is it?"

"I guess it would be pretty boring if it was."

"I'm sure your family will soften in time. Family is so wonderful. You'll pull together."

"I told them what he was like, about his flashy new wife, the big estate, and how arrogant he was. They all refused to believe he didn't ask about them. Even my mother wanted to know what he said about her. I lied to her, told her he said he hoped she was well. She fucking smiled at me when I said that, and then she got this awful look on her face. I swear to God I thought she was going to tell me to invite him for dinner. Instead she said, 'Gustav, you did a terrible thing.' Then she gave me a whack on the side of the head that made me sore for a week."

"You found him once, so you can find him again. Your brothers and sisters have all that money now. They can look for him, too," Kate said, sounding desperate.

"Don't you think my old man is thinking exactly what you just said? No, he's gone. With his obvious connections, I'd say he's in Europe or someplace in Argentina. He doesn't want to be found. I'm not sure why. I blew it."

"I still think time will heal the wounds. You said you were

a close family. Sooner or later they'll come around to under-standing and forgiving you. You have to go back, Gus. You have to be there when that time comes. You'll hate yourself if you don't."

"I know."

"Just so you know." Kate smiled and reached for his hand.

CHAPTER
14

It was downright cold, Kate thought when she climbed behind the wheel of her newly leased Mercedes 560 SL. She
was wearing a white wool coat with a champagne-colored
cashmere scarf. She looked exactly like what she was, a
highly successful businesswoman whose bank balance was
the picture of health. The last year and a half since Donald's
death had been the busiest of her life. When she'd found herself without Della and Donald, she panicked, throwing herself into her work, often staying at the office overnight. She
now had branches in Los Angeles and San Diego and was
contemplating a third in San Francisco.

She was on her way to Los Angeles to spend a few days
with Ellie and to monitor business at the second location.
And to do some shopping on Rodeo Drive.

"If I was happy, I'd have it all," Kate muttered as she slid a tape into the tape deck. Roy Orbison's clear voice relaxed her almost immediately. She fired up a cigarette and thought about Gus. She always thought about Gus when she was relaxed or about to fall asleep. She even thought about him when she woke in the morning or was in the shower. She dreamed about him, fantasized, but never acted on the dreams or fantasies.

Gus was upset with her. He'd invited her East for the holidays, but she'd declined, saying she always spent Christmas with Ellie and that maybe Della would come back. She'd been so rattled with his invitation that she hadn't thought to invite him to spend the holidays with her until later, and then she'd known he would think of it as an afterthought on her part. Sometimes she couldn't do anything right, especially when it came to Gus. Their friendship—because that's how she thought of it—had progressed to the point where she knew that if she didn't make a move, the whole thing would fall apart. It bothered her that she couldn't make a . . . What was it Gus wanted? A promise, a definite time when things would change. Commitment. The word scared the hell out if her. Commitment meant she would have to make love with Gus. In her mind and heart she was capable, but her body . . . her body was fearful. Her age was like a lighted beacon that sent shivers of fear down her spine. He was thirty-two now, going on thirty-three. She was forty-six going on forty-seven. The numbers didn't change. In three more years she'd be fifty. She'd be half a century old. She'd go through menopause. She'd start to drip sweat and get cranky; her skin would get dry and her face would turn beet-red with the hot flashes. It would be a nightmare. Her skin would lose its elasticity. Her hair would probably start to get thin on the top, her earlobes would wrinkle, and the lines around her eyes and mouth would deepen. Her rear end would droop, the skin around her knees would start to wrinkle, veins would show. And she'd just read something recently in one of the women's magazines that said facial hair was a problem at menopause.

She had three years until the nightmare became a reality. Maybe longer, since it wasn't engraved in stone that menopause started precisely at fifty. Three years to *do something*. She was entitled. She deserved to do something. The life she'd led for the past nineteen years wasn't natural. Always when she came to this part in her thinking she drew back, refused to think about being involved with *someone* in a sexual, romantic way. Gus was too young for her. She'd seen him with Ellie, teasing her, laughing with her, kibbitzing. Ellie or someone Ellie's age was more suitable for him. No matter what she did, no matter how she dressed, no matter how she thought, those fourteen years would always be there. When she was sixty Gus would be forty-six. When she was sixty-five and ready for Social Security, Gus would be fifty-one. There was no way he could catch up. Her hair would be gray and frizzy, she'd probably have a partial plate in her mouth, her fingernails would have ridges and her toenails would be yellow and ugly. Gus would be in his prime. Men in their fifties were always mature, worldly, and distinguished. She should know, she dealt with them on a daily basis—successful businessmen with wives and families and mistresses on the side.

She was an old maid, a dried-up old maid. And there was no excuse for it.

Kate's thoughts stayed with her all the way into Los Angeles. She drove straight to Olive Garden, where Ellie was taking her to lunch. "It's three blocks from the Big Eight firm I work for," Ellie had said last night. "I only have an hour for lunch, so if you get there first, order for me. Ziti will be fine. Oil and vinegar on my salad."

"Mom, you look like . . . a million bucks," Ellie now chortled happily. "I've never seen you look this good. Is there a new man in your life?"

Kate flushed. "No," she said, more sharply than she intended.

"New hairdo—and may I say it is fashionable. If I'm not mistaken, that's Sun Glitz in your hair, and I know a Chanel suit when I see one. And a Chanel bag. Come on, Mom, what's the scoop?" Ellie teased.

Her face warm, Kate said, "There *is* no scoop."

"Then what's with the trip to Rodeo Drive *to shop*?"

"Christmas is only a few weeks away. If I don't shop, there won't be any presents under the tree."

Ellie waited until the waitress had placed their wine spritzers in front of them before she spoke. "Mom," she said, leaning across the table, "I need to talk to you about something. How upset would you be if I . . . went to Denver with Pete for Christmas? He wants me to meet his parents. It's serious, Mom. I think he's going to give me an engagement ring. I want to go, but I don't want to leave you alone. If Della were here, I wouldn't feel so bad. . . . Jeez, Mom, you aren't going to cry, are you? If you cry, you're going to slop up your makeup and ruin the effect of that suit and the Glitz in your hair."

"God forbid," Kate said, dabbing at her eyes. "Oh, Ellie, of course it's okay for you to go. I'm crying because you're getting engaged. I like Pete, he's a great guy. I'm so happy for you, darling, really happy." She reached across the table to squeeze her daughter's hand.

"Pete reminds me of Gus, Mom. He's got the same laid-back attitude, the same warm, crinkly grin. He cares passionately about everything, animals, the environment. For an accountant, he's not boring at all. He wants us to open our own office at some point in the future. Nylander and Nylander. Has a ring to it, don't you think?"

"Definitely," Kate said.

"That means you're going to be loose for the holidays. That's going to bother me, Mom."

"Maybe I'll take a vacation and go see Della. Won't that be a surprise? I wish she'd write more often. God, Ellie, I can't tell you how much I miss her. I write once a week. She calls me from a store once a month. She sounds awful. All her spirit seems to be gone. I begged her to come back. I threatened to get a cat and told her it would be her replacement. She didn't even chuckle."

"Listen, Mom," Ellie said between mouthfuls of her salad, "on the off chance you wouldn't be upset about me going to Denver, I took the liberty of looking into a vacation for you. Before you say no, listen and then make up your mind. The travel agent said she could start you out from San Diego. You could have three days—two, or more if you want, with Della, and from there a trip to Hawaii. A tour trip so you wouldn't be alone. People your age. Men and women. You'll visit all the islands and have private accommodations. On Kona you'll be staying in a grass hut on a lagoon. It looks wonderful. You'll make friends, meet people, eat, put on some weight, get a tan, and come back full of vinegar. You need a vacation. I can make all the arrangements, all you'll have to do is get on the plane. I wish I could give you the trip as a present, but I can't afford it. What do you say?"

"Do you need my answer right this minute?" Kate said, flustered.

"Yes, Mom, I do. This is the holiday season. I'll need a check, too."

"Okay, I'll do it. Ellie, honey, do you need money?" The checkbook was in her hand.

"No. I'm fine. I didn't even charge Christmas presents this year. I paid cash and only bought things made in the U.S.A. Pete is real big on buying only American."

"Are you sure? Would you rather have gifts or money for Christmas?"

Ellie laughed. "I like to open presents, and I like money, too. I'll leave it up to you, Mom. Hmmmm, I can't wait to dig into this ziti, but first I have to call the travel agent. I'll drop off the check after work. Mom, you're going to have a great time. Now you can really shop Rodeo Drive. Go for the flash—on you it'll look great! I'll be right back."

Ellie sprinted like a young colt out to the foyer of the restaurant. She used her calling card, her blunt nails tapping on the hard metal tray beneath the phone.

"Gus Stewart, what can I do for you?"

Ellie giggled. "It's not what you can do for me, it's what I can do for you. It's a done deed, Gus. She agreed and is writing out the check as we speak. I don't think I'd let her see you until the plane is in the air."

"Thanks, Ellie, and Merry Christmas. I owe you."

"Damn right. Make sure my wedding present is a handsome one."

"You got it! Listen, you aren't upset over this, are you?" Gus asked anxiously.

"Hardly. I think you're the best thing that ever happened to Mom. If you can get her past that age thing, you'll both be real happy. Merry Christmas, Gus."

Ellie was breathless when she sat down at the table. "Everything will be mailed to you, Mom. All you gotta do is get yourself to the airport and do some shopping. Look for exquisite, Mom, and get one really knock-'em-dead outfit."

"You sound like you're plotting a seduction," Kate said sourly. She was already regretting her decision to make the trip.

"Mom, if I give you the money, will you pick up something for Della for me? By the time I get it, wrap it, and mail it out, it won't get there till after Christmas. You're going to see her, and it would save me a lot of worry."

"Certainly. Della is the hardest person in the world to shop for. However, I have my present all paid for and wrapped up," Kate said smugly.

Ellie fanned her mouth, string cheese dripping down her chin. "Jeez, this is hot. What'd you get her?"

"Drink some cold water," Kate said in the motherly voice she rarely got to use these days. "I had an aerial photograph made of the rainbow this summer. I got it enlarged, and it came out just beautiful. I hope she likes it. I also got her a shawl; it's got every color of the rainbow on it, fringe, too. That's what I wrapped the picture in."

"You are creative." Ellie handed over twenty-five dollars to her mother. "I know this kind of limits your choice, but do the best you can, and don't you dare add anything to it. If you do, it won't be the same. Della doesn't care about price tags."

"Have you seen or talked to your sister?" Kate asked carefully.

"You mean since Donald's funeral? Once. I ran into her in the drugstore. Can you beat that? Dr. Starr, as she likes to be called these days, now has a political science degree. She fancies herself an authority on Southeast Asian affairs. She was with a very . . . radical-looking individual. She looked great. She asked about you. She didn't mention Donald or Della. I told her about Della. This is all by the antacid section. I asked her if she had a job, and she said, 'I expected you to say something like that.' End of quote. She was dressed well. She's collecting donations from private individuals for a group of mercenary types to go on into Laos. Seems there's been some kind of sighting, and she thinks Dad might be one of the POWs in the picture that's been flashed around. She's nuts, Mom."

"Obsessed," Kate said quietly.

"No, Mom, nuts. You have to be nuts to give up your family. She doesn't care about us. She made me so damn mad, I told her about the rainbow, and I don't think she heard a word I said. I told her to drop dead and left."

"Ellie, you didn't!" Kate cried.

"Yeah, I did. I'm not sorry, either. Lord, look at the time. I gotta go. You're paying, right?" She flashed a grin, hugged her mother, and was gone a second later.

Kate finished her coffee, smoked a cigarette, and paid the bill. "Rodeo Drive, here I come," she muttered as she steered the car into traffic.

Kate whizzed from store to store, buying anything and everything that struck her fancy. Each time she returned her platinum American Express card to her wallet, she wondered if it would go through a meltdown process. She had Ellie's gifts wrapped and shipped direct to her apartment, bearing DO NOT OPEN TILL XMAS stamped on each one. She did the same to Betsy's presents and wondered if her daughter would accept them or if she would send a Christmas card in return. When she sent out her Christmas cards, she would enclose a check for both Ellie and Betsy.

On the drive home, munching a bagel she'd bought earlier, she thought about all the things she'd purchased for herself for her sudden vacation. She giggled when she remembered how she'd told the clerk, "I'll take this in every color" or "I'll take two of those, three of those, and I'll take this with me." She'd spent a bloody fortune. A case of fine wine shipped to Gus, gifts from Gucci for her office staff, gifts for everyone she knew. The United Parcel man was going to need a truck just for her purchases. But she felt really good about her day, and made a mental note to go shopping more often. She'd come a long way from the days when she used to sew her own clothes, decorating them with frills and geegaws. She winced when she remembered what she called her "artsy days."

It was late by the time Kate got home. This was the part she hated the most, coming home to a dark, cold house with no fragrant smell to greet her. She usually turned on the television, the radio, and every light in the house the minute she walked in. Then she made coffee, listened to her messages, snacked on whatever was in the refrigerator, curled up on the sofa and called Gus.

The packages she'd brought home with her were scattered

all over the den floor. She could hardly wait to tell Gus about her day. She heard the machine come on and, disappointed, left her name and the time she called. She frowned when she realized he might be out on a date. He hadn't actually *said* he dated, but he was a young, virile man. The thought perturbed her. She tried his number again at eleven-thirty before she crawled into bed. This time she didn't leave a message. Her face burned when she thought of him in bed with a *younger* woman whose skin was soft and slick. She had no strings on Gus. He could do as he pleased, just as she could do as she pleased. Only she didn't please.

Her dreams were invaded by a handsome pilot spraying bullets into her rainbow garden, which was dormant for the winter. "Run, Gus, run. He wants to kill you!" she shouted. She was running, too, dragging a huge trash bag full of gaily wrapped Christmas presents. The rat-a-tat sound of the bullets slapping into the ground around her running feet woke her. She was breathing hard, her chest heaving with the effort. She fell back against the pillow, her mind in turmoil as she tried to fathom the dream. It was raining out, the fat drops slamming against the window with the force of the wind. Patrick was the pilot, of course. He wanted to kill Gus because she was contemplating *something*. She'd been trying in the dream to protect Gus. Why? What did that bag of Christmas presents mean? All those gifts from earlier days that she and the girls had wrapped so lovingly and never had a chance to give.

Kate was awake now. "Damn!" She hadn't dreamed about Patrick for years, and she rarely thought of him these days. She must have dreamed about him now because of Ellie's news of Betsy. She squeezed her eyes shut and tried to picture Patrick. She used every trick she knew to conjure up his image, but it wouldn't surface. Instead, Gus's crazy features flashed behind her closed lids. He had such a gentle smile, such caring eyes. His touch was gentle, too. Her eyes snapped open when she remembered her last phone call with no answer on the other end of the line. Her hand snaked out from under the covers to snatch the clock. Good Lord, it was nine o'clock! Noon in New York. Gus should have called her by now. Unless he didn't go back to his apartment last night. In the past he'd always returned her phone calls.

Kate leaped from the bed. She would not think about this. By the time she showered, dressed, and made coffee, she had fixed in her mind an image of the girl she thought Gus had spent the evening with. She was twenty-six, maybe twenty-eight, a professional, wearing a crisp suit with a crisp white blouse and a single strand of pearls. She wore Bally shoes, had a French manicure, a casual wash-and-wear hairstyle. She was shapely, looked good in *anything*. She was beautiful and witty. She drove a firecracker-red Porsche, had long, shapely legs, and wore spike-heeled shoes. She carried a briefcase, and was so experienced in bed that men, Gus in particular, became addicted to her charms after only one night. Her name was . . . was Gennifer with a G, not a J. G set her above all the other Jennifers in the Big Apple. "Shit!" Kate said succinctly.

She stomped about the kitchen in search of food. The withered wrinkled apples in the fruit bowl had been sitting there for a month. The bread in the refrigerator had mold on it, as did the cheese. The lone cucumber in the vegetable bin was a slimy mass of yellow, putrid-looking seeds and skin. The bag of Oreo cookies was full of tiny bugs, and so was the box of Ritz crackers. God, how long had she had this stuff? Obviously she had to go to the grocery store, and there was no better time than right now. She would take the day off, too—go to the store, fill her car with groceries, come home, put them away, and then cook. Maybe she'd even bake a pie. Then she would sit down and eat everything. She wasn't going to call the office, either. And for sure she wasn't going to answer the phone. Maybe she'd make some fudge, with marshmallow fluff, peanut butter, and real nuts. A banana cream pie. A roast chicken with stuffing. She could eat all week. Maybe a pot of spaghetti. She could freeze everything into portions. She'd eat the whole pie through and most of the fudge. Let Gennifer What's-her-name eat the bean sprouts and yogurt. *She* wasn't trying to trap anyone, she didn't need to stay needle-thin. She was a real woman, one who liked to eat.

"Oh, shit!" she muttered as she yanked on her raincoat. "Shit, shit, shit!"

CHAPTER
15

When Kate returned home from the market with eleven bags of groceries, she could hear the phone ringing. "Ring, damn you, see if I care," she muttered as she started to put away her groceries. Earlier she'd disconnected the answering machine. She was being silly, stupid. And so *very* jealous. As she slammed boxes of cereal and rice into the cabinet any old way, she kept muttering over and over, "Gennifer with a G, Gennifer with a G." The faceless, nameless person was rapidly taking on an identity in her mind, and with each hour she grew more beautiful, more sophisticated, more upscale. Now she was model-thin, incredibly beautiful, with full, pouting lips and a mane of hair that was just curly enough, had just enough body to it, so she could toss her head and have it fly around like a moving nimbus.

Her groceries tucked away, Kate banged the frying pan on the stove to brown the chopped meat for the spaghetti. Her mind attacked Gus when the phone shrilled. He was with Gennifer with a G, a sappy look on his face. Gennifer with a G would stretch like a cat, the nipples in her breasts taut beneath the thin sheet. "C'mere, love," she'd purr. "I know what you want. We have time, love." Yes, yes, she'd call him something stupid like "love." Gennifer with a G would surely say, "We have time for a little . . . nookie. . . ." No, she wouldn't say that. She'd say, "Oooohhh, make love to me again." And still wearing the same sappy look, Gustav Stewart would oblige. Twice. But was Gennifer with a G exhausted? Not on your life. She'd get up, stretch, making Gus aware of her high, firm breasts, her perfectly flat belly, her perfectly proportioned rear end. He'd groan and maybe moan, bury his head in the pillow, and say, "Let's do it again. Soon. Real soon." Gennifer with a G would toss her mane of hair, wink slyly and say, "It all depends, love, on what you have to offer." At which point he'd rear up and say, "How does an eight-million-dollar estate in Connecticut and four million in the bank sit with you?" She'd give her tush a seductive wiggle and say, "If you're telling me the truth, love, just fine. This body, all one-hundred-ten pounds, is yours."

"You son of a bitch!" Kate screeched as the onions started to burn. She scraped at them with a vengeance. "You said you were dividing the money up, you said you didn't want the estate. You bastard! You stinking, lousy bastard!"

The phone shrilled. Kate shut the stove off. The man hadn't been born she would trust now. First Patrick and now Gus. "I always harbored a secret fear that at some time in our life Patrick would be unfaithful, but I never thought you would, Gus," she whimpered. She flung open the refrigerator and reached for one of the bottles of wine she'd put in earlier. Supermarket wine. And she'd sent a whole case of 1924 Mouton Rothschild to *him* for Christmas. "Well, we'll just see about *that*! Gennifer with a G is not going to drink wine I paid for, either."

Her purse was still on the kitchen table, filled with all the receipts from yesterday's shopping. Kate rifled through them until she found the one she wanted. On the verge of tears, she tapped out the phone number, identified herself, gave her order number, and screamed into the phone, "Cancel that order! Credit my account. Buy your own goddamn wine, Miss Gennifer with a G!"

Kate poured white zinfandel into a water glass and drank greedily. In her life she'd never had a drink of wine at eleven o'clock in the morning. "Well, there's a first time for everything," she muttered as she tripped from room to room, removing telephone wires from the jacks.

At twelve-thirty she finished the wine, went to the bathroom, and was sick. She brushed her teeth, tottered back out to the kitchen, and uncorked a second bottle of zinfandel. At two o'clock she tried to march into the bathroom and was sick before she reached the door. "Oh, shit!" she muttered as she puked. "Now who's going to clean this up? Dellllll-aaaa! . . . Ah, the hell with it."

On her way back to the kitchen, she looked over her shoulder at the mess she'd left by the bathroom door. In true Scarlett fashion she said, "I'll think about that tomorrow. Then again, maybe I won't. Maybe I'll never use that bathroom again. Oh, Della, I miss you. I'm drunk, Patrick. You should see me. I puked my guts out. Twice!" she said triumphantly. "Gennifer with a G would never throw up, never lose control. Who give's a good rat's ass? Do you hear me, Patrick? I'm using dirty language and I'm drunk. It's pissifying. I learned these words from Ellie and her friends. What do you think of me now, Patrick?"

She should make coffee. She was cooking, wasn't she? The mess on the stove smelled good. The array of bottles, cans, and packages on the counter confused her. Maybe she should just throw it all away and start over. "Waste not, want not," she said, giggling. Later, when she felt . . . different, she'd figure out what to do with all the stuff. Now she needed coffee. Any fool could make coffee, even Gus.

She started to cry as she measured coffee into the wire basket, spilling half on the counter and half on the floor. She tried a second and third time before she got enough into the basket. She slopped water all over the package of spaghetti, stared at it for a minute, and then shrugged. "Who cares? I don't." She giggled again as she staggered over to one of the oak chairs and sprawled on it in a very unladylike pose. "I'm drunk, I'm drunk, I'm drunk," she mumbled in a singsong voice. Her stomach heaved threateningly. "I hate you, Patrick, for going off and leaving me. I hate Gus Stewart for being so unfaithful. But I *love* you, Della," she cried. "What's wrong with me that you all left me?" She dropped her head into her hands and cried for her loss. She was wailing, beating her fists on the kitchen table, when the front doorbell rang. "Go away!" she cried. "I didn't invite you, whoever you are. Leave me alone." The bell continued to ring, the coffee continued to perk. "Shut up, I have a headache," she muttered. There was instant silence; the doorbell stopped ringing and the percolator offered up its last plop. "I need a cat!"

Kate's eyes focused on the two wine bottles and the mess on the counter. My God, was it five o'clock already? "Who cares what time it is. It's just another day, another hour," she said as she poured out coffee into a giant-size cup. Who the hell was going to drink all this coffee? "Guess I am, since there's no one else here and I don't have a cat. God, I need a cat," she said, her eyes welling with tears of self-pity. Maybe Ellie would get her one, a tabby with yellow stripes and big eyes. She'd call it Betsy II.

She reached behind her to a bank of light switches and flicked on all six. The kitchen blazed with light. The floodlights on the deck and in the yard made her blink. The back doorbell rang. Kate looked at the sliding glass doors and saw two policemen peering in at her. "Go away, I gave at the office!" she shouted. The doorbell rang again.

"Mrs. Starr, will you open the door? We need to talk to you."

"Why?" Kate said craftily.

"Please, it will only take a minute."

"Did I do something wrong?"

"No, we just need to talk with you. Your phone doesn't seem to be working."

"Well, la-de-da. Since when is that the policeeee's business?" she said, slurring her words. "Go away."

"We're going to stay here until you open the door."

Kate thought about the words. "You will. Even if I go to bed?"

"Yes."

"If I give you a check, will you go away?"

"If you open the door first to hand it to us."

"Oh, no, I'll slide it under the door. Come back tomorrow."

"Mrs. Starr, if you don't open the door, we'll break it."

"Then you'll pay for it," Kate said spiritedly. "That's . . . that's breaking and entering. This is my castle, you can't do that." She turned her back on the policemen and started to drink her coffee.

The back doorbell rang again. "Ellie sent us," one of the officers said. "We're friends. Now will you open the door?"

"She's such a sweet child. Did she give you the tickets to bring all the way here?"

"Mrs. Starr, open the door."

"I can't find the lock. It won't open. Guess I can't let you in," Kate said, sashaying back to the table. "Just leave the tickets on the deck. I'll call somebody to open the door tomorrow."

"Mrs. Starr, go around to the front door and open it. You can open the front door, can't you?"

"Do I have to sign for the tickets? This is such a bother." She staggered to the front door. The moment the door was open, the two officers each reached for one of Kate's arms and led her backward. "Mrs. Starr, I'm Officer Archer and

218

this is my partner, Officer Enright. Your daughter called us, she was worried about you. Then your office called us, and then a man named Gustav Stewart called us."

Kate drew herself up haughtily, shaking off the officers. "You lied, you don't have the tickets. I don't care if the President of the United States called you. I don't want you here. You should be out catching criminals, not bothering people like me. Are you going to call those people?"

"They're going to call back. Your daughter was worried about you. Why didn't you answer the phone, Mrs. Starr? Is it out of order?"

"I unplugged it. I didn't feel like going to the office. I wanted to make spaghetti today. That's not a crime."

"Did you make it?"

"What?"

"The spaghetti?"

"No." Kate sighed. "I drank wine instead. I drank too much and got sick. I made coffee, though," she said brightly. "You won't tell that to Gus, will you?" She started to cry and then to babble about Patrick, about Betsy, about being alone. "I can't possibly compete with Gennifer with a G. I'm almost fifty years old. She's got this flyaway hair and . . . she calls people 'love.' He fell for it, too."

The officers looked at one another before they led Kate back to the kitchen. Officer Archer poured fresh coffee for her before he settled her on the chair. "Tell me what to say to your daughter. She's worried about you. Think about that for a minute while I plug the phone in."

"If it rings, don't answer it! This is my house."

Archer held up his hand. "I hear you, Mrs. Starr, we won't answer the phone." He eyed the two wine bottles. "Did you drink both bottles, Mrs. Starr?"

"Yes, I did," Kate said stiffly. "I'm in my own house and can do whatever I damn well please. I can swear if I want to, too."

"What should we tell your daughter?"

"Tell her . . . tell her I screwed up. Tell her I'm sorry if she was worried. She can call the office. Don't . . . Tell her *not* to call Gus. What are you going to tell him if he calls you back?" Kate asked suspiciously. "Tell him the truth, tell him I wouldn't open the door."

"That's only half the truth," Archer said, not unkindly.

"He doesn't deserve the whole truth. I'm going to be embarrassed if I see you in town or on the street."

"Don't be, Mrs. Starr. We all have days when things crowd in on us. Alcohol doesn't make things better, but I think you already know that. Look, why don't we call your daughter from here, tell her you're all right. You're going to leave all the lights on and you're going to sleep this off. We'll check back later, come around back to make sure things are okay. We'd like it if you'd sleep on that couch over there so we'll be able to see you from the sliding doors. Will you do that, Mrs. Starr? Do you want the answering machine on?"

"Yes, and no to the answering machine. Turn the phone low."

"All right," Archer's partner said, leading her to the couch. "Does your front door lock automatically?"

"Yes." Kate leaned back on the pillows the officer placed behind her head. She listened to the officer's voice as he spoke on the phone.

"Your mother is fine, Miss Starr. She's a little under the weather right now and is about to go to sleep. She had a bad day. . . . No, I don't think you should make the drive up here. We're going to look in on her later. She said you should call the office for her. She doesn't want anything said to the gentleman who called the station. The one you said called you also. She's quite adamant about that."

Kate fought the blanket of sleep that was about to engulf her. She had to remember what the officer was saying to Ellie. It was important because it was about Gus. She surrendered to sleep with Gus's name on her lips and in her thoughts.

Archer checked out the sliding door. "No wonder she couldn't open it, there's a rod in the track. It might be a good idea for us to take the key, return it tomorrow. She could sleep for hours or for twenty minutes. She looked pretty upset to me. You know who she is, don't you, Enright? Her husband is the one who was shot down over Vietnam and has never come back. She raised her girls on her own, started up a business, again, on her own. She got fed up with the government and the Air Force and buried her husband's things. It was in the paper a few years ago. If this is all she's ever done that wasn't on the straight and narrow, I don't think we should judge her. This Gus person sounds like he's at the root of whatever it was that set her off today."

Enright grinned. "She's going to have one hell of a hangover tomorrow."

"Yeah, I don't think the lady ever had one before. Maybe we should leave her a note. 'Tomato juice with a squirt of Tabasco sauce. Drink this and it won't be so bad. Add three aspirins if the headache is unbearable.' "

Enright scrawled the note and propped it up against one of the wine bottles, then the two officers let themselves out of the house. They checked on Kate twice during the evening. She was sleeping peacefully at eleven o'clock when they went off duty. Their replacements checked on her at two in the morning and again at five-thirty. Their report to Archer and Enright was, "The lady is sleeping peacefully." By mutual consent the report they filed read, "Mrs. Starr's phone was disconnected. She was making spaghetti when we arrived. Mrs. Starr was fine when we left the house and said she would call her daughter to tell her she was all right."

Kate woke at seven the following morning with a pounding headache and a sour stomach that got worse the moment she walked into the kitchen. She ignored the softly buzzing phone as she headed for the bathroom off her bedroom. When she returned to the kitchen dressed in a vibrant purple robe, her hair wrapped in a bright orange towel, she saw the note and cringed but followed the instructions. She gagged twice, but the juice stayed down. She felt a little better an hour after she took the aspirins. She cleaned up the kitchen and the mess she'd left by the bathroom door, swearing at the same time never, ever, to drink wine again. She curled up on the couch and slept the better part of the day. When she woke at six o'clock, she played the messages on the machine. Eleven were from Gus, three from Ellie. The tape was full.

Kate made tea and called Gus at the office. Her voice sounded nasally and scratchy when she identified herself.

"What the hell happened?" he said. "I've been calling you all day and all last night. I thought something happened to you. I called Ellie and the police. Don't ever do that again, Kate. I tried calling you back the other night when I got in. Jesus, Kate, I've been sick with worry."

Kate smiled. "I'm sorry, Gus," she said happily. That meant there was no Gennifer with a G. "I don't know what got into me." Her headache was less intense, almost gone—in fact, she felt light-headed.

"I can't tell you the kinds of things I was thinking. God, an imagination, especially one like mine, is a killer."

"I know what you mean. Sometimes mine gets away from me, too," Kate said lightly.

They talked for an hour, then: "Listen, Kate, I'll call you tomorrow, okay?"

"Sure. I'm going to make some spaghetti now."

Instead of making spaghetti, Kate stretched out on the couch, the portable phone at her elbow, closed her eyes and daydreamed. Her name was Cate with a C and she was forty-six years old. . . .

CHAPTER
16

Kate looked up at the garish sign over the shop in Tijuana, Mexico. Jesus Tobacco Shop. She stepped carefully on the rotted, wooden step. The shop seemed to sell everything. She'd expected displays of cigarettes and cigars but didn't see any. She did see a telephone. So this was where Della came to make the few calls she'd placed over the past year. "Señor," she said slowly, distinctly, "Can you send someone to fetch Señora Della Rafella?"

"Sí, but it will do you no good. Señora Della has gone to help her niece. It is miles. One day if you go in a car, two days if you are walking. Then two days coming back. She will stay one week to help. New babies take much care. Many pesos, señora."

"Oh no!" Damn, she hadn't counted on this. So much for the surprise element. Four days. Her plane left for Hawaii tomorrow evening. She shook her head. "If I leave a note, will you see that Señora Della gets it when she returns?"

"Sí, señora."

Kate ripped a blank page from her address book. Thank God she didn't know anyone whose name started with an O. She handed the shopkeeper a ten-dollar bill along with the note.

"She is your friend?" the man said curiously.

"The best friend I ever had. I miss her very much. Do you know her well?"

"She does much good for her family, and for others, too. She is an American citizen," he said proudly, "and still she stays here with her people. She comes in often. Much sad eyes," he said, shaking his head. "Much like yours, señora."

"You won't forget to give her my note?" Kate said.

"No, señora, I will not forget. I do not get many American ladies here who want to leave notes. Is there anything you wish to buy?"

"Oh, yes, yes, there is. Cigarettes and . . . a lighter and these two key chains. I'll take that Bic pen and that note-book. This shoe polish and these mints and two boxes of that cherry Jell-O."

Thirty dollars changed hands. Kate knew she was being ripped off, but she didn't care. She accepted the greasy bag and left. Later she left the bag in a store she browsed through, buried beneath a pile of garish-looking shawls.

Back in her hotel in Chula Vista, Kate showered and watched television the rest of the day. She went to bed early and slept late, rising to order room service, shower, and go to church. She walked around town, had lunch, and returned to the hotel. She repacked her overnight bag, checked out, and arrived at the airport three hours ahead of schedule. She ate again and read several magazines as she waited for the tour director to arrive.

"I'm going to strangle you, Ellie," she muttered when the

tour director, a giddy young girl of nineteen or so, arrived, her charges trailing behind her. All of them, Kate noticed, were retirees with white hair. At a glance she knew there wasn't one of them under seventy years of age. She would just have to make the best of it.

An hour later when the director herded them onto the plane, Kate drew her aside and said, "Why are you patronizing these people? And do you have to yell at the top of your lungs? I'm not deaf, and neither is anyone else. I don't see any reason for you to hold up those ridiculous signs, either. I'm embarrassed for them. Think about that, Miss Tour Director. I won't be joining you once I get to Hawaii. The agency that booked me on this tour obviously didn't have my best interests at heart. Was it really necessary to have each of us stand and expound on our backgrounds? We aren't children, and I resent it. I have half a mind to cancel this tour and go off on my own right now."

"Are you saying I'm overdoing it? You have to be careful with older people. They want things explained, they wear hearing aids and bifocals."

"Which makes them see and hear better, so you don't need the signs and don't need to shout. You embarrassed all of us."

"All right," the director said stiffly. "What are you, some kind of mentor, watchdog or something? *Company spy?*"

Kate just smiled. "Or something," she said, thinking of Della and Donald. "Just because you're old doesn't mean you're a fool, and it doesn't give *you* the right to humiliate people."

Taking her seat in the smoking section at the back of the plane, Kate wondered what had gotten into her to make her speak up that way. In twenty years I'll have white hair like them and I'll be taking a trip like this, that's why, she answered herself. When she was seventy Gus would be fifty-six. She'd be doddering and he'd be pushing her along with a spring in his step. She shuddered. God, why had she allowed Ellie to talk her into this? Christmas should be spent at home with loved ones. But the few loved ones she did have had other plans. No one wanted to spend Christmas with her. She'd be with strangers who had no one, either.

At the small airport in Kona, Kate parted company with the tour. She collected her bags, rented a car, and received a map showing her the way to Kona Village. "Just watch for the little hut on the side of the road," the rental agent said. "Make a left and it will take you to the village."

Kate missed the hut and had to drive five miles before she could turn around and make her way back. "She should have told me it was set back in from the road," she muttered as she whipped the open Jeep around the corner. For miles all she could see was black lava. Where was all the greenery and bright flowers? The word *devastation* came to her mind as she drove the rutted dusty road. "I am going to kill you, Ellie, with my bare hands, when I get hold of you." Where in the damn hell was civilization?

Finally a speck of green caught her eye. A palm tree. Thank God. And water; she could smell the ocean. Kate continued to drive. At last she came to the village. She sucked in her breath: here there were flowers and greenery. People. A slice of paradise. She looked back over her shoulder but couldn't see the fields of black lava.

Kate smiled when a woman dressed in native costume came out to the car to place a fragrant lei around her neck. "Welcome to Kona Village. And you are . . . ?"

"Kate Starr. I was with the Cromwell tour, but I won't be staying with them. I understand I have my own quarters. I'd also like to make my own eating arrangements."

"There won't be a problem, Mrs. Starr. Come with me, please." The woman smiled and led the way to the office, settling Kate behind a tiny teakwood desk. "It will be just a moment until I get registration forms. In the meantime, enjoy this fresh pineapple juice," she said, offering Kate a small, frosted glass before leaving her alone.

Kate settled back and looked at the brochure on the desk. The world's most prized hideaway ... 125 thatched *hales*. She flipped over the brochure. Happy Hour at the Bora Bora Bar from five to six P.M. On Tuesday there would be a General Manager's Cocktail and Pupu Party, whatever that was. Sailing and snorkeling. Tennis. Sport fishing. Helicopter flightseeing. Therapeutic body massage. "Ah," Kate said, sipping the pineapple juice. Shiatsu, Swedish Massage. Reflexology, hand and foot massage. Hawaiian lomi lomi, electric methods of massage, local style. She made a note to sign up for one of each. Two dining rooms. Hale Moana for breakfast, lunch or dinner, and the Hale Somoa for dinner, no ties and jackets. Thong sandles were acceptable. Make dinner reservations at breakfast time. No phones, no radios, no televisions, no air-conditioning. Do not feed the wildlife. Kate closed the brochure packet.

"Did you like what you read?" the smiling woman asked, returning.

"Very much. It seems so quiet and restful here. I was surprised, though, that guests aren't given keys."

"I'm sure we can find a key if it would make you feel better."

"No, it's all right."

"I hope you brought a lot of reading material. We have a gift store with a nice selection of paperback books, and the newspapers are flown in every day. There is a phone around the corner from where we're sitting. Each *hale* has a mailbox. Should you receive messages, they will be placed there. Sign here, Mrs. Starr. Your bags have been taken to your *hale* and your car parked in the lot behind the swimming pool. Come with me now and I'll take you to your quarters."

The *hales* were thatched huts. Everything was magnificent. The lagoon was peaceful. "Is that a *black* swan?" Kate asked in amazement.

"Yes, there are several. As you can see, you have neighbors, but not too close. This is your *hale*, Mrs. Starr. If you need anything, come up to the office. There is a small map inside for walking about. Enjoy your stay with us."

"I'm sure I will," Kate said, in awe as she took in her new home.

The room was parrot bright, with a colorful spread over the bed. Two rattan chairs and a table completed the front room. A desk and a second bed/couch made up the second room. The bathroom vanity held a coffeepot with attached grinder along with a container of Kona coffee. A small refrigerator held soft drinks. Other than the shower and toilet, there was nothing else to see. She had a front porch with two chairs, the thatched fronds hanging down the sides to ward off the sun.

So far Kate hadn't heard a sound. Kona Village was certainly peaceful and quiet, but she'd have to work on the deluxe part. She bounced on the bed, checked the sliding glass door, and was relieved to see that it could lock from the inside. She turned on the paddle fan overhead. It whirred softly to life.

"I think I could get real depressed here," Kate muttered as she turned on a low-wattage lamp that did little to lighten the dim, cool room. "I do not like this!" she said aloud. "In fact, I think I hate it! I am not a sun person, I am not a beach person. I do not like living in dim, dark rooms." She kicked out at her suitcase and then yelped in pain.

"Is that a damsel-in-despair cry I just heard?" a voice called from the porch.

"Gus? . . . *Gus!* My God, *Gus*, it can't be you! I'm dreaming. I have dreams like this all the time. I cannot believe that you would show up and be staying in a grass hut the way I am. I hate this place. Do you hate it? Don't answer that. You aren't supposed to talk in dreams."

"Pinch me," Gus said, opening the screen door. Kate

pinched his bare arm. He said, "Ouch. See? It's not a dream."

"But how, you said . . . When did you get here? Do you like this place?"

"I got here yesterday. It's great, Kate. The food is out of this world. I look at it and gain weight. I had banana pecan pancakes for breakfast. I ordered seconds. The coffee is the best I've ever tasted. Both pools are super. It's a great place. For lovers," he said, winking at her. "It gets a little rowdy toward morning with different birds scratching on the roof. I got up early and had coffee on the porch. You should have seen the guests who came to call. There were twenty different birds out there, but I had nothing to feed them, and we aren't supposed to feed them anyway. God, Kate, it's good to see you. What say we shuck this place and you move in with me?"

Kate sucked in her breath. Was she ready for that? Damn right she was, she thought smartly. Well, almost ready. Sort of ready. *Absolutely not.* "Yes," she said.

"You mean it!"

"Gus, I'm forty-six years old. You're fourteen years younger than me. You're more suitable for Ellie. When I'm seventy you'll only be fifty-six."

"I want to marry you, Kate. I can make you happy. I'll love you forever. I can't picture my life without you in it."

"That's how I feel, but I don't know . . . marriage is . . . There's Patrick. . . ."

"There is no Patrick, Kate. You buried him, remember?"

"His things, Gus. Not his body."

"Do you love me?" He held his breath waiting for her reply. When it came, it *swoosh*ed out of him like a pricked balloon.

"Yes," she said without a moment's hesitation.

"Jesus. I never thought I'd hear you say that."

"Do you love me?"

"Do birds fly? Of course I love you. Why do you think I'm here? I cooked this up with Ellie. I want us to start the new year together. Guess that makes me one of those hopeless romantics. Ellie approves of me. She'll give us her blessing. My mother will like you."

"Your brothers and sisters?"

"Hey, they're coming around, just like you said. One of my sisters cashed her check. She has two kids in college. She's talking to me. It's a start."

"Are you going to kiss me?" Kate asked breathlessly.

"D'ya think I'm easy?" Gus grinned. "Not till I carry you over the threshold. We're moving in together, Kate. Grab one of those bags and let's get a move on."

He carried her over the threshold. Nothing in her life prepared Kate for the depth of emotion that swept through her. She loved this man, truly loved him, with every breath in her body. She said so.

"My God, I feel giddy," Gus said.

"I do, too," Kate said.

"We're going to do this right," Gus said nervously.

"Yes. If it isn't right, it won't work," Kate said. "What's right?"

"Jesus, I don't know, I had this all planned, I was going to ... ravage you, have my way with you, make you want me, make you want me so bad you'd kill for me."

Kate laughed shakily. "It sounds good."

"Which part?" Gus asked hoarsely.

"All of it."

His voice came out in a squeak. "All of it?"

"Uh-huh."

"I had this plan, you see. . . . What it was . . . is . . . was, I was going . . . how many 'was' was that? Whatever, I was going to kiss you, get you all fired up, and then I was going to cool it and say, 'Let's go for a walk so I can show you this place.' We need to get that out of the way. Then I thought

230

we'd come back here, mess around a little, clean up, maybe shower together, drive us both to the brink, and then we'd go to dinner. I signed you up this morning for six o'clock. We'd eat, drink a little, come back here and . . . and *do it*. What'ya think?"

"I think it all sounds like a wonderful plan. So, kiss me and let's get started."

It wasn't just a kiss, it was an event, Kate thought wildly as Gus's lips devoured hers. She moaned softly, opening her lips, felt his tongue spear into the silky recesses of her mouth and was rewarded with a deep animal sound that ground through her being. Their tongues meshed, wrapped around each other, until Kate drew away, gasping for breath. They gazed into each other's eyes. The only sound in the quiet hut was their breathing. Kate felt something primal about the way they were staring at one another. She wanted more, said so brazenly.

"About that walk and the rest of the plan . . ."

Kate's breath sighed in his ears when she said, "My feet hurt. Plans are meant to be broken. You're all the food I need."

"Brazen hussy," Gus said, ripping at his clothes. She ripped at hers.

Gus pulled down the parrot-colored spread that was identical to the one in Kate's hut. The sheets were crisp and white, unwrinkled. Pristine. Just the way I feel, Kate thought. The instant her head met the pillow, his body covered hers. There was a wild mating possessiveness to his embrace when he gathered her in his arms.

She felt a head rush, and then a small speck of alarm riveted through her, as if she were about to sail across an uncharted sea. She loosed a long, shuddering sigh as Gus's lips found and licked at the pulse in her neck. She curled into him so his lips could trail down to her breasts. She snuggled deeper, her fingers curling in the wiry furring on his chest, felt his involuntary tremor. She shivered in ecstasy when his tongue slid into the warm nectar of her mouth.

"Let go all the way, Kate," Gus whispered as his fingers skated up and down her spine, searching for the secret place between her thighs.

She could feel her body jerk to total awareness. She wanted more, much more, and said so. She was in a place now she'd never visited before, a place where she *wanted* to be, *needed* to be. She moved then, her hands cupping his face in her hands, smothering his mouth and chin with kisses before she explored his mouth with her hungry tongue.

"Oh, yeah, yeah. Don't stop," Gus groaned.

She felt powerful suddenly with his words, and proceeded to take the initiative, sliding smoothly on top of him. She smiled when she heard him groan again. The heat of his body mingled with hers, set off a banked fire she'd been holding in reserve all these years.

She teased him then, nibbling at his earlobes, whispering wondrous things in his ear while she explored the wet, slick length of him.

Before she knew what was happening, she was on her back, Gus over her, staring down at her. "You're so beautiful," he murmured. His hot breath seared her skin, making it impossible to think. All she wanted now, at this moment in time, was to feel, to taste, to *live*.

Her body was warm honey, her mouth a ranging volcano he sought to conquer. "Do you like this?" he moaned.

"Oh, yes, yes, I do," Kate moaned in return. Hungrily she brought his lips to her again. She felt his knee part her legs. "Not yet," she purred, grinding her body upward against his. She felt him shudder, drawing her up, up, until they were locked together in a sitting position, their bodies slick with sweat, grinding and rocking to the beat of some unheard music.

His hands moved, sliding up and down the sides of her

body. Needing the closeness of her, he drew her hard against him as she moaned, arching her back. He kissed her eyes, her lips, fiery kisses that trailed along her jaw, down to the valley between her breasts. The burning heat from his body transferred itself to her, scorching her skin. She was a brushfire gone wild, a raging forest fire that only Gus could extinguish. His summer-blue eyes were burning, the only bright color she could see in the dim room.

"Now," he whispered fiercely.

"Yes," Kate whispered in return.

Her body was exquisite, her responses delicious, but it was the expression on her face, the rapture and pleasure he saw there, that drove him forward. He read total joy and a hint of disbelief in her clear gaze, saw a lone tear in the little hollow under her eye. When relief came to both of them, her name exploded from him like a gunshot in the quiet room.

Kate lay still, her breathing matching his in hard little spurts. She should say something, she thought, or he should say something. Anything. What? God, she hadn't known sex could be this perfect, this wonderful. "I *liked* that," she gasped.

"You did, huh?" Gus said, smooching her cheek. "Well, guess what? I liked it, too. Hell, I goddamn *loved* it! What took us so long to get around to doing this?"

"My stupidity. On the other hand, maybe you weren't aggressive enough," she teased.

"You want aggressive? I'll give you aggressive"—Gus laughed—"but later. You wore me out, lady. I need a breather." Jesus, he was happy. He couldn't ever remember being this happy. She was his now. "You are, aren't you?" he said anxiously.

"Are what?" Kate sighed.

"Mine."

"All yours, forever and ever," she said happily. "I've never been this happy. In the whole of my life no one ever treated me the way you do. No one ever seemed to care about me the way you do. I was so afraid of this . . . afraid I wouldn't—couldn't—that you would be disappointed. Patrick was always disappointed in me. I think I was afraid of what I would see in your eyes."

"What did you see in my eyes, Kate?" Gus asked.

"Love," she said shyly.

"Kate, you will never see anything but love in my eyes. You've made my life complete. I've been trying to tell you that for so long. Do you realize what we've been missing? When are we going to get married?"

Kate's stomach lurched. "Gus, don't rush me. I have other . . . demons to set aside. Our age difference is no small thing to me. I have to work that out in my mind. Legally . . . am I a widow? I don't know. Do I get a divorce? I never . . . there wasn't any need. . . . I don't want to leave California. You live in New York. You have a good job, I have a business. Can we, for now, just enjoy what we have, and work at the rest of it?"

"Only on one condition, that this time next year we're married. We should be able to resolve everything in twelve months. Say it, Kate. I need to hear you say you want to marry me twelve months from now. We can come back here and do it. Say it, Kate," he said fiercely.

"In one year we'll come back here and get married. I do want that, Gus, more than anything. Waking up with you next to me every morning will be wonderful. Cooking for you, making love with you, doing your laundry. I want to say nice things to you and mean them, and I want to hear you say nice things to me and mean them, too. I want to be with you to watch the sun come up, and I want to be with you when that sun sets at the end of the day. I do love you, more than I ever thought I could love a man."

Gus sighed happily. "Okay, I accept that."

They talked for hours, about everything and anything.

When the torchlights were lit outside on the path, Gus said, "It's dark!"

"Now that's a brilliant deduction if I ever heard one." Kate giggled.

"I think we missed dinner," Gus said.

Kate snorted, a very unladylike sound. "Eat me," she gurgled. *God in heaven, did I say that?* "Let's go *ballistic* this time!"

Gus threw back his head and roared with laughter. He'd wakened a sleeping tiger. He obeyed the lady to the letter.

Kate stirred sleepily at three o'clock. She knew instantly where she was and what had transpired earlier. All the proof she needed was lying next to her. She smiled to herself in the darkness as she listened to Gus's lusty snores. A shout of happiness birthed in her belly, stretched upward, and was about to explode from her mouth when Gus's arms snaked out to draw her close. "Was I snoring?" he asked sleepily.

"Ohhh, you feel so good," Kate murmured, snuggling against him. "Yes, you snore, like a bull, but I like the sound. We made love four times," she said, her voice full of awe.

"You were counting?" Gus teased.

"Only after the third time. I'm wide-awake. I'm hungry. Actually I'm starved. I feel like . . . oh, I don't know."

"All charged up."

"Exactly."

"Want to go for a walk?" he asked. "We could get up, shower, go for a walk, come back to our front porch and watch the sun come up. And," he drawled, "I'm the guy who has two Hershey bars and a pack of *double* Oreo cookies in his flight bag. Plus . . . plus four bags of United Airlines peanuts and one banana. A veritable feast."

"Come on, come on," Kate said, bounding from the bed. A moment later she realized she was naked. She turned slowly to face Gus in the dim lamplight. "I want you to look at me in the light, Gus. I'm forty-six years old. I have stretch

235

marks, a bit of a potbelly, and my butt is starting to droop. This is what I am. I need to hear you tell me it does or doesn't make a difference. I need to hear it now. I'm tired of sucking in my gut, tired of wearing control-top panties, tired of trying to cover up my . . . my imperfections."

"You want to compare bodies?" Gus said, swinging his legs over the side of the bed. He stood up. "So look and tell me you like tall skinny guys covered with hair from top to bottom. I look like a goddamn grizzly bear, and my hair is thinning on top, in case you didn't notice. It is also receding. My legs are skinny and go all the way up to my chest. But to answer your question, it doesn't matter, and you would be doing me a personal favor if you didn't suck in your gut anymore. I love you just the way you are. Get it through your head. Okay, it's your turn now," he said uneasily.

"Uh, your dick looks kind of wilted." Kate whooped and ran for the bathroom. God, did she really say that? Ellie would say something like that, not a forty-six-year-old mother. She turned on the shower full blast.

"Son of a fucking bitch!" He ran after her, yanked open the shower door and said, "You forgot to mention that you also need glasses. I'll accept your apology *now*."

She gave it, one hundred percent.

Later they walked barefoot up and down and around the trails, peering at the different huts, stopping to smell the hibiscus. Gus plucked one and slid it behind her ear. She picked one for him; he stuck it in the pocket of his T-shirt. His arms around her, they threaded their way past the dining room, the open-air bar, the gift store, and up to the beach.

"This is as near perfect as anything I ever experienced," Kate said, gentle waves lapping at her feet. "Everything just feels so right. It's hard to believe there's a world we have to go back to that is so ordinary. I wonder what it would be like to live here."

"It would probably get boring after a while. Places like

this are just little slots of time God allows us to experience from time to time so we can exist in the real world. It occurs to me that we both have enough money to buy a house or condo over here if we want to. We could check out Maui. I hear it's lush and vibrant. We could get a boat. Maybe a Sunfish. Snorkeling gear. A jet ski. An open-air Jeep like the one you rented. We could be beach bums a couple of times a year."

"It sounds wonderful. Let's do that after . . . later on."

"Okay."

Hand in hand they walked back to their hut and watched the sun come up. They forgot about the peanuts, the banana, cookies, and candy.

For ten days they frolicked, always to return to their hut to make love for hours on end. When it was time to pack and leave, Kate cried. "I don't want to leave. I don't want to go back to an empty house. I don't want to have to worry about what Betsy is going to do next. I don't want to go into the office and work. I want to be with you. I don't want to give this up."

Gus started to unpack his bag, a wry grin on his face.

"I know we have to go back."

He started to repack.

"I could stay the rest of the month if I call Ellie and the office."

He started to unpack.

"But that's not fair to the office staff. If we stay, it won't be the same. You're right, we were allotted these ten days."

He started to repack.

"Don't you have something to say?"

"Are we going or not?"

"Yes, we are going, but I don't want to."

"Neither do I. It's going to be cold back home. Did you notice something, Kate? There's no air-conditioning in these huts."

237

"I know, which just goes to prove I'm more astute than you are. Did you know there are no keys?"

"Yep." Gus snapped the lock on his suitcase. He turned, placed his hands on Kate's shoulders. "These last ten days have been the most wonderful of my life. I would not trade them for anything. I love you so much it hurts me. I keep thinking I'm dreaming and when I wake up I'll know it was a dream. God, I love you, Kate. A year is too long to wait to get married. Can we move it up? I don't want you getting away from me. I'm serious, can we move it up?"

"To when?" Kate asked shakily.

"Next week. Hell, I'm ready now. I feel like dragging you back to the mainland and the nearest justice of the peace. Just soon. Will you consider it?"

"Of course." Maybe June, Kate thought. Or September. No, not June, she'd married Patrick in June, had been a June bride. August was a nice month.

They would part in San Francisco, Gus to fly on to New York and Kate to fly into LAX, where Ellie would pick her up, drive her home, and spend the weekend with her.

"I'll miss you," Kate said at the gate.

"I'll call you in the morning."

"Okay," Kate said in a choked voice. " 'Bye, Gus."

" 'Bye, Kate. I love you."

"I love you, too."

A moment later he was gone. She'd never felt so alone in her life. She was still wearing the lei he had placed around her neck. She thought she could smell his after-shave. In her hand she had a lei in a bubble box that she'd bought for Ellie. God, it was wonderful to be loved. To love someone and have that love returned tenfold.

With an hour to kill before her plane left, Kate walked into the lounge and ordered a Diet Pepsi. She fished around in her flight bag for a pen and paper to write Della a letter. She ended up with seven pages. Four lines concerned Kona

Village, the rest was about Gus and his proposal. She ended the letter with, "I want you at my wedding. If I have to, I'll come and get you. You must be here when I march down the aisle or march up the steps to the justice of the peace. I miss you terribly, Della. You are always in my thoughts, and you know there is a place in my heart reserved just for you. I send my love. Please call or write." She signed her name, licked a stamp. She spotted a mailbox outside one of the gift stores, dropped in the letter, sighed, and walked over to the gate, her ticket in hand.

It was unseasonably cold in Los Angeles when Kate got off the plane. She shivered in her cotton dress.

Heart soaring, Ellie handed her mother a heavy sweater. She'd never seen her look so happy, so full of life. She smiled from ear to ear and kept on smiling when her mother blushed. "Right now, right here, I want to know," she said.

"Ell-ieeee!" her mother admonished her.

"I don't care." She yanked her mother out of the way of the other travelers. "I played Cupid, I feel like Cupid, and I deserve to know. Was it great? Was it everything you thought it would be?—and I know you thought about it a lot. I don't want details, but I want to know that. God, you look so damn happy. Oh, Mom, I'm so happy for you. You deserve the best, and for you the best is Gus. I believe that in my heart, I really do."

"He asked me to marry him. It was wonderful, Ellie. And you're right, I have never, ever, been this happy. I said yes. My God, I really did say yes. He . . . he doesn't care that I'm forty-six. He doesn't care that my behind looks like cottage cheese. He loves *me*. I'm still a little hung up on the numbers, but I think I can handle it. I take it you approve of . . . all this."

"You got that right! You should have heard him that day

you didn't answer the phone. He was wild, absolutely wild. He thought you'd been in an accident or something. He actually called several hospitals, and then of course the police. He truly loves you. By the way, what *was* that all about, anyway? You never did tell me."

Kate told her, in the middle of the moving walkway. Ellie doubled over laughing, and so did Kate. People turned to look at mother and daughter with amusement. "Did you tell that to Gus?" Ellie gurgled.

Kate nodded. "He fell off the chair laughing. Actually, I pushed him off."

"Is he a good lover, Mom?"

"The best," Kate said. "On a scale from one to ten, I'd give him a . . ."

"Yes, yes, what?" Ellie demanded.

"A nine and a half. No one is a ten," Kate said glibly.

Ellie hooted and she yanked at her mother's arm as they neared the end of the walkway.

Kate spent the weekend with her daughter, cooking and hanging out in the hot tub. At night they rented videos, all horror flicks to which Ellie was addicted. On Monday morning when Ellie left, Kate hugged her. "Thank you for going with your instincts and . . . and for arranging everything. I don't know if I could have done it on my own. I needed that push."

"It was all Gus's idea. I just went along with it."

"Ellie, does Betsy know about Gus?"

"Not from me she doesn't. If she knew, she'd be making all kinds of noise. If you want some advice, and I hate to say this, I don't think I'd mention it until it's a done deed. I keep hoping that one of these days she's going to get all her ducks in a row and come back to whatever is normal for Betsy."

"I think I'll take that advice, Ellie. Thanks for picking me up at the airport, and thanks for spending the weekend with me. I'm really glad you like your prospective in-laws. I knew they'd love you. Happy New Year, honey!"

"Same to you, Mom," Ellie said, hugging her mother.

The new year started out in a legal mode, with Kate paying visits to the Mancuso law office on a weekly basis. She wanted the Air Force to issue a death certificate, which they were reluctant to do. "I'm not going to fight or argue," Kate said after the sixth visit, in late May. "File for a divorce. I want it done quickly, and if it can't be done quickly, I'll go someplace else, like Nevada or Mexico. I want this behind me. I'm getting married, and I don't want any surprises along the way. I want everything legal."

Mancuso shrugged. "I'll do my best. I did manage to get you a clear title to the house in New Jersey. Anytime you want, you can sell it. Do you have a buyer?"

"As a matter of fact I do. I'm going to divide the money between Betsy and Ellie. Mr. Stewart is buying the house for his mother. I imagine he's going to put the deed in her name. It's a cash sale. He'll be sending all the papers to you. You have Ellie's address, so you can send all the papers to her. She does my taxes and the taxes for the corporation. This sale isn't going to come back and haunt me later on, is it?"

"I don't see how it could, Kate. Everything is legal. Don't worry about anything. Go home and plan your wedding. By the way, when is it?"

"I was hoping for August or September, but it looks more like December at this point. I can't wait," she said, a girlish ring to her voice.

"I hope you'll be very happy."

"I don't just hope. I *know* I will be. Thanks for all your help, Nick. I never would have gotten this far if not for you."

"Kate, about Betsy. Do you have any idea of the kind of

money she's been spending on all these searches she's been doing over the years?"

"A lot. She's dedicated her life to finding her father. It makes me sad when I hear she's begging for money on the streets to finance . . . whatever it is she does. Every lead fizzles, and still she keeps at it."

"Do you give her money?"

"When she asks, which isn't often," Kate said, then added nervously, "She doesn't know I'm planning on getting married."

"I see," Mancuso said, which meant he didn't see at all.

"I hope so. Keep in touch, Nick."

"Good luck, Kate," Nick said, extending his hand.

Would she need luck? She wasn't sure. What's more, she didn't care.

Three days before Labor Day, Gus called, his voice full of excitement. "Kate, how would you like to go to Costa Rica with me for a week? Can you get away? I won this crazy trip and the tickets just arrived. I took my mother to this senior citizen thing and they were raffling off this prize and I goddamn won. Of course I bought all the tickets, so it was only natural that I would win. Pack your duds. I'll meet you at LAX."

"You bought all the tickets!"

"No one else wanted to buy them. The raffle was my mother's idea. I was with her when she was considering the prize. I had a feeling no one would want to buy them so I held out for Costa Rica. She wanted Disney World. Write this down. We're going to live in the bush, so don't bring any fancy clothes. You game, Kate?"

"I'll be there," she said breathlessly. "Did you really buy all the tickets? How much?"

"Ten grand's worth. The group had to make a profit.

They're taking a bus trip to Atlantic City. I'm giving each of them twenty-five bucks for the slots and lunch and dinner at Resorts. "I love you, Kate Starr, soon to be Kate Stewart."

"I love you, too, Gus Stewart."

"You have a passport, don't you?"

"Yep."

"Thank God. Now write."

Kate stuck the paper in her purse, stood, straightened the hem of her tailored jacket, looked around the office and said, "I'll be leaving now. I'm not sure when I'll be back. I have things to do and places to go. Carry on, ladies and gentleman."

From home she called Ellie, who squealed in delight. "In the bush! I love it. Go for it, Mom. When are you leaving?"

"Tomorrow."

She was light-headed, giddy, as she packed her bag and searched for her passport. She was going to see Gus again. "I'm blessed, truly blessed. Thank you, God, for sending him to me."

CHAPTER
17

Komsomolets Island, Russia

"Captain Starr, there is someone here who wishes to talk with you. Mr. Gorbachev himself has sent this visitor," a Russian guard said in broken English.

Patrick's heart leaped. He had a visitor. "What does it mean?" he said in Russian to his guard. They were friends now, teaching each other English and Russian.

"I do not know. Perhaps something to do with the American inspection of the missile sites. We are scheduled to destruct the launchers and ancillary equipment. The Americans are to supervise. Perhaps they want your opinion," he said slyly.

"And your ass goes in a sling when they see me. How are you guys going to explain keeping me here all these years?

The shit is going to hit the fan. Finally. Come on, Sergi, is my visitor an American or Russian?"

"Both," Sergi said.

"You shittin' me?"

"That means what?"

"That means are you lying to me, you asshole?"

"Ah, yes, asshole I understand. Two visitors, one American, one Russian. They look important. Maybe American Express."

"You mean American embassy. You are stupid, Sergi. Well, let's go."

"First you shave, comb hair, wear clean shirt. Asshole!"

"Up yours," Patrick said, excitement rushing through him. It must mean something. It had to mean something. He cried when he shaved and combed his hair. He wiped at his tears with the back of his hand when he put on a clean shirt. He was shaking so badly he could hardly button his shirt. "Please God, let this be what I want it to be."

"It is time, asshole," Sergi said from the open doorway.

"No, no, I call *you* 'asshole,' not the other way around. Say you're sorry, Sergi."

"I'm sorry, what do I call you?"

"Try Captain Patrick Starr. I like the way that sounds."

The guard spit on the bare floor. "Move," he said sharply.

Patrick squared his shoulders and followed Sergi to a cold room with a table and four chairs. Seated at the table was one obviously Russian-looking man and an American who was thirty or so years of age—a good-looking young man with sandy hair and warm brown eyes that were now filling with moisture. His voice was husky and filled with emotion when he said, "Captain Starr?"

"God, yes. Yes, I'm Patrick Starr, United States Air Force. You found me!"

"Yes sir, we did. You're going to make your family very happy, sir."

The Russian held up his hand. "We talk first."

"I'm David Peterson, this is Vladimir Suidnetzy. Sit down, Captain Starr. We have things to discuss."

Patrick sat down, his breathing shallow. Why weren't they just taking him out of here? Now that they knew he was here, he should be walking away with this David Peterson, who was as old as he was when he bailed out over Vietnam twenty years ago. He felt frightened and tried not to huddle on his chair. He blanked everything out, moved himself to Westfield, New Jersey. He was a kid again, riding his bicycle up and down the street, waiting for the guys to come out and play stickball, one ear tuned to his father's call. Out of the corner of his eye he could see Kate Anders carrying a bag of trash to the curb. He sidled down the street, his feet propelling the Schwinn bike. "Whatcha doin', Kate? Need any help?"

God, she was pretty, probably the prettiest girl in school. He liked her smile and the thick blond braids that were always tied with colored ribbons to match her dress. She had on the same dress she'd worn at school, red-and-white checks with some kind of X-ing around the hem. "You going to the picnic on Saturday? They're gonna have all kinds of food and races and stuff. Huh?"

Kate's saddle shoes scuffed at the cracked concrete walk. He noticed they were polished, the white part real shiny and the laces just as white as the tips of her shoes. "If you go, I kind of thought we could walk around together. I have two dollars I've been saving. I bet I could win you something."

Kate blushed and continued digging at the crack. If she didn't watch it, she was going to scuff the leather off the tip of her shoe. "Maybe. If I get my chores done. I don't have any money, though. What could you win for me?" she asked shyly.

Maybe was almost as good as a yes. "You know, one of those things on a stick. Maybe a monkey, maybe a bear.

Something like that. Jack's mother is working at the hot dog stand. He said she'll give us all hot dogs."

"For free?" Kate asked in amazement.

"Well, sure. Will you try to go? I can meet you by the gate. Maybe you can get up early and do all your chores. I could even come by and ride you out to the picnic on my handlebars."

"What if my dress blows up?" Kate asked anxiously.

"Well heck, Kate, hold it down. I don't think there's going to be any wind. I've been paying attention to the weather reports. They always give 'em in advance when it gets close to the date of the picnic. There's gonna be an air show late in the afternoon. You're the prettiest girl in school," he blurted.

Kate turned beet-red. "You're good-looking, too. All the girls make goo-goo eyes at you. Janie Chalmers wants you to kiss her."

"Well, I'm not going to kiss her or anyone else. I'd kiss you, though, if you'd let me. Will you let me?"

"On the lips? I don't know about that. I'm only thirteen. My mother says I can't date or kiss boys until I'm eighteen."

"That's five years from now. Don't tell her. Kisses are nice."

"How do you know?" Kate asked suspiciously. "Who else did you kiss? I didn't think you were that type. You know, going around kissing girls. Who'd you kiss?"

"Swear you won't tell."

"I swear I won't tell," Kate said solemnly.

"Nancy Eggers."

"Nancy Eggers! Nancy Eggers! She's older than you and she has pimples. Why'd you kiss Nancy?"

" 'Cause she's the only one would let me. I wanted to see what it was like. I liked it. You'll like it, too. I'll show you how to pucker up. Don't wear lipstick."

Kate inched closer to the curb. "I'm not allowed to wear lipstick. C'mere . . ." She motioned him closer to the curb, leaned over, and planted a wet kiss on his lips. Then she jumped backward and ran into the house.

"Oooheeee, we saw that, Pat!" his friends hooted from across the street, where they'd been concealed behind the hedges. "Pat has a girl, Pat has a girl. Pat loves Kate. You love Kate, don't you?"

"Shut up, Danny, or I'll punch you in the mouth. Now, you want to play stickball or not?"

"Patrick . . ."

"Captain Starr, are you listening to me?"

"What?" Patrick said, returning from his youth to the room he was in and the two men sitting across the table from him.

"Listen to me very carefully," David Peterson said.

"We should be walking out of here. Now. We shouldn't be sitting here talking. I'm a United States citizen and an Air Force officer shot down in the line of duty, and you want to fucking talk to me. Get me the fuck out of here!" Patrick said belligerently.

"I'm going to get you out of here, but first we have to talk."

"Why can't we talk on the way out?" Patrick snarled.

"Because we can't, and that's the best answer you're going to get at the moment. Now I want you to tell me what happened from 1971 until 1973 when you were brought here. We think you were sent here in 'seventy-four because that's when we lost track of you."

"How's my family? Do they think I'm dead? Do you have pictures of them? I want to see my family."

David Peterson opened his briefcase and withdrew several photographs. "Your daughter's graduation picture. Their faces are circled. Your daughter Betsy has a doctorate degree. Your daughter Ellie is a CPA. This is a picture of your wife taken at your younger daughter's graduation."

Patrick's eyes filled with tears as he brought the pictures

up close to his eyes. "I need glasses," he said. "My teeth are rotten and need to be fixed."

"That will all be taken care of. Now, tell us what happened."

"Do you know any of it?"

"No, Captain Starr, I don't. I guess you could say I was sent here because I was in the U.S. embassy in Moscow when the call came in. I was the one who could get here the fastest. We don't want you here one minute longer than necessary. Please, the sooner you get on with it, the sooner we can get you out."

"During my first tour I was flying Thuds. You probably know them as F-105 Thunderchiefs. I shot down four North Vietnamese aircraft, one shy of making me an ace. On this tour I was flying an F-4E Phantom 11 fighter-bomber. I'd only been flying bombing and flak/missile suppression missions, so I didn't get a chance to get my fifth MiG to win ace status. That ate at me.

"The F-4E was a real honey of an aircraft—she could drop bombs on a dime in support of ground troops, *and* handle recon, radar/flak/missile suppression, and MiG hunting. I was carrying eight tons of ammunition, bombs, air-to-ground missiles, napalm, and a combination of fuel tanks. I also had a Vulcan—that's a twenty-millimeter cannon to you—that fired six thousand rounds a minute. God, I loved that plane.

"I was flying out of Ubon Air Base, Thailand, on this tour, as a member of the 547th Tactical Fighter squadron, part of the Eighth Tactical Fighter Wing. It was December fifth, 1970, and we were fragged, that is, scheduled to hit targets in North Vietnam. My primary target was the Radio Hanoi AM transmitter site—the NVA main propaganda and communication network. We were never able to put it out of commission.

"I was the leader of Romeo Flight. There were four F-4s, each of us equipped with two 'smart bombs'—two-thousand-pound laser-guided bombs. Our mission was to take out Radio Hanoi.

"The site was surrounded by a twenty-foot-high wall. I put every one of the fucking bombs right into the target area. At one P.M. Hanoi time, right in the middle of a vicious anti-American broadcast beamed in English to our troops in South Vietnam, I cut off their transmission.

"I zoom off at five hundred knots. My weapon-system office reports the bombs smacked in the middle of the transmitter compound . . . when suddenly a surface-to-air missile detonates very close by with a hell of a flash and bang. Exploding fragments killed my WSO. My aircraft had serious damage to the hydraulic system. Christ, I had holes in my wings. I tried for as much altitude as I could get. I knew I'd never make it back to Thailand. The best I could hope for was to get out over open water where the U.S. Navy could pick me up. The others in the squadron who dropped their bombs warned me I was on fire. My cockpit filled with smoke and the F-4 started to yaw to the right, wanting to go into a roll. I knew then I couldn't control it. My wingman is yelling for me to punch out before the F-4 explodes.

"I knew my WSO was dead, he wasn't answering my calls, so I released my canopy and fired the ejection charges. I was dazed with the force of the ejection explosion, but I was okay. I'm swinging underneath this parachute. I activated my survival radio in my vest in case any rescue aircraft can locate my position once I'm on the ground. I didn't think there would be any rescue, but I hoped. I prayed all the way down. I landed in a rice paddy swarming with Vietnamese.

"Man, I literally fell into the arms of my captors. They immediately stripped me of everything but my flight suit. They didn't hurt me then. The next thing I knew, I was in a truck and driven blindfolded into Hanoi.

"I guess I was treated to the standard North Vietnamese routine for the first three days. I was yanked into the commandant's office at the end of the third day. He told me I was the lead aircraft that bombed the Hanoi transmitter site—" Patrick's voice faltered and broke. "It seems his fiancée was the one doing the broadcasting when I pulverized her. He was in such a fucking rage I thought he was going to kill me. They threw me in isolation and beat me senseless. There wasn't anything they didn't do to me. They told me they broke me. I have to believe they did, but I have no memory of it. The commandant got a kick out of repeating the things I told him.

"There were other Americans there. I heard them talking, but I was so bad off, I couldn't talk. They left me alone to rot in my cell for a week, maybe it was longer, I don't remember. I tried to scratch my name in the wall, but I don't know if I did. Maybe I thought I did it.

"More time passed. Maybe weeks. Maybe months." Patrick shrugged. "Anyway, one morning—it was still dark outside—my guards took me to the commandant's office, where he served me up this speech. He said he'd informed the Russians that I was a highly skilled pilot and someone they would like to talk to. It was his revenge, he said. He said I would never see my country again or my family. Then I was brought here to this missile base.

"At first the KGB was all over me, questioning and testing me, demanding long technical descriptions of various American fighter aircraft and aerial weapons and electronics gear. They wanted to know it all. I resisted at first, but they wore me down with drugs. One of the guards told me I was like a vegetable for a long time. I don't know how long. That was the end of it. The guards told me that over the years they forgot about me. They'd go off on a furlough and come back, and after a while we almost became friends. Once or twice they even brought me a woman. I never had enough to eat, was never warm enough. Sometimes they gave me aspirin. Once, one of the guards took pity on me and pulled out a molar that was decayed. With pliers.

"I was passed from one commandant to another. I guess

you could say I was their mascot. Life was tolerable. I was alive, but that was all. I never gave up hope I would be found.

"I learned Russian, and I tried to teach two of the guards English. We managed to communicate. Sergi told me about the Strategic Arms Treaty and said maybe I'd be sent home. I hung on to that. I've been counting the days, just waiting for the American inspection of this missile site. I figured they'd hide me when that happened, so I've been working on Sergi, hoping he'd let something slip or outright tell the Americans I was here. I told him if I got out, I'd take him back to America with me. The jerk wants to meet Jane Fonda.

"That's my story, Mr. Peterson. Now, how did you find me? Who told you I was here? There hasn't been an inspection."

"Gorbachev has taken over and he's initiated glasnost," Peterson said. "You know about START. They called. On the telephone. The White House. They offered to return you if you agree to keep your mouth shut until Gorbachev's government reforms are securely in place. The question now is, will you keep your mouth shut? If you agree, sign on the dotted line, you walk. That means no parade. No interviews with the press. No nothing. We move you home, you join your family. We say, if necessary, you are a cousin of Patrick Starr. The government will compensate you. You have to understand you will not go home to a hero's welcome. Unfair, I grant you, but that's the way it is."

He was back in Westfield at his high school graduation, decked out in his cap and gown. He was valedictorian of his graduating class, his speech firmly in mind. He was going to locate Kate and speak directly to her so he wouldn't get nervous. She'd curled her hair and was wearing pink lipstick.

It was all planned; they were going to run away together after graduation. He had $700 and Kate had $290. They'd get other gifts of money at graduation, enough for them to pack up his clunker and head out to Texas, where he'd been accepted at Texas A&M. He was going for his B.S. in engineering. He was going to join ROTC and get his commission in the USAF. From there he'd go on to get his M.S. in aerospace engineering. If he was lucky, with Kate at his side, he'd try for the U.S. Test Pilot School at Edwards AFB, California.

Kate was confident she could make a home for them cheaply, baby-sit children for extra money. He'd work part-time. Kate said they could do it. He believed her.

Off we go, into the wild blue yonder . . .

"Captain Starr, I'm waiting for your answer."

"Does my family know?"

"Not yet. No one is jumping the gun here. We take you home, quietly, if you agree to the terms."

"I only survived because of Kate. All I did was think about her, about the girls. I always knew I'd get home. Do you pray, Mr. Peterson?"

"Yes."

"I didn't, not for a long time. I thought God forgot about me. Of course I wasn't thinking clearly. Why is it when things are the hardest, when it can't get any worse, people turn to God? It's almost an afterthought. I thought God wiped me out of the picture, but I knew Kate would never forget me. Kate loved me, loves me," he said, his voice breaking. "I'll sign your damn paper, but only because I want to see my wife and children. You'll have to read it to me since I can't make out the print."

Patrick listened to Peterson's flat, emotionless voice. "I guess you know I'm signing this under duress. I have no lawyer here to advise me. I want that understood. You're fucking me over. You know it, I know it, and this asshole sitting next to you knows it." He signed his name, an illegible scrawl. Later he would tell the truth. For now all he wanted was to get back to Kate, to smell her heavenly vanilla-lemon-scented hair. He wondered if she'd bake a chocolate cake for him. Would it be sitting in the middle of the kitchen table?

"If you talk, we say you defected," Peterson said coolly.

He was crying when he walked out of the bare, cold room in his coarse shirt and baggy wool trousers that hadn't been washed in a long time. His boots had holes in the soles and were stuffed with rags.

Jesus Christ! He was going home!

CHAPTER
18

"Can you believe we've been here a whole week?" Gus asked from the shade of a lush tree.

Kate finished the banana she was eating. "Time has whizzed by. You know, I never thought I would ever see a rain forest. I'm so happy we came here. It's a beautiful country, but I wouldn't want to live here. There's no place like the good old U.S. of A.," she said, snuggling in the crook of his arm.

"What I like best is there are no phones, no newspapers, no radios. I feel so insulated. The word *safe* comes to mind, but it isn't the one I'm searching for. I'll say one thing, though, I'm probably never going to eat another banana."

"And give up all this wonderful potassium?"

"Uh-huh. Have you come up with a date, Kate?"

"I feel guilty going off and getting married in a strange place. I'd like my girls to be there. At least Ellie. I doubt if Betsy would come. And I want Della, and the girls from the office. We could still get married by the J.P. if you want."

Gus cuddled her close. "I don't care either way. I just want us to be married. Period. I can deal with anything as long as that's the outcome. Women like that stuff. Men don't care. A date? I need to hear a date."

"What about a candlelight service at a Unitarian church and a small party at the house afterward? We can fly out that night from LAX and be in Hawaii the following morning. Or we can have a dinner party at least, in a hotel in Los Angeles. I haven't found a dress yet," Kate fretted.

"Burlap will do nicely. A date. I'm not hearing a date."

"How about Saturday, December fifteenth?"

"God, you actually set a date," Gus said in awe. "I've been thinking you'd switch up on me or change your mind. It's a given, then?"

"It's a given," Kate said quietly.

"Kate, we've never really talked about Patrick. Maybe we should. I don't want ... what I mean is, I don't think I could handle it if you made comparisons. I don't want a third person living with us even if he's a memory. You have let go, haven't you?"

"Of course. Many years ago. Time, my darling, heals just about everything. It's sad to say, but I can hardly remember what Patrick looked like. I could never compare you to him. You are so totally different, so warm, so caring, so giving. Patrick wasn't like that. I loved him, though, very much. He was the father of my children. There will be no ghosts between us. I packed up all his pictures and the few things I kept in a drawer that belonged to him. I cried my tears then. Part of me will always wonder what happened to him. I think that's natural and normal. If I think about him from time to time, I'll tell you about it. There won't be any secrets between us."

"I love you very much, Kate Starr. I can't wait to call you Mrs. Kate Stewart. Do you think you'll have trouble adjusting to your name?"

Kate laughed, a joyous sound. "Hardly. I practice writing it every chance I get. I guess we're going to have to get a his and hers checking account. Speaking of checks, when do you think your other brothers and sisters will cash their checks?"

"I'm hoping by Christmas, so I can wrap up that chapter in my life. I can't sell that damn estate, though. Seems like no one wants to pay eight mil for it. I dropped the price five hundred thousand and had no takers. Until some moneybags comes along, it's just going to sit there. The siblings want no part of it. So they say."

"Did you keep your share of the money? You should, you know."

"Yeah, It's in an investment account at Merrill Lynch. I got a real savvy broker named Gary Kaplan. Mike Bernstein, the CPA I hired, is just as savvy. They take care of everything. Jeez, I forgot Ed Grueberger, the estate planner I hired. You need to know all this, Kate, in case anything happens to me."

Kate went rigid in his arms. "Do not *ever* use those words to me again. I don't want to know, don't want to hear about wills and junk like that. I can't go through all that. Swear to me, Gus," she said vehemently.

"I swear. Okay, okay, relax. Come on, let's go skinny-dipping before you get your knickers in a twist."

Kate was peeling off her clothes as she ran to the water. She dived in, her rump in the air. Gus whooped his delight and followed her, overtaking her with five sure, deft strokes. "Want to make love?"

"We've done that for seven straight days. Why do you think I tricked you into the pool?" Kate gurgled.

A long time later she said, "That was delicious."

Gus hugged her. "Speaking of delicious, what are we having for dinner?"

"Bananas, crackers, and Hershey bars. It was your idea, Mr. Stewart, for us to go off on our own. We'll live off the land, you said. The only thing growing on this land as far as I can see is bananas. Take it or leave it. Tomorrow when we get to the airport we can eat real food. Maybe a steak or a chunk of chicken with stuffing and gravy. God, I could eat a whole cow right now," Kate muttered.

"Cows give milk. Steers are for meat," Gus said, nibbling on her ear playfully. "So it wasn't one of my better ideas. I thought there would be other fruit. I really don't care what we eat as long as we eat it together. Still, a steak would be nice."

"It's been a wonderful vacation, but I don't think I want to come back here, do you?"

"Nah, it's too primitive. At least we know what we like and what we don't like. I'm really looking forward to our trip to Hawaii—our honeymoon. As Mr. and Mrs. Gustav Stewart. I didn't think it would ever happen."

"I didn't either," Kate said softly. "I love you so much, I ache sometimes just thinking about you. I'm afraid something will go awry, that you'll meet one of those Gennifer types and not want me. I worry about that. Those numbers won't go away."

"I can't change the numbers, Kate. But they don't mean anything to me. They shouldn't mean anything to you, either. We're getting married and will spend the rest of our lives keeping each other happy. That's all that matters to me."

"You are the dearest man, Gus Stewart. When I'm seventy years old and drooling, I'm going to remind you of those words. I'd like to make love again, if you don't mind."

"Whatever you want, lady," Gus said, smothering her face with kisses. "Whatever you want."

"I want," Kate purred.

The following evening, while Gus checked their baggage, Kate presented her tickets to the agent behind the counter along with both passports.

"Mrs. Starr, there's a cablegram here for you. One moment while I fetch it."

Kate's heart leaped in her chest. She looked around for Gus and immediately panicked when she didn't see him. Something must have happened to Ellie or Betsy. "Oh, God, no, please, let them be all right," she murmured. He was coming toward her, in silhouette, the sun from the doors at his back. She felt herself sway, heard the ticket agent call her name.

"What's wrong?" Gus asked, his face masked in worry.

"Mrs. Starr, I have your cable."

She saw Gus reach for it and then felt him lead her away to a quiet area. He fingered the yellow square gingerly. "We have to open it," he said nervously.

"I know, but I'm afraid. I just know something's happened to the girls. Maybe they were in a car accident. I wasn't there for them. I was off in the damn jungle fucking my brains out. I'm their mother. How long have they had that cable?"

"I don't know," Gus said quietly. He felt something between his shoulders he'd never felt before.

"Ask. I'm not opening this until I know," Kate cried. "God, what if they're dead?" She was talking to herself; Gus was at the ticket counter.

"Five days."

"Five days!" Kate cried in anguish. "Five days!"

"That's what she said. Do you want me to open it, or will you do it?"

259

"You do it," Kate said, burying her face in her hands. "Which one? Please, God, don't make this be serious, whatever it is. Please, God. I'll do anything. Let my girls be all right."

"Kate."

Kate looked up, her heart in her eyes. Her shoulders slumped when she saw Gus's white face. "Which one?"

"Neither. Your daughters are fine."

Kate jumped up, her arms waving wildly. "Thank you, God, thank you! Did the office burn down, what is it? I can handle anything as long as I know the girls are okay. Della! It's Della, isn't it?"

"No, Kate, it isn't Della. The office didn't burn down, either. It's your husband. He's on his way home. The telegram reads, 'Dear Mom, a Mr. Peterson called to say he's bringing Dad home. He wants us all at the house for his arrival.' It's signed 'Ellie.' "

Kate slid to the floor in a dead faint. Gus dropped to his knees to gather her close to him. "Kate, Kate, snap out of it! Come on, we're going to the bar. We need to talk this over . . . we need to call your daughter. Kate, please snap out of it." Lightly he whisked his fingers back and forth across her cheek.

"I don't believe this," Kate said when she came out of it and struggled to a sitting position.

A crowd was gathering. Gus waved them away.

"This can't be happening," she said in the bar as she gulped at the fiery brandy. "It must be a mistake. I don't know a David Peterson. It's a mix-up. Twenty years is too long. I'm sure it's a mistake. We have to call. You do it, Gus. I can't . . . I don't . . . please," she begged. Her eyes rolled back in her head. Gus reached for her, his heart pounding like a triphammer in his chest.

"Kate," he said harshly, "get it together. I know this is a shock, but I can't have you going off the deep end here.

We'll deal with this." Yeah, sure, he thought, that's got to be the understatement of the decade.

Kate shook her head. "It has to be a cruel joke. Something Betsy would do. Gus," she said frantically, "see if there's an American newspaper in one of the shops. If what that cable says is true, there will be something in the paper."

Kate watched as Gus sprinted off. Watched and waited. A group of college students loaded down with camping gear and backpacks straggled past her, their boombox blasting. She kneaded her thighs and knew she was going to be bruised.

At last she raised her eyes to see Gus loping toward her, his face white beneath his tan. She wondered how white her own face was. She felt herself start to grieve. "There's nothing in this paper," he said, holding up a three-day-old copy of the *Wall Street Journal*. "Some woman had a copy of the *New York Times* she'd brought with her yesterday. I asked if I could look at it. There was nothing in it, either."

"I told you, it's a cruel joke of some kind. Who would do such a terrible thing?"

"The telegram has Ellie's name on it. She wouldn't play a joke on you. We have to call her, Kate. As it is, I think we're going to miss the plane. I have no idea how this telephone system works down here. Then there's the time difference." He waited for Kate's response. His heart and gut told him it was not a cruel joke. And why the hell should anything go his way? All along he'd known it was too good to be true. He'd lived in fear that Kate would change her mind about him, but the one thing, the only thing, he'd never factored into his fear was Patrick Starr's return.

"I don't know what to do," Kate whimpered. She held up both hands. "I'm not going home. I can't deal with that. I wouldn't be able to hold up to all the publicity, living in a fishbowl. They can't make me go back. Gus, what's going to happen to us?"

"You filed for a divorce," Gus said desperately, knowing it made absolutely no difference. Kate's first loyalty, her *only* loyalty, was to her husband, and that left him out in left field without a mitt. He felt like crying. He didn't want to say it, but the words trembled from his lips, driven by a force he couldn't control. "You have to go back, Kate. If all this is true, I can't even begin to comprehend what your husband must be feeling. He deserves . . . to have you and his daughters. I could never fight that."

Kate cried softly into a wad of tissues. "I can't even remember what Patrick looks like. He won't be the same person. He can't be the same person. *I'm* not the same person. Why is this happening to me? I know why," she said, jumping to her feet. "Because I've been unfaithful. God is punishing me."

"Kate, honey, you can't look at it like that. God doesn't punish his children. He's sending Patrick home after . . . God, after nearly twenty years. That itself is a miracle in my eyes. How it affects us isn't important."

"My God, Gus, you sound like you're on his side," Kate cried desperately. "What about us? What about all the plans we made?"

Gus dropped to his knees as the loudspeaker called their flight. "Kate, my feelings for you will never change. You have to know that and believe it as well. Because I love you with all my heart and my soul I can . . . try to step aside. Let's call your daughter now and find what's going on. That was the last boarding call, so we have time now. We've had our shock and we're going to deal with it."

Kate followed him in a trance, her gait stiff-legged. She watched as Gus fished out his calling card, placed the call, and then handed her the phone. She shook her head violently.

It was an hour before they were able to reach Ellie. Their hands clasped together, Gus and Kate sat on hard plastic seats, eyes glued to the telephone three feet away. When it finally rang, they went to answer it with their hands still locked together. His voice was rough, sounding raspy when he said, "Ellie, did you send the telegram?"

"Yes, I did, Gus. Can I talk to Mom?"

"Then it's real. There wasn't anything in the papers," Gus said, as though that fact alone would make it all unreal. "We're still at the airport, we missed our flight. Ellie, your mother is in shock. She asked me to call. She's standing right here. Now, tell me what happened." He sucked in his breath as he listened. Kate stared off into space.

"The day after you left, a man named David Peterson called me, and then someone else came to my apartment. They had Betsy with them, so they told us together. Dad's been in Russia all this time. The Vietnam government turned him over to them after he was captured. He's here in the United States—Washington, I think. They didn't tell us. All they said was he was in a holding area. They won't bring him home until Mom gets here. It's all hush-hush. Betsy claims to know what's going on, and she won't share her information until Mom gets here. She's like an angry hornet right now. I wouldn't tell her where Mom was, only that she was on vacation and I'd try and get in touch."

Gus's shoulders slumped. "Why wasn't anything in the papers? I would think the world would want to know. I'm a reporter, for Christ's sake! I know about stuff like that."

"They know all about you, Gus. Not from me, so don't think I spilled my guts. Betsy doesn't know, but *they* know. They want to talk to you, too, when you get back. But separately. Someone is going to be at LAX at customs. I don't know who *they* are. Important people from the government, I guess. How's Mom taking this, Gus?"

"She's in shock, like I said." They wanted to talk to him. His reporter's antennae went up and his nose started to twitch. "As I told you, we missed our flight. The next one out is around nine tonight. Can you meet your mother?"

"Yes. I'm supposed to call Mr. Peterson."

"Is this call being monitored?" Gus asked suspiciously.

"I wouldn't be a bit surprised," Ellie said quietly. "These people are . . . very cold. They made me feel like I did something wrong. They don't smile. Look, tell Mom I love her. I love you, too, you big schmuck. Take care of her. She loves *you*, and don't you ever for one minute forget it."

"All right. See you later."

"Well?" Kate said hoarsely, when Gus had hung up.

He repeated his conversation. "I don't know what it means. If I were to assume—and a good reporter never assumes—I'd say they're waiting for you to get home and then they'll spring this wonderful, joyous homecoming. I'm sure there's an avalanche of accusations, denials, and all kinds of shit hitting the fan. How the hell did he get to Russia, and why? Somebody is going to have to come up with some answers. Ellie said it's all hush-hush, so I assume the parties concerned are busy trying to cover their asses."

"It's true, then."

"Yes, Kate, it's true," Gus said quietly.

"I buried him . . . his things. But I also buried him in my mind. I really believed he was dead. Ellie believed, too, because of me. Betsy was the only believer. God, I wish I were dead," Kate moaned.

"Don't say that," Gus said, his arms about her shoulders. He led her back to the hard plastic chair. "Something's not right about all of this," he muttered. "Ellie told them where you were. They could have found us in a heartbeat if they really wanted to. Listen, can I have your permission to call my paper and ask a few questions?"

"Of course. No one told us not to ask questions. I'll wait here for you."

Kate watched him walk away. What would she say to Patrick? Hi, how are you? I've missed you. Gee, it's good to have you back. By the way, I'm in love and I'm getting married in two months. You understand, don't you? No, I don't have feelings for you anymore. I buried you. I sold your father's house to Gus and gave the money to Ellie and Betsy. I thought you were dead, never coming back. I have a life, too. I put it on hold for twenty years. What about me? What about me?

She cried harder, sniffling and blowing her nose every few seconds. "Damn you, Patrick! Damn you for ruining my life a second time."

Forty-five minutes later Gus took his seat next to her. "No one knows anything. *Nada*. I had my chief call the foreign chiefs, and there've been no leaks of any kind. Everyone is going to be sniffing now. I might have stirred something up."

"So what?" Kate said belligerently. "I can't let his coming back ruin my life. Again."

"Kate, don't think like that. This is something you have to do. You owe it to your husband. The selfish part of me doesn't want you to go back. While I was waiting for news at the phone, I thought about all the money at Chase and the estate. I thought about running off with you, but that's not what you and I are all about. We're decent, normal human beings who had the good fortune to fall in love with one another. I'm telling you, you have to go back, face your husband, and do whatever is best for the two of you. It is the decent, human thing to do. And you know it."

"What about us?"

"I have this feeling that when we land at LAX, there won't be any 'us.' I might not have the chance to tell you later, but I understand. I will always love you, that's never going to change. Whatever you decide to do, I'll accept."

"I can't picture my life without you in it," Kate said quietly. "I've been unfaithful to Patrick."

"Not knowingly," Gus said.

"It doesn't matter. I broke my marriage vows. That's a sin in the eyes of God."

There was nothing for Gus to say, so he remained quiet. He reached for her hand.

"I feel like smashing something," Kate said a long time later.

"I could probably destroy this entire airport single-handedly," Gus said an hour or so before their flight was scheduled to leave. "Let's go get a drink. I think we deserve one."

In the bar, Kate held her glass of beer aloft, her eyes blazing angrily. "I want to drink to the would-haves, the should-haves, the could-haves."

Gus chomped down on his lower lip before he clinked his glass against hers.

"Will we stay in touch? Can we still call each other?"

Gus nodded. "Anytime you want. I'll always be here for you. Listen to me, Kate. I have this feeling . . . my reporter's instinct, that all is not what it seems. I want you to promise me something. When we get back, listen to what people have to say. Don't agree to anything. Don't disagree with anything. The most I want you to say to anything, is, 'I'll think about it.' Then call me, but not from home. Call me from a phone both and at the office. Can you promise me that?"

"Yes. Yes, of course. You sound so . . . dramatic, so . . . What is it you're trying to say?"

"I think I'm remembering the way my story got squelched and that 'keep quiet policy' they bound all you wives to. Government agencies have power you wouldn't believe. They use power against people like you, and they try to use it against big papers like mine and reporters like me. Don't make promises you'll regret later. It's important, otherwise I wouldn't ask it of you."

"I think you just scared me, Gus."

"Good. Keep it that way."

266

"Will you call me?" Kate asked wistfully, in a small voice.

"I don't think that will be a good idea. What if Patrick picks up the phone? Your office probably isn't a good idea, either. It'll be best if you call, when you can, from outside. Tell Ellie the same thing. Betsy is sharp, she probably already figured all of this out, whatever *this* turns out to be."

"There's something fishy here, isn't there, Gus?"

"The newshound in me says yes. Kate, I . . ."

"I know," Kate said softly.

The four-and-half-hour flight was made in virtual silence. They held hands, their knees touching, each of them busy thinking. When the plane landed, they were the last to leave, postponing the inevitable as long as they could. When they walked through the door, two men stepped forward. They had a twin look about them, a government look, Kate thought. One called her by name and one called Gus by name. They spoke at the same moment: "Come with me, Mr. Stewart."

"Come with me, Mrs. Starr."

Kate felt a hand at her elbow and flinched away. "Take your hands off me right now," she said viciously. "If you don't, I'll scream my head off."

"Easy does it, Mrs. Starr, I'm here to help you. Don't do anything foolish." His voice was the same as Bill Percy's, her old caseworker. They must have all studied under the same elocution teacher, she decided.

"Where are we going?" Kate demanded.

"To a private room where we can talk. Your daughters are there waiting for you."

"Then why was Mr. Stewart taken separately? What's going on?"

"Shouldn't you be asking questions about your husband?" the man said coldly.

"Don't tell me what I should and shouldn't do. I asked you questions and you asked one in return. I'm going to ask

267

you again, and if you don't answer, be advised my lungs are strong." She stopped short, slamming up against the agent to make her point. Those long-ago days of bullying and intimidation were gone.

The man at her side stared at his charge, correctly interpreting her state of mind. This was one woman who'd make good on her threat. "Mr. Stewart is a reporter," he said curtly.

"What does that have to do with anything?" Kate demanded, her feet rooted to the carpet.

"In matters of national security we have a certain protocol to follow. Your daughters are waiting. They've been waiting for hours. You weren't on your scheduled flight," he said coldly.

"So what!" Kate snapped.

"So you've kept everyone waiting. I suggest you move along here, Mrs. Starr."

"And if I don't?" Kate said belligerently.

"Then I'll have to resort to other measures."

"You can't talk to me like this. Maybe once because I was dumb and thought I had to take it. Not now, Mr. whatever the hell your name is. You—you're kidnapping me!"

"I'm *not* kidnapping you, and my name is Eric Spindler. I work for the State Department."

"You *say* you work for the State Department. How do I know that? You didn't show me any identification." But even as he reached into his suit coat pocket for his wallet she said, "I've changed my mind. I'm not going anywhere with you. Now what are you going to do?" she asked him. "You're invading my privacy and . . . and you can't make me do anything unless you're arresting me. I want a lawyer and I want one now!"

"You're being unreasonable, Mrs. Starr," he said, managing to flex open his wallet as they walked, revealing his badge. "All I want to do is talk to you in private with your daughters in attendance. Thirty minutes at the most and then you're free to go."

"I'm free to go now, isn't that right, Mr. Spindler? I have rights, and you are stepping on those rights. I want a lawyer present when we talk."

"For every minute you delay this, that's another minute Captain Starr is being detained. Do you have any idea how those minutes count to him? Put yourself in his place, Mrs. Starr. Look, I understand how this must seem to you. I have orders, I follow them. You have every right to an attorney, and you're also right, I cannot make you go with me. I told you the truth—all I want to do is talk to you and your daughters."

"Mr. Stewart?"

"Mr. Frazer is talking to Mr. Stewart. Same deal. No one is going to be held against their will. It's been a long night, Mrs. Starr, for everyone concerned. Please cooperate."

"I'm going to hold you to that thirty minutes, Mr. Spindler."

"Fine. This is it," Spindler said, holding the door open to a small cluttered room with three desks and four chairs and stacks and stacks of baggage tickets. The room was airless, with no windows, and smelled like garlic and peppers. Four suitcases rested one on top of the other. Kate wondered if they would fall over if one moved the wrong way.

"Mom!" Ellie and Betsy said in unison, rushing to her. The suitcases toppled. No one picked them up. Kate held out her arms to them, tears dripping down her cheeks.

"All right, Mr. Spindler, you have thirty minutes. The clock is ticking," Kate said, looking at her watch.

"Your husband is safe and sound. He's in a . . . what we call a holding area, going through a process of debriefing and medical testing. As a matter of national security, your husband must be returned to you and your family as . . . Harry Mitchell. Captain Starr has agreed to this. It was one of the

269

terms of his release by the Russians. Now do you understand why Mr. Stewart is not involved? His first loyalty is to the paper he works for." Kate and her daughters said nothing.

"Your husband will join you tomorrow. He'll leave Washington in the morning and arrive on your doorstep at approximately three o'clock in the afternoon. We need the same assurance from you, in writing, that we got from Captain Starr, that you will not divulge to anyone that he is indeed your husband."

"What he's saying, Mom," Betsy said, "is our side screwed up and we pay for it. Dad is denied a hero's welcome. He gave twenty years for his country, and his country now wants to deny his very existence. The end does not justify the fucking means, Mr. Spindler," Betsy snarled.

"There are no choices here, no options, ladies," Eric Spindler said coolly.

"He's right, Mom. If we don't sign his damn paper, if we don't do whatever he says, they'll stick Dad somewhere else for another twenty years. He has us all right where he wants us."

"Is that true?" Kate demanded, knowing her daughter spoke the truth. "How did this happen?"

"I'll tell you how. No one wanted to listen to me," Betsy spat. "I believe, and can just about prove, that the Defense Intelligence Agency and the CIA had a pretty good idea at least one American was being held in the USSR who was reported MIA in Vietnam, but nobody in the White House wanted to act on the information because they were afraid of both domestic and overseas reactions to such information. So to avoid embarrassment at home and to ensure friendly talks with the Russians, the information was buried. Dad is the loser. Tell me I'm wrong, Mr. Spindler," Betsy said tightly.

She's right on the money, Kate thought as she stared at the expression on Eric Spindler's face. She hated him the way she'd come to hate Bill Percy. So many lies. Everything was a lie.

"What's more," Betsy said, "we'll all be under surveillance from now on. Our phones will probably be bugged, our mail gone through. Someone will always be watching us. One false move and we're all history. People die every day. People disappear. I'm not saying it will happen, but it is a possibility. Ellie and I talked about this all night, and she agrees. Sign the paper and let's go home, but I think we should rent a car. At least we'll know it isn't bugged. Our life as we knew it is gone, and we can only imagine what it must have been like for Dad."

Gus, Kate thought. He wasn't overreacting. He'd told her to watch and listen, but not commit herself to anything. "For how long?" she asked coldly.

"Until we tell you otherwise," Spindler said.

"That means forever. Otherwise you'll be considered a traitor to your country. Don't waste your time reading it, it's all bullshit," Betsy said, taking a fountain pen from her purse. She scrawled her name and shoved the paper toward her sister along with the fountain pen. She had no other options. Patrick was the only thing that mattered now. Kate had to borrow it from Ellie to sign her name.

"I don't suppose we get a copy of this?" Betsy snapped.

Spindler's face registered disgust.

"Is this the same agreement my husband signed?" Kate asked.

"I can't tell you that." He folded the papers and placed it in his briefcase. "Customs has been taken care of. Your baggage is alongside Carousel Three. You're free to go."

"Dickhead," Betsy spat as she shouldered past Spindler to get to the door.

"Fuckface," Ellie snarled.

"Asshole," Kate snapped. But, that wasn't true, an asshole served a purpose.

"This is not a happy time," Betsy said bitterly. "I thought there would be a parade, the President would shake Dad's hand, the whole nine yards."

"It's sneaky. They're making your father sound like he did something wrong. Knowing him, I'm surprised he didn't spit in their faces and refuse to sign the paper. We should have read it," Kate said.

"I'm going to get a rental," Betsy said. "I'll meet you right in front."

"Is all this necessary?" Kate asked Ellie, her face puckered with worry. "Did you tell her about Gus?"

"No, but fuckface did. I think she knew. She didn't say a word. Mom, it'd blow your mind to know what she knows. All those groups, all those organizations she belongs to. She says there are still men in Vietnam. She can prove it, too. No one will listen, no one will help. All these years . . . and she was right. I gotta tell you, when Donald died, she went to mass—she converted, you know. She had mass said and she went to the cemetery a few days . . . after. She's the one who put the flowers there. She'll go up against anybody, like she did to that guy back there, go to the wall and not think twice, but she couldn't handle Donald's death. She's got guts, Mom. More than I'll ever have. She's going to apologize. If we want her back in the family, we have to take her as she is."

Kate nodded. "I thought she was going to . . . to punch out his lights back there."

"Me too. Mom, how did Gus take all this? You must be devastated. You can handle it, can't you?"

"I hope so. I'm numb right now. Gus was . . . was . . . He said he understood. I think he does. He's a good, kind man."

"I know that. It's you I'm worried about. Can you handle this?"

"I think so. I don't see that I have choices or options at this point. Whatever is best for your father, I'll do. Without reservations. What about you, honey?"

Ellie shrugged. "I'll be meeting a stranger. I really don't remember Dad. I'm open to a father-daughter relationship. I can stay a few days if you think it advisable. Betsy is, too. He's going to be like a stranger, even to you, isn't he?"

"I'm afraid so. It's been twenty years since I've seen your father, give or take a few months. Betsy . . ."

"Has a mouth on her. Guess she gets it from all the people she hangs out with. I still can't believe she has her doctorate. When did she do it, in her sleep? Who does she get her brains from?"

"From her father. You do too. I was the slow-witted one. I always felt so inferior to him, like I could never measure up."

"He's going to be real proud of you now. You have a degree and a successful business with three offices. That's not shabby."

Kate felt pleased with her daughter's compliment. "Do you think Betsy is overreacting? That bit about the CIA and that other organization . . . is that possible?"

"Betsy says it is. I believe her."

"Is she right about the surveillance? Gus more or less said the same thing. He made me promise not to agree with anything, and what do I do? I do the exact thing he warned me not to do."

"We didn't have a choice, Mom. Anything else would have been cruel to Dad. We did the right thing. We'll live with it."

"I don't have a good feeling about this, Ellie, and it has nothing to do with Gus. That's my bag, the one with the flowers. It has wheels."

On the walk to the sliding doors where Betsy would be waiting, Kate said to Ellie, "I just came in from a foreign country and didn't go through customs. There's no stamp on my passport. Officially Gus and I are still in Costa Rica. I thought you *had* to go through customs."

"This is what Betsy was talking about. The power. He whisked you two right off the ramp. Nobody said boo."

"It's scary," Kate said, shivering.

273

"I swear, Mom, you're losing your tan just standing here."

"Fear will do that to you," Kate muttered. "Here's Betsy," she said, moving to the curb. "In a Lincoln Town Car, no less. Where does she get her money?"

"She gives speeches and she tutors. She's not hurting. She charges thirty-five dollars an hour to tutor and gets a grand a speech. She knows her stuff. I feel bad we missed so many years. We talked all night. I kind of like her. I think she liked me. We agreed to work on this sisterly thing."

"What about the mother-daughter thing?" Kate asked quietly.

"I don't know how to open the trunk," Betsy called out, "so slide your bag on the backseat. Do you have enough room?"

"Plenty," Kate said, sliding onto the seat.

Four hours later Kate and her two daughters were soaking in the hot tub, glasses of wine in hand. The portable phone rested on the ledge. "The bottom line here is if we open our mouths and admit Dad is back, we become an embarrassment to the government and endanger national security," Betsy said over the rim of her glass.

"If your father agreed, if he can handle it, so can we," Kate said.

"Mom, if you were in Dad's position, you would have signed anything to get out of there. He was coerced, threatened. We all have to remember that. Duress. But try and prove it. They'll call him a defector."

"We don't know that, Betsy," Kate said.

"Well, what do you think happened to us at the airport? Weren't we threatened and coerced? It opens up all kinds of cans of worms. How many others are there? Where are they? Why hasn't something been done? The press, of which your friend Mr. Stewart is a member, would have a field day. It would rock this country, and the government would have egg on its face. Listen, let's talk about something else for a little while. What are we wearing tomorrow for the big moment?"

"I don't have anything with me," Ellie groaned.

"Me either," Betsy said.

"We'll get up early and go shopping," Kate said. "Mr. Spindler said your father won't arrive till three or so. We can have lunch together like we used to. We also have to think about dinner. For the life of me I can't remember what your father likes to eat. I should remember, but I don't. I don't remember what he looks like, either," Kate said, crying softly.

"It doesn't matter, Mom," Ellie said gently. "He won't look like he did back then. It doesn't matter if you don't remember."

"You must be very happy, Betsy."

"Is this where I get to say I told you so?" Betsy said, pouring more wine.

"Only if you want to," Kate replied. "How am I going to explain that . . . burial?"

"Mom, you don't have to make explanations. You have nothing to hide. You did what you had to do. That's the end of it."

"Your grandfather's house. I sold it."

"So what?" Betsy said. "Dad isn't Dad anymore. He's Harry now, a long-lost cousin. The house went to you rightfully. I'm all for not even mentioning it unless Dad does, and then you tell him straight. Boy, is he going to be surprised when he sees this house. I almost fell out of the car when I saw it. Pretty pricey, Mom."

"I bought it with Donald and Della's help. It's paid for now. I made a will a few years ago, girls. In it I left half of everything to Della's family. There are so many of them. I hope that's all right with you."

Both girls nodded.

CHAPTER
19

Time passed, as they knew it would, but slowly. They slept curled on the recliners in the large glass-walled family room, rose, ate, hot-tubbed again, ate some more, slept, and woke to what Ellie called "the day."

They canceled the shopping trip by mutual consent, the girls preferring to wear Kate's clothes with a few minor adjustments. The decision not to shop for new outfits allowed them time to stew and fret, to dither and wring their hands in anticipation of Patrick's return.

It was barely light out when Kate plugged in the coffee maker. Her chest felt heavy, her eyes heavier still. The girls seemed to vacillate between a state of euphoria and total despair. Kate just felt numb. She dreaded the upcoming meeting, but some part of her couldn't wait for Patrick to see and comment on her success. *Dear God*, she prayed at the kitchen table, *don't let this be the nightmare I think it's going to be. Please help us all to get through what I know is going to be a traumatic reunion.*

Reunion. A happy time. Laughter, hugs, kisses, talking about old times. Happiness.

"The early bird gets the worm, is that it, Mom?" Ellie said, coming up from behind to plant a kiss on her mother's cheek.

"This early bird is shaking in her slippers," Kate said quickly.

"That's natural," Ellie said. "We're all going to do our best. I'm sure Dad is going through the same thing. I can't even begin to imagine what he must be thinking and feeling. No one said a word about his mental state. I wish one of us thought to ask."

"Ask what?" Betsy said, yawning elaborately from the kitchen doorway.

"What your father's mental state is," Kate said.

"Shaky at best," Betsy said.

"Do we wait for his move, or do we . . . I don't . . . what I'm trying to say is, do we react to what he says or does? What if he doesn't like the way we turned out?" Kate fretted.

"What's not to like?" Ellie muttered. She smeared three inches of jam on a piece of toast, looked at it, and pushed it aside.

"Change is never easy to accept. For anyone," Kate said quietly. "I don't think I'm being overly melodramatic when I say our lives as we know them are not going to be the same. That frightens me."

"I feel the same way," Ellie said.

"This may surprise you, but I do too," Betsy said. "All these years it was so easy to say I'll do this or that, I can't wait to show, tell, and now it seems . . . I think what I'm trying to say is I more or less thought we'd carry the ball, but that's not the way it's going to be. Mom's right, we're going to do whatever we do based on what Dad does or says. We are *incidental*."

How sad her voice is, how tortured she must be feeling, Kate thought.

"Have you spoken to your fiancé?" Betsy asked.

"Last night. Why?" Ellie asked fearfully.

"These government guys seem pretty thorough. They have to know you're planning on getting married. They aren't going to overlook him. They're going to want assurance he doesn't talk. Can he hold up to what we're all going to be going through?"

"I don't know," Ellie said.

Gus's cautionary words rang in Kate's ears. "We sound like we've done something wrong and . . . we're going to be under government scrutiny night and day."

"We are, Mom. Try, just try, to picture newspaper headlines, newscasts, talk shows, all of it. You . . . we simply cannot embarrass the government. We cannot endanger national security. I'm sure Dad will be able to tell us more. We're beating a dead horse here. Until we talk to Dad, we have to accept everything. We signed away any rights we have. I don't know if that would hold up in a court of law or if we could get a lawyer to defend us if we decided to go public. My best advice for all of us is we go with the flow and take a wait-and-see attitude."

"Your father was never known for his patience," Kate said.

"Dad is an officer in the United States Air Force. He's not going to go back on his word. It's that 'do or die, defend your country' thing." At her mother's worried look she said, "I have an idea. It's a beautiful day, so let's go to work on the flower garden. It looked a bit straggly to me yesterday. You guys did a real good job on it, it really does look like a rainbow."

"We did it for Donald," Kate said.

"I know," Betsy said, staring out the window.

"What are you making for dinner?" Ellie asked.

"I have everything defrosting. I thought I'd wait to see what your father wants. Besides, I'm all thumbs."

"Sounds good to me. I'll clean the pool, you guys do the gardening. I hate getting dirt under my fingernails." Betsy hooted. Then they were off, racing down the hallway the way they used to do when they were younger. At least one good thing had come of this, Kate thought. Her daughters were friends again. And she had Betsy back. For that she would be eternally grateful. She remembered the promise she'd made to God at the airport. *Don't let anything be wrong with Betsy and Ellie. I'll do anything. Anything.* One did not break a promise made to God. Ever. She started to cry, silent tears of anguish.

"Promise me tomorrow," she whimpered. Patrick was keeping the promise he'd made so many years ago. Where had her faith gone? Why hadn't she believed? Why hadn't she trusted her husband to make good on his promise? Why? *Why?*

Kate squeezed her eyes shut to stop her tears. All she could see was years of counseling ahead of her. Even when she was in a rocking chair on the deck, she'd be trying to explain, trying to understand where she went wrong.

Abruptly, she slapped her hands, palms down, on the table. "You're going to do your best, and you aren't going to look back. Yesterday is gone, tomorrow isn't here yet, and today is all that counts. So there." She slapped at the table again for emphasis. She didn't feel one damn bit better, but she wasn't going to think about that. She was going to get dressed and work in the garden. With her daughters.

It occurred to Kate later as she was pulling on her gardening gloves that they were almost a family again. She wondered why the thought didn't give her any comfort, since *family* was her most favorite word in the English language.

"Hey, guys, it's one o'clock. Shouldn't we be breaking for

279

lunch and showering up?" Ellie called. "Three o'clock is going to get here real fast." She propped the skimmer against the Sunrise fence. "Hey, it looks good. Tidy. Looks like you trimmed with a scalpel. Real good job."

"God, it's a nice day, isn't it?" Kate said. "Anytime the sun shines it's a nice day." She looked around at the garden, at the empty cottage in the back and the flowers bordering the little front porch. A cluster of birds sat sentinel on the rail on the deck. Waiting. She'd forgotten to put out the seed this morning. How patient her feathered friends were. Maybe that was the key to life: patience. The birdbaths were empty, too. She looked up at the lower limbs of the Joshua tree, where birdhouses hung.

The huge redwood-and-glass house stared down at her. An architect's delight. She'd done a rendering of it that hung over the fireplace. She loved it, felt as if it were her first real home. Shortly there would be an intruder, a stranger, living here.

"Who's doing lunch?" Ellie asked. "What are we having?"

"You girls make it. Tuna or grilled cheese is fine with me," Kate called from the toolshed. "I have to feed the birds and fill the birdbaths."

She saw her daughters running for the deck, their bare legs flashing in the sun. The pool sparkled, the hot tub bubbled, the birds waited.

"How do we look?" Kate asked nervously at 2:45.

"We look beautiful," Ellie said. "We look like we belong together. You know, cut from the same mold or whatever it is people say about families."

There it was, that word again, *family.*

"You look great, Mom," Betsy said.

"I'm not overdone, am I?" Kate asked nervously.

"You mean the gold hoops in your ears? Nope," Ellie said.

Her dress was electric-blue, designed by Donna Karan to

expertly disguise her thickening waist. It stopped two inches above her knees and reeked with chic.

"I don't want to know how much that dress cost," Ellie said.

"Good, because I'm not about to tell you," Kate said. "Does my hair look okay? I had the gray colored before I went to Costa Rica. I used to have this long . . . *ponytail.*" She was about to say Gus loved her new Princess Di style, but she bit down on her lower lip to squelch the words. It was simple, wash and wear, and fit her needs perfectly. The fact that it looked good on her was a plus. Having a natural wave to her hair helped.

"I remember the buttons and bows you used to deck us out in. God, we looked like dimity orphans." Betsy giggled. "Even our socks had ribbons and bows on them."

"You looked adorable," Kate said defensively.

"Mom, we looked like dorks. Everyone else was wearing blue jeans and tie-dyed shirts, and there we were in our rick-rack and trailing ribbons. It's funny now, but it wasn't then."

"I'm sorry," Kate said.

"The boys liked our outfits, though," Ellie said.

"Yeah, they did, come to think of it. God, is that a car I hear?"

"Yes, it is," Kate said, swallowing hard.

"Are we going to go to the door or stand here? Nobody said what we were supposed to do," Ellie said.

Kate looked at Betsy, whose eyes were glazed. "The screen door is open. He can just walk in. I . . . I don't think I can walk all the way to the front door."

"We're going to stand here and wait, is that it?" Ellie demanded.

"Yes," Kate floundered. "We look like . . . like—"

"Half of a family who's waiting for the other half to make it complete," Betsy said softly. "The screen door is opening."

Kate's heart thumped in her chest. What was she supposed

to do? Run to her husband, throw her arms around him? Wait to see what he did? Go with her feelings? *I don't have any feelings.* She was so tense, she felt brittle. Ellie, on her right, felt stiff; Betsy appeared to be loose, but her facial features were tense, expectant. *Please God, make this right for her. She's waited so long.*

He appeared, the sun from the open front door at his back. Kate fought with her tongue and lips. He was drawn, his face pasty white. The clothes he wore were big on him, almost baggy; he'd lost a lot of weight. Somehow she'd expected him to appear in uniform, but then he wasn't Captain Patrick Starr anymore. He was Harry something or other. She had to say something—or was it Patrick who had to say something? He advanced farther into the room, shuffling, his shoes squeaking on the oak floors. How shiny his shoes were, she thought; they must be new. This couldn't be her husband, not this terribly old-looking man. Where was the dashing fighter pilot she'd married? God in heaven, what had they done to him?

He was in the room now, staring about intently. He spoke in a voice that sounded strange, unused. With a Russian accent. Kate felt tears burn her eyes.

"Kate? I know I look like ten miles of used road, but I'm here. I kept my promise."

"Welcome home, Patrick," Kate said.

The girls ran to him while Kate stayed rooted to the floor. She watched as her husband stared at Betsy, then at Ellie. "My eyesight is bad. I need to see you up close. You're beautiful, just the way I knew you'd look. I won't always look like this. Some good food, a little sun, some exercise, and I might pass for something human."

God, Kate prayed, *please let me feel something. Please.*

His arms around his daughters, Patrick advanced into the room. Kate stepped forward. "It's good to have you home, Patrick." The girls stepped aside until she couldn't see them in her peripheral vision. She felt his arms go around her, tentatively at first, as though afraid she would vanish. She smelled his foul breath, noticed the white film over his left eye, the scars around his neck and forehead. He was trembling, about to cry. *Please God, let me feel something. I want to. Please.* She hugged him, tears streaming down her cheeks.

Patrick pushed her away, held her at arm's length. He stared at her. "What did you do to your hair? You have on too much makeup," he said critically. "I don't like your hair. You smell different. For years I'd close my eyes and bring you to mind. You always looked the same. You smelled the same, like vanilla and lemon. I don't like the way you smell. Is that real gold in your ears? How much did they cost? You all look so well off," he said, peering at the hemline on his wife's dress and then down at her high-heeled shoes. "You never wore high heels before."

The sisters exchanged glances. Kate stammered, "I—I'm sorry, Patrick. I wanted to look nice for you. We dressed up for your homecoming."

"I don't like it." He moved around the huge family room, peering at everything, touching the things he wanted to see better. "Whose house is this? How much rent do you pay here?"

"It—It's my house, Patrick. I don't pay . . . rent. I own it outright."

He was shuffling again, yanking at the sliding glass doors. "Why don't you let those goddamn birds out here? Don't tell me you feed them. If you feed them, they never go away. I hate birds. Get rid of them," he said forcefully. "Where did you get the money to buy a house like this?"

"I—I worked for it. Friends . . . friends helped," Kate said in a choked voice.

"And what did you have to give those *friends* in return?" Patrick demanded. He made the question sound obscene.

"Just our love," Ellie said hoarsely.

"I didn't ask you, I asked your mother." He was moving again, shuffling his way out to the kitchen. "Well?" he called over his shoulder.

"Ellie told you, just our love. Nothing more." Her eyes were wild when they focused on her daughters huddled close together.

"I don't smell anything. Didn't you make a welcome-home meal? The prodigal returns, that kind of thing. I don't smell anything. I expected smells. I expected . . . I guess my return caught you all by surprise. Well, Kate, aren't you going to make something?"

"What—What would you like, Patrick?"

"You know what I like. Or did you forget? I want stuffed chicken, pork chops, steak, lobster. You must be able to afford that, living in this rich house. Where did you say you got the money?"

"I said I worked for it." Kate began to get food out of the refrigerator.

"You could never make enough money to buy a house like this. It must cost sixty or seventy thousand dollars."

"Try half a million, Dad," Ellie said coolly.

Patrick grabbed Kate by the arm. "Just what kind of work do you do?"

"Mom has her own business," Betsy said, coming up close to where her father was standing. Ellie took up her position on the other side of her mother.

"Do you sell Avon products? You don't know how to do anything."

He must be laughing. That sound *must* be laughter, Kate thought wildly. She dropped the chicken she was holding.

"Mom went to college and got her degree," Ellie said, her face a tight mask. "She does architectural renderings. She has three offices," she added proudly. "She's been written up in magazines. She's a professional woman. They call her a "woman of the nineties.""

The chicken was in the sink, Kate's tears splashing on the plump breast. Her children were defending her. To their father. It wasn't right. She whirled about in time to hear her husband say, "You won't be doing that anymore. I'll take it over. You belong here at home taking care of me the way you used to. You aren't going back to work."

"No!" The single word was like a gunshot. "No, you will not take over my business. No, I will not stay home taking care of you. Listen to me, Patrick. We must all make adjustments here, and I am prepared to make my share. It is my business, I worked at it twelve, fourteen, sometimes sixteen hours a day. I was the one who went out and knocked on doors, I was the one who did without when I could barely make the rent, and I will not turn it over to you. If you want to work with me, that's fine. I can teach you the business, but I will not turn it over to you. I will not stay home. I've become a career woman out of necessity. I will take time off if you need me. If we work together . . . together we might be able to pull all this together." She was shaking so badly, her daughters closed in protectively.

"You just said no to me, Kate," Patrick said. He glanced into the sink at the chicken. "I can't eat this stuff." He pulled back his lips to show a row of rotten stubs. Kate winced. "Make me something soft that smells good. Meat loaf. You don't have to worry about my not knowing how to run your business right. I know how to make money. I can probably show you a profit of fifty thousand in the first two years."

A devil perched itself on Kate's shoulders. "My net last year was three-quarters of a million dollars," she said proudly.

"When did you become such a liar?"

"She's not lying, she's telling you the truth," Ellie said. "I'm a CPA. I do her books. Betsy has her doctorate. Do we sound like we don't know what we're talking about?"

Her voice was icy. She did not like this man who claimed to be her father. It didn't look like Betsy liked him much, either.

Kate dumped chopped meat into a bowl. She was searching for an onion when Patrick said, "I don't feel like meat loaf. Make some chicken soup. Where are the bedrooms?"

"The meat loaf is down the hall— I mean, the bedrooms are down the hall. Your room is the one at the end. It's blue, your favorite color."

"Where's your room?" Patrick said.

"It doesn't matter where my room is. *Your* room is down the hall. It is the blue room. Until we go through this period of . . . of adjustment, you will be sleeping there."

"Atta girl, Mom," Ellie whispered.

"Oh, God," Betsy said.

Patrick was back a moment later. "I don't see my pictures anywhere in the house. Why is that?"

"I thought you were dead, Patrick. I put them all away. I had to. I had to get on with my life."

"Don't you feel stupid now?" he said belligerently.

"In a manner of speaking."

"There's nothing in this house that belongs to me. It's your house. Whose name is on the deed? I want my name on the deed. This is California. I own half of what you own. The Air Force told me my trunks were sent to you. Where are they?"

Kate felt herself wilt. "I buried them in the cemetery. I held a service for you. Then I had them dug up and buried in the plot next to your mother and father back in Westfield. I'm—I was going to say I'm sorry, but I'm not sorry, Patrick. I had to make sense of my life. I had no stability, no hope of your ever returning. I didn't think I had choices. I did what I felt was right."

He slapped her in a rage, and would have slapped her again if Betsy and Ellie hadn't grabbed his arm. He was no match for his young, athletic daughters. Kate wept into her dish towel.

Patrick thundered out of the room.

"Mom, forget this damn dinner business," Ellie said. "Please make us some coffee, and we'll all sit down on the deck, in the sun where it's warm, and talk. I'm not leaving you here . . . alone with *him*, until I feel . . . comfortable."

"I agree," Betsy said.

"All right," Kate said through clenched teeth. The last thing in the world she wanted was to drink coffee and talk. *Who was this person?* There was nothing even remotely resembling Patrick in this stranger.

The stranger—that's how she thought of him—didn't seem to have much of an attention span. What was being done for him? Surely the military and the government wouldn't just turn him loose like this—wash their hands of him, cast him aside, and dump him in her lap. Kate measured coffee into the basket, filled the pot with cold water, plugged it in. The reality was, they'd done exactly that. Now what was she supposed to do? Pity for her husband she'd lost so long ago welled up in her.

Kate sighed. What was going to happen when the girls left for Los Angeles and she was alone with Patrick? She didn't think twice; she reached for her address book and flipped through it till she found the tobacco store in Mexico. When she heard the familiar voice of the man she'd handed the note to over a year ago, she identified herself.

"Please, you must get a message to Señora Della Rafella Abbott. Tell her Kate needs her immediately. Tell her Captain Starr has returned and to come as soon as possible." A sob escaped her. "Can you get this message to Señora Della?"

"Sí, señora. Señora Della will be in my shop shortly. I saw her go by an hour ago. I will tell her."

"Thank you, thank you very much."

The coffee was done. Kate heaved a mighty sigh. With

287

Della here, she might survive what she knew was coming. She filled the tray and carried it out to the deck. She went back for the coffeepot.

In the bright sunlight, Patrick looked even more ghastly. "I don't want you wearing clothes like that anymore. I like the old things you used to wear."

Should she humor him or talk straight from the shoulder? Was it too soon to set down the rules? Someone should have told them how to act, how to deal with Patrick. But no one cared; it was that simple. "I go to work, I have to dress appropriately. I'm sorry you don't like my dress. It happens to be a fine dress. I think I look good in it. I deal with businesspeople. I have to look professional. I don't make my clothes anymore, Patrick. I don't have to. This is the style. I like it. We'll have to think about taking you shopping, too. I didn't see any bags. Didn't they give you anything?"

"A change of underwear, some shaving gear and a toothbrush. I left the bag by the front steps. If you hadn't thrown my things away, I wouldn't have to go shopping."

"The things wouldn't fit you now anyway. I can't imagine you not wanting new clothes. You have to fit in, to look like—"

"Harry. You have to start calling me by name."

"All right, Harry," Kate said, sitting down on the redwood chair. She wished she could fall asleep and never wake up.

"I'm glad to be home even if I never saw this house before," Patrick said quietly. "I know I look like ten miles of bad road. I said that before when I first got here, didn't I? I expected . . . thought I would see revulsion on your face. All those years I never had a mirror. You used to say I was handsomer than any movie star. Star, get it?" He made that strange sound that had to be laughter.

Kate told him about Betsy's rainbow and pointed to the border around the house. "She thought you would fly overhead and be able to find the little house we used to live in.

288

We believed for so long that you would come back. We hoped. We prayed. I wrote to the President six or seven times, and anyone else I could think of. Anytime we even got close to finding out something, it would be squelched. What did you sign, Patrick?"

Patrick slurped at his coffee. Some of it dribbled down his chin. Ellie handed him a napkin. "I agreed to what they wanted so I could come home. They don't want me to tell anyone where I was or what happened to me. I asked them how long I had to remain quiet, and they said until they told me otherwise. I might never be Patrick Starr again. I might have to be this Harry fellow for the rest of my life."

"You'll always be Patrick to us," Kate said, her voice sounding desperate.

"We had to sign a paper, too," Betsy said.

"Do you regret it?"

"No," they chorused.

"When are you going to get rid of the birds, Kate?"

"I'm not going to. I love waking up and hearing them chirp. They depend on me for their food. I would think you'd like having them around. You used to fly. You told me once you could fly better than any bird and they were doing what came naturally. I don't mean to sound nasty or over-bearing, but you are going to have to make some adjust-ments. The birds are God's creatures."

"I don't want them here. They remind me of my flying days. I'll get rid of them myself."

Ellie and Betsy both fidgeted on their chairs. Kate was off hers in the blink of an eye. She dropped to her knees, keep-ing her distance from her husband. "Patrick, listen to me. You are not to touch the birds. Not now, not ever. If you do, I will have to . . . have to . . . think about having you live somewhere else until we can adjust to this situation. I'm go-ing to try very hard to get . . . to get to know you again." She saw the kick coming and leaped backward in time.

"Don't you tell me what to do! For nineteen and a half years people told me what to do. I'm a free man and I don't have to do anything I don't want to do," Patrick snarled.

"In my house you do," Kate said quietly. "Do not ever, ever lash out at me again. You will be out of here so fast your head will spin." Her husband sneered at her. She didn't back down.

Kate turned to her daughters and with a slight nod of her head indicated they should go into the house. She mouthed the word *cook*. Both girls seemed reluctant to leave but did as their mother wanted.

Kate pulled her chair around so she could face her husband, but far enough away so he couldn't kick out or lunge at her. She settled herself, the skirt of her dress hiking up to mid-thigh. She tugged at it. She'd taken this dress with her to Hawaii last year, had worn it to dinner with Gus. He liked it, said she looked like a rare flower and that the color became her. She in turn said it matched his eyes perfectly. How happy she'd been then. She tugged at the skirt again.

"Patrick," she said gently, "we need to talk. I think we should start over. We're different people now, both of us. We can't go back to nineteen seventy. That time in our lives is gone. We have a tremendous adjustment to make, both of us. I'm more than willing to seek out a therapist, and I know the girls will agree. I don't know what you went through, and if you tell me, I probably couldn't begin to imagine your pain and suffering. I'm sorry for that, but you can't take your anger out on me and the girls. I simply will not allow it."

"I was never warm, never comfortable. I was always hungry. All I thought about was you and the girls. That's what kept me going," Patrick said, staring across the garden.

"And we thought of you. For years. When I finally gave up, Betsy didn't. She worked tirelessly. My heart ached for you. I dreamed of the day you would walk through the door. For so long I lived in a fantasy world, hoping, dreaming of your return. You're angry, and justifiably so, but your anger is directed at the wrong people. We aren't the enemy. I thought you would be so proud of the girls, of me. You . . . you shot us down. We wanted to share, and you didn't want to hear. You haven't smiled once since you've been here. With skilled help, you can be whole again. We have the patience and the resources to help you. Don't take your anger out on us. We've lived in our own hell for a lot of years."

"Nothing is the same," Patrick said flatly.

"Time doesn't stand still, Patrick. Surely you knew things would be different," Kate said gently.

"I wanted it to be the same. I wanted to see that small apartment, trip over those damn ducks. In my dreams I could smell you. I could see the girls with the little bows on their socks and in their hair. They're grown up, and I missed all that. I always knew I would come home someday. I'd swagger in, be the conquering hero, sweep all of you off your feet. I dreamed about the hugs and the kisses, the big welcoming dinner. I expected a ticker tape parade, meeting the President, being invited to go on television and give interviews. None of that happened."

"Oh, Patrick, I'm so sorry," Kate said in a choked voice. "It's not right for your country to deny you, to pretend you're dead. You deserve much more. If there was a way for me to give you all of what you deserve, I'd move heaven and earth to do it. A man named Spindler made us sign papers, too. I hated doing it, but he said if we didn't you would be kept someplace. Betsy said they could do that. She said we should sign."

"They meant it," Patrick said. "Do you know how I kept my sanity all those years?"

"You said you thought about us."

"Besides that. When things were bad, I retreated into my mind, back to Westfield. I went door to door. I'd knock, and when someone opened the door, I'd say 'Hi, I'm Patrick

Starr. I used to live here.' I'd pet their dog or cat, and they'd ask me to come back again. I knocked on every door in Westfield. I visited every single store. As the years wore on, I paid a second and third visit. I saw the dogs and cats die, got invited to weddings. Hell, I went to two of them. In my mind. Both of them were held in the VFW hall. I went to a couple of funerals, was even a pallbearer. One person even asked me my opinion on choosing wallpaper for the kitchen. I told her she should get green and white, the kind you had in our kitchen. You know, so it would look like summer in the winter. The woman said it was a good idea. When I was really cold in the winter, I'd visit this one house where an older couple lived. They had a fluffy white dog that liked to lie in front of the fire. I'd carry wood in for them, and they let me sit by the fire. The lady made hot cocoa, and we toasted marshmallows. The dog liked them, got the sticky stuff all over his whiskers. They were nice people. No one had names, though, but they all knew mine. Isn't that strange?" Tears were streaming down his cheeks.

Kate moved her chair closer and reached for her husband's hands.

"This isn't going to be easy, Kate. I think I must be a terrible person. It's like I can't control myself. I'm not going to be easy to live with."

"I know. You're disappointed in me, aren't you? I wanted you to be proud of the success I've made of myself."

"I didn't think you had enough brains to go to college."

Stricken with her husband's words, Kate murmured, "I guess no one can ever know everything about another person."

"You turned your doodling into a business. It must really be a crazy world."

"One of my renderings hangs in the White House, Patrick. I don't exactly doodle."

Patrick's eyebrows shot upward. He seemed to cringe into

himself. "I don't want you working. Wives shouldn't work. I want you home."

"Cooking, cleaning, and working my fingers to the bone? You want me making crafts again, the crafts you once hated. I can't do that, Patrick. We can't go backward. We can't re-capture the past. We have to move forward, adjust to what we have and deal with the here and now. If your mind is still working on that California property split of fifty-fifty, you're going to have to readjust your thinking. You are no longer Patrick Starr, and since you are no longer Patrick Starr, you cannot claim anything. You are not my husband any longer. You're Harry. Don't threaten me, Patrick, I won't stand for it."

"You're full of piss and vinegar, aren't you?" Instead of waiting for her response, he rushed on. "I can make your life miserable."

"And I can boot your ass right out of here. I don't have to take you back. I cannot believe we're having this conver-sation. We're actually threatening each other. And to what end?"

"I'm the man of the house. You used to accept that. You never had a thought in your head. All you wanted to do was use that damn glue gun you had and make things. Now all of a sudden you're an authority on everything."

"I'm sorry you see it that way. I've had to survive, and I did it the best way I knew how. Please don't punish me for that. I made myself into an extension of you. You should never have allowed me to do that. I believed you when you said I couldn't do anything but keep house and have babies. I had nothing to compare it to. When you were shot down, I couldn't cope. I didn't know how to do anything but keep house. By the sheerest accident I met up with a wonderful woman in the park, and together we both managed to sur-vive, helping one another. I was so ashamed that I was thirty years old and didn't know the first thing about *living*. With-

293

out her and Donald, our kids would have been put in foster homes and I would have been carted off to the loony farm."

Patrick stared at his wife as though she were a stranger. The sun was dropping. Soon it would be twilight and the end of the day. He hated the darkness. "Do you have lights out here?"

"Yes. Lots of them. Why?" Kate asked, confused.

"I don't like the dark. What you say you went through was no more than a pimple on your ass. You don't know the meaning of misery. I'm not going to be able to fly again. I always felt good in the air. They're taking that away from me, too. I hate them. I'm not even sure I like you, Kate."

"I'm not sure I like you, either," Kate said quietly. "You can fly if you want to. We can even buy a plane, if that will make you happy. You can get your pilot's license under your new name. That shouldn't be a problem. I wish everything would be as easy for you. A good dental surgeon will take care of your mouth. An eye specialist will take care of your cataracts and fit you with glasses. You're alive, Patrick. Be grateful for that. Good food, warmth, and fresh air will aid your progress."

"You left out the vitamins, the orange juice, and a weekly laxative," Patrick said nastily. "It's getting dark."

Kate walked over to the outdoor switch and turned on the floodlights. Artificial light bathed the yard in a warm, bright glow.

"What's that little house?"

"That's Della's cottage," Kate said.

"Maybe I should move in there."

"Maybe you shouldn't be alone. Maybe you should think about that. You've been alone too long."

"Are you telling me what to do?"

"It was a suggestion. The cottage belongs to Della. You would need her permission."

"Where is she?"

"Mexico," Kate said, her heart thumping in her chest.

"She's Mexican? She owns a cottage on your property? No, that isn't going to work. If you have all the money you say you have, buy it from her. I've had enough foreigners to last me the rest of my life."

"I'm sorry, I can't do that. I *won't* do that."

"Yes, you will. I'm your husband and I'm telling you to do it."

"The government says you aren't my husband. I'm not doing it, Patrick. You cannot make me do anything."

Patrick lunged at her, reached for Kate's hair and dragged her off the chair. His rancid breath swept past her fear-filled face. Her daughters barreled through the door and were on their father within seconds. They dragged him backward, each pinning one arm. Kate coughed and sputtered as she fought for breath.

"Mom, what—"

"I gave your mother a direct order and she refused to obey it," Patrick said, trying to jerk his arms free.

"This isn't the Air Force, Dad," Betsy said. "What was the order?"

"I told her I didn't want any foreigners here. Your mother said a Mexican owns that little cottage. I told her to buy it back and she said no. Let go of me!"

The girls dropped their father's arms at the same moment and then joined their mother on the deck. "Della will be here tomorrow," Kate told them in a low voice. "I called her before."

Patrick shrugged his shirt down over his shoulders and stomped into the house.

"He's like an animal," Betsy said wildly.

"Mom, you can't stay here with him. He could have killed you. What's going to happen when we leave?"

"Della will be here. She'll come, I know she will. Your father has been through a lot. He needs a few days to adjust. I think he feels betrayed, and rightly so."

"That has nothing to do with us," Betsy said, hanging on to her mother for dear life. "I didn't know . . . I had no idea . . . what did they do to him?"

"Every terrible thing you could think of, I imagine. If things get bad or if I think I can't handle it, I'll call that man . . . what's his name?"

"Do you have his phone number?" Ellie asked in disgust. "Don't you have it?"

"No. Betsy doesn't have it, either. They didn't hand out cards. They contacted us, remember?"

"This is unreal," Kate muttered. "All we have to do is something they told us not to do and they'll be all over us. I think we can get help if we need it. He doesn't like us, me especially," Kate said.

"He's disappointed in us," Ellie said. "He wants yesterday."

Betsy sat down on the deck and hugged her knees. "Would it be wrong if we tried to give it to him? I didn't think it would be like this. I knew he'd changed, but I thought . . . hoped, he'd still be the father who went away."

"Yes, honey, it would be wrong to try and go back. All we can do is be here for him. He's going to have to work real hard, but then so are we."

"What's going to happen when Della gets here?" Ellie asked fearfully.

"I don't know. Your father suggested moving into the cottage. I feel that would be a mistake, though. He needs to be around people and learn how to interact again. All of this is going to take time."

"I'm not leaving here till he settles down." Ellie said. "You don't think he'll do anything to us when we're sleeping, do you?" she asked, her eyes wide with fear.

Kate had been wondering the same thing. So had Betsy, from the look on her face. "I think we can all sleep in my room this evening. It will be a slumber party. My God, did I just say that? I did, didn't I?"

"We started dinner," Ellie said nervously.

"What did you make?"

Betsy giggled hysterically. "We took all the meat and dumped it in the Crockpot with some vegetables. It's kind of soupy, so maybe he won't know the difference. Ellie poured a lot of spices and stuff in it. It even smells kind of good. Mom, did he say even one nice thing? Did he say he missed us, loved us?"

"In his own way he did. He feels those things, but I think he's afraid it's all going to be taken away from him again. He turned in one set of fears and accepted another set. It's not fair, what they're asking him to do. It's not fair to any of us. I just don't understand any of this," Kate muttered.

Through the open window they could hear the phone ringing. As one they moved to enter the house in time to hear the phone picked up in the middle of the third ring. From the kitchen they heard Patrick's voice say, "Don't call here again."

Kate bristled. "Patrick, who was that?"

"She said her name was Della, that foreigner you said owns the little house."

"And you hung up on her?" Kate sputtered. "Don't you ever do that again! You don't hang up on people I know or do business with."

Patrick's response was to yank the yellow phone from the wall. He threw it across the table. Carrots and string beans flew in every direction. The phone bounced twice before it skittered across the black slate floor. "Now we don't have to worry about any more foreigners calling here," he said, smacking his hands together. "I need some money."

The women stared at him speechlessly.

"Mom, let's get in the car right now and get the hell out of here," Ellie said tightly.

"I'm all for that." Betsy pulled her mother toward the front door.

"What do you need money for, Patrick?"

"You *said* you have all the money. I don't have any, so you should give me some. The government gave me a check and it's been deposited, but they said it won't clear for seven to ten days. It's hush money."

"What do you want money for? The stores are closed now."

"You never used to ask questions, Kate. Now you ask too damn many." He was rummaging along the counter, pushing and shoving everything in his way till he found the Betty Crocker cookbook. "You used to keep money in the back. I bet you thought I forgot about that. Well, I didn't forget anything, Mrs. College Student with her degree."

"Does that intimidate you?" Kate said quietly.

"Why should it? I have a master's. Do you have one of those?"

"No, but I have a doctorate," Betsy said, stepping forward. "Does that intimidate *you*, Dad? Don't put Mom down. I did enough of that over the years. She doesn't deserve it."

"You raised a disrespectful snot here, Kate," Patrick said, lifting the lid of the Crockpot. A rush of steam surged upward. He jerked backward, swinging wildly.

"Oh, God," Ellie wailed as vegetables and meat sailed up and out.

Kate raised her eyes to see a chunk of celery on the ceiling. When it dropped, it landed on the tip of her shoe. She wanted to bellow her outrage, to call Gus and tell him to come and get her out of this nightmare. "Why don't we change our clothes, clean the kitchen, and order a pizza," she said calmly.

In her bedroom, with the door closed and locked, mother and daughters clung to one another. I'm supposed to be the strong one, she thought, the guide, the one who leads her daughters in the right direction. She wanted to scream, run, run as fast as she could and not look back.

"He's a tormented soul," she said.

"He's nuts, Mom. He should be in a hospital with trained people to help him," Ellie said tightly. "He could seriously hurt one of us. You better start thinking about what's going to happen when Della gets here."

Kate looked at Betsy. "I think he needs intensive therapy, but I don't know if he'll agree to it. What if . . . *they* don't want him in a . . . place like that? He could say something that would . . . blow it all away. How can he have therapy when he isn't allowed to talk about his past?" The horror of what she'd just said hit Kate full force, her daughters, too.

"They took him out knowing there would be problems, made him swear to secrecy, us too, and now they expect him and us to survive? What kind of people are they?" Betsy demanded.

"Does that mean we scratch any kind of therapy?"

"Yes, I'm afraid that's exactly what it means," Kate said quietly.

"What do you suppose he wanted money for?" Betsy asked.

"Men need to have money in their pockets. It's right he should have money. I'll give him whatever he wants," Kate said.

"He wants to buy a gun so he can shoot the birds," Ellie blurted. "Don't let him buy a gun, Mom."

"I won't. Let's change now. I don't think we should leave him too long."

They scrambled into jeans, shirts, and sneakers, and they looked like triplets when they walked out to the kitchen. Kate pulled up short. The table was set, most of the mess cleaned up. The contents of the Crockpot were in a big bowl in the center of the table. Patrick was sitting at the head of the table.

"I'm used to eating things off the floor," he said. "My

guards used to throw my food at me. Sometimes it had rat hairs on it, but I ate it anyway. We shouldn't waste food. I didn't think you would eat it, so I made you jelly bread sandwiches. Is that okay, Kate?"

Kate burst into tears. She shook her head. "I don't think the food is done, Patrick. I can fry you some eggs or open some soup."

"No, this is fine. I ate raw meat. This is a luxury. Sometimes I just had fat and grease on bread. This is good. I like it," he said, trying to chew the food with his bad teeth.

"These are good sandwiches, Dad," Betsy said, her mouth full. "I remember you used to make them for us when you had a day off."

"I used to sprinkle sugar on the top and tell you not to tell your mother. Do you remember that?"

"Yeah, I remember," Betsy said, tears streaming down her cheeks.

"Don't cry," Patrick said.

"Okay." She wiped her eyes on the sleeve of her shirt.

"Kate, do you think I could get a dog? A big one. I think I'm going to need a friend, one who will tolerate me when I do something wrong. I think I need someone to love me. I thought . . . all this past week I thought I could handle anything as long as I was home. I can't. It's like everything is rushing at me, smothering me, and I have to do something. React in some way. For many years I wasn't permitted to do or say anything. I used to whisper to myself so I wouldn't forget how to talk. They beat you if they heard you clear your throat. Did you say I could or couldn't get a dog, Kate?"

"Yes, of course. We can go tomorrow if you like." God, maybe this was going to work out after all. "Patrick, I have to talk to you about Della. I don't want to upset you. Will you please listen?"

"Yes."

Kate told him about Donald and Della, with the girls

chiming in from time to time. "She took care of us, Patrick. She and Donald made us whole again. They wiped away our despair, made us want to live again. We wouldn't be here for you now if it wasn't for Donald and Della. Will you accept her and be kind to her?"

"Do you think I'm a monster, Kate?"

"No, of course not."

"If I say yes and you say yes to the dog, does that mean we are both working at"—he waved his arms about—"all of this?"

"Yes, it does."

"Should we vote?"

"Voting sounds good," Kate said.

"I vote yes," Betsy said.

"Me too," Ellie said.

"You always did that when you were little," Patrick said. "You have to say, I vote yes."

"I vote yes," Ellie said carefully.

"I vote yes, too," Kate said.

"I vote yes, too. No hot peppers."

"I'll tell Della."

"I think I'll go to bed now, unless you want me to finish cleaning up."

"No, we can do it, Patrick. Sleep well."

"I love you all," he said brokenly.

"Is he trying or is it a trick?" Ellie said when she heard his door close. A moment later the door opened. She heard her father say very loudly, "I don't like doors that are closed."

"Let's believe he's trying, and let's all try harder," Kate said, clearing the table.

"Maybe it will work out." Ellie sounded as though she didn't believe what she was saying.

"The Captain Patrick Starr I knew would never give up," Kate said staunchly. "He was the best of the best. He'll . . . make it. I know he will."

CHAPTER
20

"I think I know what happened," Kate said, wiping her eyes. "Your father has been locked up for so long, his thought processes can't be normal. He's got justifiable rage in him, and he lets it out the only way he knows how. He can't vent that rage on the people who freed him, so who's left? Us. The good part of him, the part they couldn't take away from him, came through. It's mixed up in his mind and tied to . . . how he must have lived, afraid of doing something wrong and being punished or tortured for it—for no reason, more often than not. He may have . . . thought, for just a little while, that we were his captors. That we would punish him for what he'd done. The good part, the Patrick part, cleaned up and tried to make it right with the jelly sandwiches. Does that make sense?"

"It's as good as anything I can come up with," Ellie said, rinsing the dinner plates.

"None of us are qualified to offer therapy," Betsy said. "You're absolutely right, Mom, we can't take him to any kind of professional. He can't tell them where he's been all these years and what he's gone through. Those bastards really covered their asses on this," she said bitterly. "I always dreamed this would be such a happy time. Damn it, I wanted it to be happy. Think about how we feel, and then think about what he must be feeling. My God!"

"Della will . . ."

"Della will what, Mom? Clean up after him? Cook his meals? Wash his clothes? That's not what I'm talking about. *You're it.* You are Dad's only chance of surviving this. It's going to be a twenty-four-hour job. You're the only one who can make him whole and well again."

And when he's whole and well again and able to function in this big world we walk around in, then I can . . . then I can go to Gus. "How long do you think it will take?" Kate asked, hating the desperate tone in her voice. When her daughters shrugged, she sank onto a kitchen chair. The shrugs had to mean a year at the very least, maybe longer. Would Gus wait for her to do her duty to her husband? How awful that sounded. How terribly selfish.

"Mom, this is probably going to sound . . . weird, but did you notice how Dad talked, how he moved? He said all these strange things, and some of them he repeated like he was trying to make a point. It didn't seem like he *heard* you. Do you think . . . is it possible he has a hearing problem, too? If they beat him, maybe they punched him in the head or something. I kept watching him. He heard us at the table because the table is small and we were close. What do you think?" Ellie said.

"We'll find out tomorrow. I'm taking your father for a complete physical, and from there to the best oral surgeon I can find. Hopefully the doctor who gives him a physical can recommend a good eye doctor. I think when they see his condition, they'll want to do everything they can for him as soon as possible. The question is, do I take him to L.A. or go local? People know us in town. Questions might be asked that I can't answer."

"I think you just answered yourself," Betsy said. "L.A. is your best bet."

"All right, that's what we'll do, then. I'll follow you girls back to the city. I know you want to stay and help and . . . protect me. However, I think I'll do better with your father one on one. Come up on the weekends, call, that sort of thing."

"What about your business?" asked the ever-practical Betsy.

"I was hoping you'd step in, Betsy, and take over for me. If I have to worry about the business, I won't be able to free my mind and give a hundred percent to your father. Besides, your drawings were always as good as my own."

"What about Gus?" Ellie blurted. She covered her mouth instantly, her face full of guilt.

"Oh, for heaven's sake, I know all about Gus Stewart," Betsy said sourly. "Nothing you two did escaped me. So I was an ass. Let's not go into all that old stuff. Well, Mom, what about Gus? Why don't we go outside on the deck or walk around the yard," she said suddenly.

Ellie's eyebrows scooted back almost to her hairline. Kate strode to the door and outside, her daughters right behind her. They sat down on the lounge chairs by the pool and whispered.

"None of us would make good spies," Kate said hoarsely.

"The point being we are ordinary people thrust into an extraordinary situation. What about Gus?"

"For now there is no Gus. It's that simple."

"You love him, don't you?" Betsy said.

"Very much. We were going to be married in December."

"And now?" Ellie said.

"And now we aren't."

"Do you love Dad at all?" Betsy asked.

Kate was tempted to lie, to wipe the miserable, hurt look off her daughter's face. "Not in the way you mean. Your father was my first love. One never forgets that. But it was never a healthy relationship. I idolized him, worshiped him to the exclusion of all else. I was like some kind of robot going through the day-to-day motions. I existed. I only came alive when your father came home. I did everything by rote. I had all these schedules that only an idiot like me could follow. All they did was allow me to exist until your father walked through the door. I came alive then. In the morning when he left, I went back to being a robot. I thought I was normal. That's why I couldn't function when your father was shot down. I simply didn't know how. All I ever wanted was his approval, a pat on the head, but he never gave it to me.

"During our therapy sessions—do you remember, when you were sixteen or so?—Dr. Tennison asked me if Patrick loved me, and I said, without a moment's hesitation, He doesn't even like me. Then he said it was possible for someone to love another person but not like them, and vice versa. I pretended I understood what he was saying, but I really didn't. I still don't know what he meant. I don't see how a person can love another person and not like them. Do you understand that?" Her daughters shook their heads. "So, I'm not so dumb after all," Kate said ruefully.

"In my stupidity, I would have made you two girls clones of myself. If your father hadn't been shot down, if I hadn't met Della and Donald, I might have ruined your lives. You shook me, Betsy, when you rebelled, but deep inside I cheered you. You forced both Ellie and me to change. So, some good did come of all this."

Kate's daughters wrapped her in their arms. They cried together for the past, the present, and the future.

A long time later Ellie said, "Do you think Dad will ever be okay?"

"I think so," Kate said, not knowing if it was the truth.

"I'll take over the business," Betsy said. "If I screw up, don't blame me."

"I'll be watching you, big sister. Just because you're the oldest doesn't mean you're the smartest," Ellie teased.

"Oh, yeah, who else do you know who got their doctorate at the age of twenty-six?" Betsy retorted.

They were needling one another. To Kate it sounded wonderful. This generation had such a strange way of communicating. For a few minutes she felt almost happy.

"Why don't you girls go in the hot tub. I have to make some phone calls to see if I can get some appointments tomorrow for your father. Bring the phone down with you and some sodapop. With all the lies I'll be telling, my throat is going to be dry."

They listened, the water bubbling and whirling about them as Kate called one person and then another until she got the promises she needed. "A distant cousin is here from Poland and needs extensive, immediate medical help. Can we schedule the appointments all for the same day? . . . Of course I'll do a rendering of your brother-in-law's house. It will be my pleasure. How about by Thanksgiving? . . . Sooner? Absolutely. I'll drop everything and do it right away. Call the office and give them the addresses. . . . Framed? I wouldn't have it any other way. Thank you, Stephen."

"What say we fake him out, Mom, and I do it," Betsy said, giggling. "I'm going to flatter you now, and tell you I've seen just about every one of your renderings in town. I even bought one that was hanging in the bank. What do you think of that?"

Kate laughed. "Tell me how much you paid for it." Betsy told her. She laughed again and said, "Guess I made a hundred and fifty percent profit on that one."

"Two years ago I had the flu and nothing to do, so I

amused myself by trying to copy the rendering. I had it matted and framed, and except for my signature, you wouldn't be able to tell them apart."

"She said with no trace of modesty," Kate said, and smiled.

"If you got it, you got it. All I'm trying to say is I can do the renderings, and if you feel they're as good as yours, maybe you'll sign them for this guy. It'll make me feel like I've done my part in helping Dad."

"That's not very honest," Kate said.

Betsy's mood and tone of voice changed instantly. "I don't want to hear about honest right now. Just take a look at the position we're all in. Let's just forget that word right now."

Trying to head off something she didn't want to get involved in, Ellie said, "What about me? Do I carry your pencils or what?"

"You carry my pencils and add the numbers in the ledgers. Maybe we can shame this guy into paying."

"Not a chance," Kate said. "You might give some thought to signing them with just 'Starr' and the date. The next ones I do I can sign the same way. It'll make it less dishonest."

"I'm ready for bed," Ellie said, climbing out of the tub. "This thing knocks you on your butt, but you sleep like a baby afterward."

There was anxiety in Kate's voice when she said, on her way to her bedroom, "Are we sleeping together?"

"Yes," both young women said at the same time, following her.

"Good. I guess we better leave all the lights on in case your father wakes up. We should check on him, too."

Kate stopped short as she peeked in on her husband. "Oh, my, he's sleeping on the floor. He must have six blankets wrapped around him."

"Maybe he thought he'd fall out of the bed. It is kind of high," Ellie said.

"Maybe he's used to sleeping on the floor," Betsy said.

"Maybe he didn't have a bed. This carpet is thick enough to be a mattress."

"He looks so ... alone," Kate murmured. She advanced into the room and dropped to her knees. She was about to brush his hair back from his forehead when he woke, his eyes filled with total, complete terror. He huddled into himself and muttered something in Russian that Kate couldn't understand. "It's Kate, Patrick. It's all right," she crooned, patting his shoulder. "Nothing is going to happen to you. Not while I'm here."

"Kate? Kate?"

"Yes, Patrick, it's Kate. Go back to sleep. I'll stay here with you for a while." Her touch was gentle when she brushed at his hair. Because she couldn't remember any lullabies, she started to croon, "Mary had a little lamb, its fleece was—"

"White as snow, and everywhere—"

"Mary went, the lamb was sure to go."

"Sing it again, Kate."

Kate waved off her daughters. When she finished with Mary and her lamb, she started on Jack and Jill. There was a smile on her husband's face when he drifted back to sleep. Kate's heart swelled in her chest as her tears splashed on her husband's shirt-clad shoulder. Anger, hot and scorching, rushed through her. They hadn't even given him clothes. A change of underwear, he'd said, that was all. Because he wanted to be warm, he slept in his clothes. She wanted to kill someone for what they'd done to him. "I promise you, Patrick, your day is coming," she whispered.

In the morning, Kate handed Patrick an overlarge cable-knit sweater. "It's chilly out," she said. "We're going to Los Angeles. I made appointments for you. It's going to be a full day, Patrick. Are you up to it?"

"Yes, Kate," Patrick said quietly.

"Tomorrow we can get you some new clothes. Or the girls can follow us later. They can shop for you so the clothes will be here when you get back. Yes, that's a good idea. Do you agree?"

"Do you think it's a good idea?"

"Yes, I do, but what do you think?"

"I think I want my own things. I think I want to throw away these clothes. Not the sweater. You gave me the sweater. Yes, it's a good idea. Did I do that right, Kate? Did I make a decision? I'm not allowed—I wasn't allowed to talk or ask questions. I have not made . . . decisions."

"Well, you just made your first one. Today you are going to make more," Kate said gently.

"What if I make the wrong one?" Patrick asked. "What will happen?"

"Not a goddamn thing." The scorching anger ripped through her again at the nameless, faceless people who had done this to her husband. She tried to force a smile in her voice. "Sometimes it's fun to screw up because you get a second chance to make it right."

"I'll get two chances, then."

"You bet. More if you need them," Kate said, her voice breaking. Where did the anger, the rage and hostility, go? she wondered. Was he being submissive for a reason? Fear did strange things to people. She fought with her scorching anger. *Your day is coming, Patrick.*

"Who's going to make breakfast?" she asked cheerfully.

"I will," Betsy said.

"I'm going to shower. Patrick, did you shower?"

"I . . . it was too cold."

"You have to take a shower every day. And you have to shave and brush your teeth. I understand what you're saying about it being chilly. I'll show you how to work the fan in the bathroom. There's a blower. It will take five minutes for the room to warm up."

Patrick moved alongside Kate down the hall and into the bathroom. He watched her carefully and nodded to show he understood how to turn the blower and the fan on and off. "Don't close the door, Kate."

"I won't."

"Are we going to get the dog today?"

Good Lord, she'd forgotten. Well, the girls would have to help with that, too. "Yes, Patrick. Do you have a particular one in mind?"

"A man's dog," he said sprightly.

"A man's dog it is. You'll have to train it, you know. Do you promise to take responsibility for it?"

"Yes, I promise. They treated me like a dog. I would never treat a dog the way they treated me. I want to prove that. I have to prove that. No, let's not get it yet."

Kate's throat closed. Somehow she managed to say, "We're going to get you the best dog in the state of California. Not yet, though. You're going to be real buddies." Patrick smiled at her. *You son of a bitching bastards. I'm going to get you for this.* She rushed from the room to her own bathroom, where she showered and washed her hair, all in under five minutes. She was out, dressed, and in the kitchen in twelve minutes total.

"You look nice, Mom. I bet Dad approves of those slacks and sweater. Peridot is your color."

"Thanks. What's for breakfast?"

"Pancakes. They're soft. I melted the butter and warmed the syrup. Betsy squeezed the orange juice. The coffee's good, too."

"Girls, I have another job for you. If you have time, bake a chocolate cake with lots and lots of frosting. Pick up some ice cream."

"What kinds of clothes should we get? We need sizes," Betsy said, reaching for the notepad. "And what should we do if Della gets here while you're gone?"

"Hug her. Buy large. Casual. He doesn't need a suit yet. Loafers, maybe moccasins, size eleven. Real warm socks. Think warmth. His underwear is probably thirty-two. Flannel pajamas, a warm robe. Lots of sweaters. Warm trousers, a lined windbreaker. A wool hat and some gloves. Just go through the men's store and use your best judgment. Later on I'll pick up a flight jacket. I think he'd like that."

"If we have any time left over, do you want us to paint the house?" Ellie quipped.

"Don't forget to bake the cake," Kate said, lighting a cigarette from the stub of the old one.

"Hi, Dad. Sit down, I made pancakes," Betsy said proudly. She layered six onto his plate.

"They look very nice," Patrick said.

Betsy giggled. "They taste very nice, too."

Patrick ate everything on his plate, then finished his juice and coffee. "I never leave anything. If you left something, they didn't feed you the next time," he volunteered.

"You don't have to worry about that anymore," Kate said. "If you feel warm enough, we should be on our way. I'll call you this evening, girls. The credit card is with the money in the desk."

"Don't you use the cookbook anymore?" Patrick asked.

"Sometimes I do. But sometimes I forget and just stick it in the desk drawer. You said you wanted money, Patrick. I'll get it for you. How much do you want?" she asked, and saw Patrick's face fill with panic. "How does fifty dollars sound?" she added gently.

Patrick's face relaxed. "Fifty dollars sounds . . . okay." There was such relief in her husband's voice, Kate wanted to cry. To the girls she said, "Get a wallet, too." To Patrick she said, "You can keep the money in your pants pocket for now. We'll see you girls later on."

"We'll come up to see you on the weekend, Dad," Ellie said.

"Okay. Do you want me to kiss you good-bye?"

"Sure," Betsy said, her eyes wet.

Ellie hugged her father and said, "I wish I could remember you."

"I remember you. You used to pull my ears when I carried you on my shoulders. Betsy pulled my hair. I remember everything. One time they told me you all died in a car crash. I knew that wasn't true because your mother was a good driver. I told them I believed them, but I didn't," Patrick said proudly. "I don't have much hair left," he said suddenly.

"You have enough," Kate said. He was so docile, so mellow. When would he erupt again, she wondered, or was yesterday's anger a one-shot deal?

"You never lied to me, Kate, so I believe you."

"No, Patrick, I never lied to you. I won't lie to you now, either."

They were on the highway, the heater blasting in the Mercedes, when Kate said, "Did you ever love me, Patrick?"

"I'm not sure. You were a good mother and you kept house good. We were happy, weren't we?"

"I thought I was. I loved you with all my heart and soul," she said quietly.

"That's a lot," Patrick said in amazement.

"Yes, it was. I'm not sure you even liked me. Why did you volunteer for that mission?"

"I wanted to get my ticket punched. It was the only way to make rank. It was a mistake. I didn't use to make mistakes, did I?"

"Not too many."

"I wanted everything to be like it was. I'm sorry about yesterday."

"I'm sorry, too. Did you really think I was dumb, that I needed you to think, that I never had a thought in my head?"

"Yes, but only because it was true."

312

Kate cringed. "You don't hear well, do you?"

"No, I don't. I guess I had too many blows to my head. One ear is good."

"Why didn't you say something?" Kate asked sadly.

"Because there were so many other things wrong with me. You couldn't see inside my ears."

Please God, help me get through this. Help me to be kind, to understand. "We'll get that taken care of today, too."

"When do you think I'll be normal, Kate?" Patrick asked.

"I don't know. We're all going to do our best for you, but you're going to have to work hard. I'll do whatever I can."

Kate almost laughed when Patrick said, "Because you love me heart and soul?" Almost. "You don't love me anymore, do you?" he asked, his tone conversational.

Kate thought about the question before she answered. "Part of me will always love you, Patrick. But I'm not *in love* with you." Please, she prayed, don't let him ask me if I love someone else. Don't let him ask me that. "Do you love me?" she asked, hoping to forestall the question she felt was coming.

"I think I was in love with the idea of marriage. I needed a wife. You need a wife in the military or you don't get ahead. I liked you. Most of the time." It was said so matter-of-factly, Kate found herself half smiling. Maybe, she thought, it doesn't sound so bad because of the Russian accent; when things were quiet, when her head was together, she would think about what her husband had just said. That and the fact that suddenly, with Patrick's words, she could feel her guilt start to wash away.

"Today is going to be difficult, Patrick. Tell me something. I don't understand why you weren't given medical treatment. I don't understand how they could just . . . send you off in your condition. They're treating you like an animal," she blustered.

"It was my choice. They took me to someone, and I had

a going-over, a quick one. My eyes and ears were scheduled for later. I also had to go through extensive debriefing. Once I told them how I spilled my guts, they more or less lost interest in me. I've had nineteen and a half years to think about all of this, and I know in my heart no human could have held out against the torture and the drugs. I wanted to come home. They said they would reimburse us for all the medical bills. They lie, Kate."

"I know that."

"If I get better and start to look normal, do you think we could go out to dinner? In a public place."

"Would you like that?"

"The thought is a goal. Right now. I'll pretty much have to learn to walk like everyone else. I shuffle, and sometimes, most of the time, I move in jerks. That's because I was scrunched up a lot."

"We'll work on that. We'll take walks, ride bicycles. Remember how you used to ride past my house on your bike? You always pretended you had a flat tire when you got to our driveway."

"You saw through that, huh?"

"Pretty much so."

"Are you really rich, Kate?"

"I'm comfortable. I don't think we'll have to worry about starving. I have an investment planner. Ellie oversees it all. You should be very proud of the girls. Betsy . . . Betsy understands all this business with the government. I don't pretend to understand how she . . . She takes after you, Patrick. When you're feeling up to it, you should talk to her. Ellie says she's an expert in international government affairs. I guess that means she knows how the system works or doesn't work."

"They're fucking me over, Kate, and there's nothing I can do about it."

"We aren't going to worry about that now, Patrick. For

now we're going to defy them and get you on your feet. We're going to make you robust and . . . and we're going to work on your anger so we can all deal with this reasonably and logically. I don't believe that nothing can be done. I refuse to believe that."

"We're caught up in the system now." Kate heard the fear in his voice and reacted angrily.

"I don't want you quitting on me before we even get started. If we believe we can take on the system, we're halfway home. It's not always the winning that counts. What counts is calling them to accountability. When the time is right, Patrick. It all depends on you."

The rest of the trip was made in silence, the radio playing softly, the heater blasting.

At the hospital Kate was told to come back at four o'clock. Patrick would have his physical, visit the dentist and eye specialist. His hearing test was scheduled last. The doctor assured her that when she picked up her cousin Harry, he would have glasses and his hearing aid. If possible, dental work would be started.

With time on her hands, Kate treated herself to lunch and a long walk. She stopped for coffee in the middle of the afternoon so she could use the bathroom. The phone on the wall made her light-headed. If she was lucky, Gus would still be in the office. Generally he ate lunch in the office, unless he was out in the field working on a story. She counted her change. She had enough to make the call, but if Gus wanted to talk, he'd have to call her back.

The moment she heard his voice she started to cry. She was still crying when he told her to hang up and he would call her back. They talked for thirty minutes, about the weather, about Betsy and Ellie, and about how certain she was that Della would be at the house when she got back. "I miss you," she said. "I dreamed about you last night."

"Kate, I'm worried about you. Can you handle this?"

315

"One minute I think I can, but the next minute I think it's hopeless. I have to try. You said you understood."

"I do understand, but that isn't going to stop me from worrying. Is there anything I can do?"

"How did it go with the man who picked you up?"

"Not well. They tend to work on intimidation. He thought he was intimidating the *New York Times*. I told him to go screw himself. I signed his damn paper, and underneath my signature I wrote, 'Under duress.' He tried to tell me I wouldn't be permitted to leave until I signed a second form. We looked at each other for five goddamn hours. He went out to make a phone call, and finally he let me go."

"I wish I'd had the guts to do that."

"You need to be in a position of strength to fight them. You had nothing going for you. You have your husband back. They played on that, the bastards. As long as I know you're okay, I can live with this. When can you call me again?"

"I'll try every few days. I'll try to work out some kind of schedule. A routine is going to be important to Patrick. I've been thinking about enrolling him at a gym. I can take him into town and wait. I can't give you anything more definite right now. I have to do this, Gus."

"Yes, you do. The poor bastard deserves the best. If there's anything I can do, let me know. I love you, Kate, more than life itself."

Kate squeezed her eyes shut. She wanted to tell him she loved him just as much, maybe more, but the words wouldn't come. She had no right to say them. Not now. Maybe never.

"Take care of yourself, Kate. You're in my thoughts every hour of the day."

"Don't eat too much fast food," Kate said, choking back a sob before she hung up.

When she took her place at the table to finish her cold

coffee, she looked around. The few customers who had been there when she'd entered were gone. A man who absolutely reeked of suspicion, right down to the propped-up newspaper, stared at her. Kate stared back, her eyes defiant. She was chagrined, to say the least, when she went up to the cash register to pay her bill and the man said, "Mrs. Starr?"

"Yes?"

"I thought I recognized you. I'm Reverend Timmins. You did a rendering of our rectory several months ago. I've been meaning to write you a letter to tell you how many comments I received from my parishioners." His hands went to his tie. "Sorry, but today is not my collar day."

"We all need days like that," Kate said, offering a huge smile. She felt like a fool as she walked out into the afternoon sunshine.

At the hospital, Kate settled herself in the waiting room to wait for the doctor. He found her at ten minutes of five.

"Well, Mrs. Starr, I'm happy to report your cousin Harry is not as bad as we thought at first. His EKG is fine. His lungs are a little congested, but medication is going to relieve that. His kidneys are good, his bowels are okay, too, considering the strange diet he's been living on. Our resident dentist filled nine cavities and pulled six front teeth. A partial plate is being made up. It will be ready in three days. Soft diet, of course. His cataract is not ready yet to be removed. Laser surgery will take care of that, and he will have the use of his left eye. He's already got his new glasses and can see quite well out of his right eye. His hearing has been severely impaired, but he's now wearing the latest in hearing aids. He was quite fascinated with it. It goes behind the ear and is hardly noticeable. His entire mouth is numb and will stay that way for about six hours. The man is exhausted and is napping in one of our recovery rooms. Oh, yes, his preliminary blood and urine tests seem to be okay. We'll know more when you come back for his partial plate. You can take your cousin home, Mrs. Starr. But"—he wagged an invoice under her nose playfully—"stop at the office and give them this."

"Thank you, Doctor," Kate said, and glanced at the bill in her hand. Two thousand, eight hundred dollars. A small price to pay for Patrick's health. She wrote out and signed the check with a flourish.

Back in the waiting room, she stood quietly as Patrick tottered toward her. "I feel like hell," he said around the packing in his mouth.

"You look like hell, too," she said cheerfully. "You can sleep on the ride home."

"I could hear every word you said," Patrick mumbled, his face full of amazement. "Every word. I can see you clearly, too. You're very pretty, Kate, but you're too fat around the middle."

Kate didn't know whether to laugh or cry when Patrick poked her playfully on the arm. "If I wanted to be nasty," she said, trying to hide her smile, "I could tell you you look like shit right now. So *there*." She dug her elbow into his arm. A sound escaped his mouth. He's laughing, Kate thought. He's really laughing. She grinned from ear to ear.

Patrick fell asleep the minute the car started to move, and he was still sleeping when Kate pulled into the driveway. The house was lit up like a Christmas tree. She was out of the car in a flash when she saw Della's plump figure outlined in the lighted doorway. They laughed and cried, hugged and kissed, and then they babbled like magpies. Patrick continued to snooze in the car while they walked around the garden.

"I really need you, Della, can you stay? Will you stay?"

"Of course. Now you need me. Before you didn't. Those girls left such a mess. It took me hours to clean up. The cake was such a disaster, the top slid off onto the table. Even the birds wouldn't eat it. I made another one. I made chicken soup and spaghetti and pudding and all kinds of things. It's all ready. I hung Captain Starr's clothes up. Your daughters have good taste, Kate. Betsy hugged me. She told me she loved me. We cried and cried. Everything is fine now. They did tell me that Captain Starr might not take to me because I'm Mexican. What should we do about that?"

"It's not that you're Mexican, but that you're not American. I settled all that. He might be a little standoffish for a while, but I know Patrick—he'll come to love you like we do. And stop calling him Captain Starr. Actually, we're supposed to call him Harry. 'Hey you' sounds better to me than Harry."

They were in the middle of the yard under one of the many Joshua trees when Della said, "What about Gus?"

"I spoke to him today," Kate said softly. "I thought my heart would break. He told me how much he loves me. I wanted to tell him how much I loved him, but I couldn't. I don't have that right anymore. I don't know what's going to happen. Patrick told me on the ride to the city that when we got married, he was in love with the idea of marriage more than he was in love with me. He said he just *liked* me, 'most of the time.' *Liked* me! How could I not have known that, Della? Was I that big a fool? I would have died for him if he'd asked me to. Everything I thought was real, wasn't. I must have been the stupidest person in the world. A woman should know if her husband doesn't love her. But not me—I was so busy making chickens and ducks, bows and ruffles, that it never occurred to me. How am I supposed to know if Gus loves me? Patrick used to tell me he loved me."

Ever practical, Della said, "Ask him if he's in love with you."

"I can't do that," Kate faltered.

"Then I'll do it," Della said.

"No, you won't." Kate wrapped the older woman in her arms. "We have to get Patrick into the house and into bed. He's had a tough day."

"I see it's taking its toll on you, too, Kate. Well, I'm here now. Does he want to have sex with you?"

"Delllllaaa!" Kate sputtered. "I think sex is the furthest thing from Patrick's mind right now."

"He's a man," Della said. "When it becomes in the front of his mind, what will you do?"

"I don't want to talk about this, Della."

"You're going to have to think about it sooner or later. Captain Starr is a man. He's not always going to be in such a *delicate* condition."

"Then I'll think about it later, but not now. Definitely not now." There was an edge to Kate's voice.

Della shrugged. "Life is never easy," she said philosophically.

Kate's heart leaped to her throat at the sight that met her eyes when they returned to the driveway, the floodlights glaring down on the candy-apple-red Mercedes. Patrick was cowering in the front seat, his hands scrunched around his head. The sounds he was making were those of a trapped animal. "It's the lights. He must think he's being interrogated. He doesn't like the dark. The girls must have turned the lights on before they left," Kate whispered.

"Patrick, it's me, Kate," she said soothingly as she approached the driver's side of the car. "We went to the hospital today. You fell asleep on the way home. I want you to get up now and climb out of the car. No one is going to hurt you. These are good lights, Patrick, they make the dark go away." She ran to the passenger side of the car and opened it.

"I thought it was a bad dream," Patrick said.

"It's all right now," Kate purred. "Della is here, Patrick. I want you to say hello. She's going to help us. She's also going to make a poultice for your gums. Come along now."

"The lights weren't this bright before, were they?"

"Yes, they were, but you can see better now with your

320

glasses. "Della, this is my husband, Patrick, also known as Harry."

"I'm very pleased to meet you, Captain Starr. For years I heard about you from your wife and daughters. I feel like I know you."

Patrick stiffened. Kate exerted pressure on his arm. "Hello," he said, relaxing almost immediately.

Della fussed then, hustling them inside, where she immediately set about making a poultice of tea bags for Patrick.

When Patrick was settled for the night, the wet tea bags clamped between his gums, Della said, "You have a long road ahead of you, Kate. The bottom line is, what happens when you get to the end of that long road?"

"Like Scarlett said, I'll worry about that tomorrow," Kate said wearily. "Della, will you sleep in my room with me?"

"That's where my things are. I think you should turn in, you look exhausted."

"Della, having you here means everything to me. I feel better just looking at you across this table. As usual, I'll never be able to thank you."

"And as usual, no thanks are needed. Are you sure you don't want anything to eat?"

"I'm positive. Besides, Patrick told me I was fat today. I guess I could lose a few pounds around my middle."

The following morning, Patrick's new routine began. To make it official, Kate carried a ruler. She wasn't sure why, and Patrick didn't ask. He was attired in gray Nike sweats, L.A. Gear sneakers, and a Mets baseball cap. He was still biting down on the wet tea bags. His tinted aviator glasses were in place, his hearing aid turned to full volume. He looked at Kate expectantly.

Kate waved the ruler and cleared her throat. "You ate a good breakfast, hot cereal, mashed banana, pudding and juice. Now we're going to . . . to do a few simple exercises. Simply because *I* probably can't handle anything more strenuous. Then we're going for a walk. A long walk. If we get tired, we'll rest, come back, eat lunch. Della has spaghetti, soup, and a lot of soft stuff, and you'll need to change your tea bags. You'll rest or nap an hour and then we'll do it all over again. If you're up to it, we'll go to town, maybe see about joining a health club. We'll stop by the drugstore and get some Grecian Formula to color your hair. Then we'll have high tea, cake and whatever else Della makes. We'll swim, soak in the hot tub, and I'm going to hire a masseur to give you daily body massages. Maybe me, too."

"You need it," Patrick mumbled.

"I heard that," Kate snapped. He made the funny sound she knew was laughter. From the kitchen window Della smiled.

On the third day, when they made the trip to the city for Patrick's partial plate, he didn't sleep at all. Kate giggled most of the way home as she watched him admire his new bridgework in the visor mirror. When she stopped for a light, he skinned back his gums and smiled, and then made the funny laughter sound.

"I know you're probably saying something profound," Kate said as they neared the exit for Bakersfield, "but I'll be damned if I know what it is. I guess it's because you aren't used to the bridge yet, and that Russian accent isn't helping. I think we should hire a tutor. One-on-one will be good for you. Don't worry, we'll fit it in somehow. What's another sixty minutes out of your life?" Patrick rolled his eyes, then patted her on the arm. Kate felt touched with his simple gesture.

"Why don't you freshen up now," she suggested as they pulled into the drive. "I'll make some iced tea and we can drink it out on the deck."

"Okay," Patrick said agreeably, and he trotted off to do as

she'd ordered. She watched him shuffle down the hall, her eyes full of pity.

It was all too much. He felt trapped and free at the same time. His mind whirled. His room ... He didn't like the sound of that: his room. *The* room didn't sound any better.

He'd wanted everything to be the same, had expected just that. He'd even allowed for the change in the girls, but not Kate. Kate was ... Kate was ... a slick chick. He used to call her that, but at the time it was just words. Kate had been plain, a comfortable person, a warm person with love shining in her eyes.

His eyes searched the room. It looked like a man's room, with the box-pleated, navy-blue bedspread and matching drapes. Even the pillows had special covers. He wondered why that was. Maybe they were afraid he had lice or dandruff. The room was too big, it had too many windows. He needed a smaller space, some place where he could huddle. All this openness confused him.

This was a stranger's room in a stranger's house. Was he ever going to belong here? He sniffed, hoping for some kind of familiar scent. Mothballs. The room hadn't been used. A guest room. He was in the guest room. He looked at the light blue walls, at the deep blue shag carpet that was one shade darker than the spread and drapes. He wondered if he could ask for yellow or maybe light green. Red would be good, even orange. He thought about orange then as he crunched into himself.

He saw it then. The closet. He hadn't gone near it. He wondered why. "Maybe I didn't see it," he muttered. He opened the door and a wave of cedar washed over him. He sniffed again and again before he decided he liked the smell. The closet was small, with a rod and one shelf he could reach if he wanted to. His hands were shaking when he stretched to remove the bar. The shelf came away easily. He placed both outside the door, then walked into the closet. His shaking stopped when he leaned into the corner, his thin arms wrapped around his chest. His hands crept upward. He beat at his face, his shoulders, yanked at his sparse hair. His shoulders started to shake as he slid down to the floor. His feet clawed at the fluffy shag carpet.

"I need you to help me, God. I can't do this myself. Please, help me. I can't bear the looks on my family's faces. I'm scaring them. I don't want to do that. Why am I in this closet? Why can't I stand in the middle of the room? Why do I need this dark, narrow space? Kate won't punish me. The girls won't whip me. Show me what to do. Show me how I'm supposed to act. I forgot. Somebody has to help me," he pleaded. "Give me a sign, something I can hang on to when it gets bad. Anything. My mind will recognize it. I want this so bad. Please, God, help me."

"Patrick?"

His sign. He struggled to get up.

She stared at him.

He stared back.

"Are you going to ask me why I'm in here?"

"I think I know why. You're comfortable there. All the rest of this kind of . . . scares you. It's going to take time," Kate said softly, a smile in her voice.

"Kate, can I ask a favor?"

"Of course."

"I don't like these colors."

"Oh. Well, we can change that. What color would you like?"

"Something . . . sprightly."

"Like . . ."

"Yellow. Maybe green. I like red."

"It's a done deed, Patrick. Tomorrow I'll have someone come out and do it over. How about a nice moss-green with daffodil yellow accents? That will look . . . sprightly."

"Yes, sprightly." Patrick grinned crookedly. Kate was his sign. Kate was going to make everything right. "Thank you, God," he murmured.

As the days and weeks passed, Patrick improved so rapidly, it boggled Kate's mind. By the time the new year rolled around, He'd gained fifteen pounds. Twenty more would put him in his proper weight class. His face had filled in and begun to fit the aviator glasses he loved. His movements were less jerky, and if he paid close attention, he could actually stride, and even at times glide, to Kate's amusement. He had color to him now, thanks to the tanning bed at the health club. "It's just temporary, Patrick, sun isn't good for you," she told him.

By St. Patrick's Day, when Della cooked a huge corned beef and two heads of cabbage along with small white potatoes, Patrick was walking five miles in the morning, working out with minimal weights at the gym, swimming, and then walking another five miles before dinner. Afterward he had his body massage and worked with the tutor.

Kate was exhausted and had lost only seven pounds.

In June Patrick passed his driving test and Kate bought him a Jeep Cherokee, a bright red one to match her Mercedes. He still carried the original fifty dollars in his pants pocket that Kate had given him on his arrival.

By the middle of August he'd gained another eighteen pounds and was constantly at the refrigerator. He ran and jogged, swam and continued to work out.

One bright, golden afternoon, Patrick sneaked away from the house while Kate was taking a shower. He drove to the pound, where he turned over his fifty dollars and bought a dog that had been picked up off the freeway. It was a mangy, unkempt, filthy mutt with huge sad eyes and half a tail. He liked Patrick's hand. "This one. Does he have a name?"

"We've been calling him Jake. Kind of fits him, if you know what I mean." Patrick didn't know and wasn't about to ask.

Jake smelled so bad, Patrick had to roll down the windows for the drive home. "We're going to catch hell when we get home, Jake. I'm not supposed to go anywhere on my own." This last was said with barely a trace of his former Russian accent. "You know what, Jake? You look like I did when I got here. You know what else? My wife is okay. She's putting her life on hold for me. I want to say something to her, but I don't think the time is right. She doesn't like me too much."

He rambled on, from time to time looking at the dog as though expecting him to answer.

"She's not what I expected. Nothing like I expected. She has *opinions*. Before I left, she didn't even know what an opinion was. Now, look at her! I guess I'm jealous. I wanted it all to be the same, and it isn't. I want to love her. I think she expects me to love her. I think she's waiting for me to ... *do something*. You know, get horny or drag her out to the bushes. She's being so good to me, trying to help and all. She should, she owes it to me. I want to feel something besides gratitude, and even the gratitude eats at me. Why is that, do you suppose, Jake?

"You know, back then I had to get away from her. She was smothering me, and then when I got captured, she was all I could think about. I care about her. I cared about her back then. She was almost perfect in a ... smothering kind of way. For a wife. You take me, now, I was the perfect pilot, everyone said so. And what did that get me? Twenty fucking years out of my life, that's what.

"Kate has a secret. I can see it in her eyes. The girls know what it is, but they aren't talking about it." He laughed, a strange sound that made Jake's ears go flat against his head.

"The thing of it is, Jake, I've intruded in her life. She

doesn't want me around, and she feels guilty for the way she feels. See, I know this woman.

"If someone came up to me now, this very minute, and said, 'Come on, Patrick, I'm going to let you fly again,' I'd be out of here so fast, I'd leave scorch marks on Kate's fluffy carpet. That's all I want, Jake, to fly again. Kate and the girls, they have their own lives. I wish I loved her, really loved her. I wish there was a chance for us, but there isn't. Kate doesn't know that yet. She's the world's best fixer-upper. She thinks she can make me over, make our marriage work. Yesterday is gone, Jake. She keeps saying that all the time. She thinks my brain is gone. Now she's trying to make me an extension of her. That's what got us into trouble in the first place. Back then she made herself an extension of me. But I'm smarter; I'm not going to let that happen. No, sir, I'm not going to let that happen.

"Well, we're here, Jake. This is where I live these days. It's temporary. Kate thinks she's here for the long haul, but I can read her like a book. What she's doing, Jake, is her duty. Okay, let's get out so I can show you what a really good life you're going to have."

When he climbed from the Cherokee, Jake stayed in the back and refused to get out. He's afraid, Patrick thought. "This is freedom, Jake. We're gonna give you a steak, the biggest one you ever had, and we're *throwing away that bone*." If the dog had been a cat, he would have purred at Patrick's gentle touch. "Come on, boy, I'm going to clean you up. You can sleep in my room, and if *she* says anything, we'll tell her how it is."

A minute later he came back outside to Jake, a sheepish expression on his face. He could hear his wife still screeching his name from the deck. "She's pissed," he said. "I'll tell you how I know she's pissed, Jake. When she calls me Harry, she's mad. When she calls me Patrick, it's okay. We are in deep shit this time."

Kate burst through the front door, eyes flashing fire. "You know the rules, Patrick. I was worried sick! Why didn't you at least *say* something? . . . Well? What do you have to say for yourself?" she snapped.

"Meet Jake. I drove to the pound. I used the fifty dollars and bought him on the spot. He smells a little. Kind of the way I did when I got here. I guess nobody wanted him."

"What fifty dollars?" Kate demanded.

"The fifty dollars you gave me when I got here," Patrick said patiently. "I have change."

"I thought you said you weren't ready for a dog."

"Then, I wasn't. Now I am. This is my kind of dog. When I spruce him up, he'll be okay. Don'tcha think, Kate?"

It was the first time Patrick had taken the initiative to do anything on his own. She'd forgotten about the fifty dollars. He looked so anxious, and the dog looked . . . petrified. Despite herself, she stooped down and scratched him behind the ears. "He's going to need *a lot* of sprucing up."

"That's what I thought. I think we should feed him. I told him we'd give him a steak and throw away the bone. I think that's good, don't you?"

"Yes. On the grill or under the broiler?" she asked.

"The grill. I'll do it."

"Did you have any trouble finding the pound?"

"No. I asked for directions. I saw a mailman and he told me. I was . . . very anxious. But I was careful. I wore my seat belt."

"I would have taken you. All you had to do was ask."

"I needed to do this myself. I think you're getting tired of me. You need time to be by yourself. Jake can go with me on the walks or when I run. I don't want you to start to hate me, Kate." He shuffled his feet at the bottom of the deck stairs. "In a few weeks I'll be home a year. A year is a very long time."

"I don't mind. Betsy is running the business better than I

did. I made a commitment to you and to myself. I could never hate you. I don't want to hear you talk like that."

"Okay, Kate. My motor skills are good now."

"Yes, they are. I'm very proud of you."

Patrick beamed.

In the kitchen, Kate sat down at the table. She could see Patrick turn on the grill and flop the steak on it, Jake at his side. "Why do I feel so funny all of a sudden?" she asked Della.

"Pretty soon he isn't going to need you. It's hard to believe he's the same man I saw when I first got here. The biggest hurdle, at least to me, was when he started sleeping *in* the bed. I might be wrong, but I think by next year he's going to be ready to go off on his own. Legally, that leaves you in limbo more or less, but you will be free to go to Gus."

"Shhh," Kate whispered.

"He wants to fly again," Della said.

"I know. I don't think he's ready for that yet. On the other hand, maybe that's the last thing he needs to make him whole again. I'm going to talk to him about it. Just last week he told me the amount of money the government gave him—two hundred thousand. I never asked him how much it was, and he never mentioned it. He seems to be doing a lot of thinking, and he's not talking about whatever he's thinking about." She sighed. "Christ, I have to start getting ready for the Chamber of Commerce meeting tonight. I picked up the videos he asked me to get. I don't know if it's good or not for him to watch all those Vietnam movies."

"It's one way for him to find out what went on while he was in Russia. He read all the material you and Betsy gave him. He soaks it up like a sponge and then grows quiet for a day or so. Your husband carries many demons, Kate."

"He needs professional help for that. I'm certainly not qualified. Every time I ask him something, he changes the subject. I wish I didn't get so irritated when he takes so much time to think and act before he does anything. It's been almost a year. I think he should have lost some of his fear by now. He hasn't had a bad dream in a long time."

"Perhaps he is afraid of you," Della said softly.

"Me! Why in the world would he be afraid of me? All I've done is help him."

"I think you intimidate him. Perhaps the way he used to intimidate you. The mind is a curious instrument, Kate. He was looking for your approval when he came home with the dog, but I saw the fear in his eyes, too. I was watching from the kitchen window. He did wrong, but he did right too. He wasn't sure which way you would react. I think you handled it just fine."

Kate sniffed as she marched into her room to get dressed. She would not go to the Chamber of Commerce meeting, she decided. She would find a phone booth in a restaurant, call Gus and talk to him for an hour. Then she'd get something to eat and come home. She was being sneaky and devious. In the beginning Patrick had questioned her about the meetings, but he didn't do that anymore. He was content to settle himself in front of the fifty-six-inch television with a bowl of popcorn for hours on end. Tonight was what Kate called a free evening, which meant no tutoring, no anything, just relaxation.

She flicked at the hangers in the closet with impatient fingers. She always wore a suit to the Chamber dinner meeting, so she had to play the part. A wave of guilt washed over when she picked out a dove-gray suit and bright crimson blouse with a bow at the throat. It was what she called her neat, tidy look. Her hair, long now, was pulled back into a chignon. She slipped into a pair of Ferragamo heels and stood back to assess her image in the free-standing pier glass. All she needed to do was add the double teardrops to her ears and spritz on some perfume.

She was ready to talk to Gus. She felt good, looked good.

It was all she had.

She was in the hall, wondering where she'd left her car keys, when a whirlwind of soap suds slammed her up against the wall. Stunned, she let out a shriek and saw Patrick stop short, his hands flying into the air.

"What . . . what happened?"

Patrick was backing up, his face drained of all color, his hands in the air. From down the hall she could hear Della shouting at the dog. So that was what it was. Some internal instinct warned Kate that this was do-or-die stuff for Patrick.

"Oh, well," she said cheerfully, forcing laughter into her voice. "I didn't want to go to that damn meeting anyway." *I'm sorry, Gus, I'll have to call you later in the week.* How long would he wait at the paper for her call? All night, she answered herself.

"I think," she said, kicking off her heels and yanking at her suit jacket, "we should rethink this bath business. Now mind you, I've never had a dog, but on television they always jump out of the tub. What you have to do is close the door, and one person stands ready to catch the dog if he bolts while the other person scrubs him down. Now, the way I see it, since we can't close the door, Della will stand guard at the door and I'll help you. Between the two of us I think we can get Jake here squeaky clean. I'm ready if you are." She rolled up the sleeves of her crimson blouse.

Della led a bedraggled Jake into the bathroom, and between the two of them, they managed to wrestle the dog into the tub. "This was not a good idea, was it, Kate?" Patrick said.

"It was a great idea," she replied. "We just didn't count on Jake being so frisky. He's a nice-looking dog. I think we can put some cream rinse on him so his coat will be easy to brush when he's dry. I bet we could blow-dry him, too. That way he can sit on the couch with you while you watch your movie."

"He smells like a wet dog. Lord, when did he have a bath last?" Della grumbled.

"Probably never," Patrick said with an edge in his voice.

"That would explain why he's so afraid. I can feel his heart beating. You remember what that was like, don't you, Patrick?" Kate met her husband's gaze.

"You aren't upset that you can't go to the meeting? Your clothes are all wet."

Something was brewing here, something she didn't understand. "That's trivial, Patrick. You have to learn what's important and what isn't. In the scheme of things, this would go down as a big zero."

"It's two mistakes in one day," Patrick said.

Kate could sense the tightness in her husband's shoulders, and the set of his jaw bothered her. Was he going to fly into a rage? "You didn't make a mistake getting the dog. All I said was you should have told me you were going. I was worried about you, but it wasn't a mistake. If you don't want to tell me something, you can leave me a note."

"You look sad, Kate."

She wanted to say, I am sad, I looked forward all week to calling Gus tonight; I have the right to be sad. But she didn't. Instead she said, "I'm sad because this poor dog is beside himself at what's happening to him. We need to rinse him. Della, would you fetch something from the kitchen so we can end his misery? No, no, that . . . it was a poor choice of words, Patrick. What I meant was we have to get him out of the tub and dried so he can go back to being a dog. We agreed you weren't going to take everything I said so literally."

"I'll try harder," Patrick said, his shoulders relaxing slightly, but not enough to reassure Kate trouble wasn't brewing.

Jake suffered through his blow-drying better than Patrick did. It looked to Kate as though he were relating somehow to the dog. She'd found over the past months that Patrick talked when he wanted to talk and not one minute before. But then he'd always been like that. She was more or less pleased that he'd retained one of his original traits.

Their evening began the way it usually did. They had dinner, and Jake begged at the table, even though he'd had a three-pound T-bone steak. Patrick's voice sounded sharp when he told the dog to lie down. Jake's tail wagged, his sad eyes imploring when he sat up on his haunches, his tongue lolling out of the side of his mouth.

Kate saw it all in slow motion, saw Patrick's face contort, saw him raise his arm, saw Jake, eyes trusting, trying to lick the hand that was about to strike him, saw Della's swift movement, saw Patrick literally pulled from his chair onto the floor, Della standing over him, her chest heaving. Jake thought it was a game and proceeded to lick Patrick's face. Patrick rolled over on the slate floor and beat at it with his clenched fist.

"I thought you loved Jake? You fed him, bathed him, gave him a name," Kate said hoarsely. "He trusts you, and you were going to strike him. If you had done that, the dog might have turned on you and gone after you, and it would have been your own fault. What is it, Patrick?"

"I think I'll take Jake for a long walk," Della said. "Don't worry about the dishes, I'll clean up later when I make the brownies I promised . . . Harry."

"I understand, Patrick," Kate said, brushing his hair back from his forehead. Her voice was low, soothing, almost a croon. "In your mind it's all mixed up. You were treated like a dog, and you fed the dog and he was still begging, much the way I imagine you had to beg for food. You've come a long way, Patrick. These flashes . . . whatever they are, they're getting to be fewer and fewer. It's over now and Jake is okay. He thought it was all a game."

Patrick sat up and wrapped his arms around his knees. "I

333

could have hurt him, turned him against me. When . . . when I told . . . said something about giving Jake a bath, Della said maybe we should just turn the hose on him, but then she said it was too chilly and he might catch a cold. That . . . that one word, hose, triggered all this. The V.C. turned a hose on me once. Who the hell even thought they knew what a hose was? It was like one of those fire hoses where the water comes out a hundred miles an hour. It drove me against the wall and then into a rack of bamboo spikes. That's what all those scars on my back are from. I thought I was going to drown. They laughed and laughed, poking sticks at me to force me back into the stream of water when I'd try to crawl away. That was probably the only real bath I ever had. Without soap." He grimaced.

Dear God in heaven. "Come on, Patrick, we don't sit on the floor in this house. It's over; everything is okay now."

"You're wrong, Kate, it's never going to be okay. I can't ever get those years back. I won't ever be able to forget. I'm not permitted to talk about this to anyone but you and the girls. How can I put it behind me if I can't get it out in the open and deal with it? You said writing down everything in those stupid journals would be a start. I did it because you said it would help me. Well, guess what? You were wrong, it's worse now than it was when I first got back. It's almost a year—a whole goddamn year—and I was ready to kill that poor dog," Patrick said miserably.

"But you didn't, and that's what's important. You won't ever do anything to Jake. You'll always be aware, and you have control now," Kate said quietly.

"Do you realize it's been a year and no one has been in touch with us? No one has called to see how I'm doing. No one has checked up on me. Once I signed that paper, I became a nonperson. Patrick Starr doesn't exist anymore. I'm goddamn sick and tired of being honorable. Honorable should work both ways. All this past year you've talked me up when things were bad. You were always there. You never got mad, you never fought with me even when I was at my worst. And you don't even love me," he said, his voice full of awe. "I always know when you're pissed off, though. You call me Harry."

Kate laughed. "Yeah, I guess I do. So, now what? I can tell you've been doing a lot of thinking. It would be nice if you'd share your thoughts with me."

"Well," Patrick said thoughtfully, "I thought I'd stick around to participate in that one-year anniversary party you and the girls are planning for me. I overheard you talking," he said sheepishly. "I can hear a pin drop with this hearing aid." He laughed at the look on Kate's face. It was a nice laugh, full of amusement at his wife's embarrassment.

"And then?" Kate said anxiously.

"Then I thought I'd go back home and start a new life. Maybe I can buy my dad's old house in Westfield. I guess if you have enough money, you can buy almost anything."

"Not always. And after you do that?"

"Maybe sign up for some flying lessons, using the Harry name. Maybe I can even get a job at the Linden airport. I can try Newark, too. If there's one thing I know about, it's planes. I'll have Jake. I'll get a bike and pedal past your old house. If I have any money left, I might buy yours, too. This way Jake and I can pedal by and sit on your front porch and pretend you're going to come out and chase us away."

Kate bit down on her lower lip so hard she could taste her own blood. She wanted to cry. "That was one of your dreams. I don't understand. You said you weren't in love with me. Why would you want to sit on my old front porch?"

"It's one of the nicest memories. Back then things were simple. We were kids and pretty damn innocent. I don't think it's ever going to get any better than that. If you give me that old Betty Crocker cookbook of yours, the one with the pocket in the back, I'll be okay."

She did cry then, great hacking, gulping sobs. Patrick put his arm around her, pushing the button on the VCR at the same time. "I think you're going to miss me, Kate. Who are you going to miss, me or Harry?"

"Shut up, Patrick. Just shut up, do you hear me?"

"With this hearing aid I can hear—"

"Go to hell!" Kate cried, jerking free of his arms. She stomped her way down the hall to the bedroom. She slammed the door and locked it. Howling like a banshee, she threw herself on the bed. When she'd exhausted her tears, she rolled over on the bed and reached for the phone. Not caring who was listening, not caring about *anything*, she punched out Gus's private number at the *New York Times*. "Hi," she said, "I'm calling from home." The word *home* would set the tone for the balance of the conversation. "How are you doing with your Pulitzer?" It was a standing joke with them. She forced a chuckle into her voice she didn't feel.

"How's Harry?" Gus asked.

"Harry had a bad day today, but he also had a good day. He went out and bought a dog. He calls it Jake. Ellie is going to be married in February. Romantic that she is, she wants the wedding on Valentine's Day. Betsy is doing so well running the business that I don't bother calling in anymore. I'm thinking of taking up ceramics."

"God!" Gus said.

"Maybe I'll hook rugs."

"God," Gus said again. "You sound nasally, are you catching cold?"

"I think so," Kate lied. "I'm thinking about buying an airplane."

"Do you plan on flying it, or are you just going to look at it?" Gus asked.

"Look at it. More or less. I have this fear of heights."

"Me too. I mean I have a fear of heights, too. We have a lot in common, don't you think?"

"I always thought so. It's been almost a year since . . . since Harry came back. The girls are planning an anniversary party. Streamers, balloons, that kind of thing."

"Sounds like . . . fun."

"Depending on your point of view, it could be, I guess."

"Kate—"

"Well, I think I've taken up enough of your time. I've been thinking about you all day, and when I do that, I have to make sure my friends are okay. Go back to your Pulitzer writing."

"Kate—"

"Good-bye, Gus. I'll call again."

Kate waited until he broke the connection, then stayed on the phone a few seconds longer. She cleared her throat. "Whoever you are, you son of a bitch, I hope you go straight to hell." Then she put her finger between her lips and whistled the way Patrick had taught her when they were kids back in Westfield. "I hope your eardrum is ruptured!" she cried before she slammed the receiver back into the cradle. There were times, like now, when she wondered if she was paranoid. Patrick assured her she wasn't, that there really was some faceless man sequestered somewhere listening every time the phone was picked up. He believed it, so she believed it.

Kate threw her suit skirt and the crimson blouse in the corner and donned a pair of sweats and sneakers. Maybe she could snitch a couple of brownies if Della hadn't given up on the idea of baking them. She did love her sweets.

The movie playing on the VCR was *Private Benjamin*. Patrick was laughing while he fondled Jake's ears. Della, she could see at a glance, was removing the brownies from the tray. She snitched one then, dropped it immediately when she burned her fingers.

"Serves you right," Della snapped. "Load the dishwasher."

"What are we cooking for Patrick's party?" Kate asked.

"Don't you mean banquet? Your daughters have a two-page list. If you look at it carefully, you'll see the desserts are first. Four-layer chocolate cake, homemade pineapple ice cream, ambrosia, cherry cobbler. Shrimp cocktail, lobster bisque, roast capon, prime rib, candied sweet potatoes, string beans and almonds, garden salad, homemade dinner rolls, and there's a question mark next to the creamed corn. I have no idea what that means. Betsy wants pickled beets and eggs with lots of onions in the juice. Be sure to use balsamic vinegar, she writes. What would *you* like?"

"An Italian hot dog. Coleslaw and a slice of that four-tier chocolate cake. How about you?"

"A taco would be nice."

"How long do you think it will take us to make all this?" Kate asked curiously.

"It depends on how long it takes us to blow up the balloons," Della grumbled.

"Oh, shit," Kate said. "Della, I want to thank—"

"Kate, take these brownies in to Patrick. Two of them are for Jake. You better hand-feed him so he doesn't get it on the carpet."

Patrick smiled at her she handed him the plate of brownies. She started to break one apart for Jake. "I'll do that, Kate. I want him to know I'm the one who feeds him. You don't mind, do you?" he said, fondling Jake's ears.

"No, of course not." But she did mind, and she wondered why that was. She watched man and dog for another minute before she got up and went to her room.

Kate rose early the day of the party. For days she and Della had cooked and cleaned. The girls would come up together around five. She made coffee and carried it out to the deck. A year ago today she'd thought her world had come to an end. She felt proud of herself. She'd had the same feeling the day she received her college diploma. Well done, Kate Starr. She patted her shoulder, tears burning her eyes.

"The early bird gets the worm," Patrick said quietly. "Listen, you were right—it's a wonderful, happy sound. And I wanted to shoot them. I don't know too many sounds that are as pleasing as the chirp of a bird. I want to thank you for not letting me . . . and last night, too. Jake woke me up in the middle of the night to let him out. He's a quick learner, better than I was."

Kate smiled. "But you started out with a tremendous handicap. I'm very proud of you, Patrick."

"That means a lot to me, because I know you mean it."

"I bought you a present," Kate said, suddenly shy with her husband's compliment. "If you wait here, I'll get it."

"I have something for you, too," Patrick said. Like kids they raced into the house to get their presents for one another. Kate returned to the deck first and handed hers over when Patrick came out.

"It's kind of silly," she said.

"A giant Slurpee cup. For my drive cross-country. This is great, Kate."

"Are you going to come back, Patrick?"

"Nah, me and Jake . . . we're gonna be nomads." It was a lie, but Kate didn't know that. "I really didn't know what to give you. It would be pretty stupid of me to buy you something with your money, since I haven't made the effort to work out that account I have." From under his Izod pullover he withdrew four spiral-bound notebooks. He handed them over as though he were offering her a priceless gift. And it was a priceless gift, it was twenty years of his life he was giving to his wife, who could never be his wife again.

"It's all there, Kate. Every single minute of my life for the last twenty years. You were right, I needed to write it down. It . . . it's right to the minute, right up to the part where I pull out of the driveway at dawn tomorrow. It's all I have to give you."

"Thank you," Kate said, tears streaming down her cheeks. "I'll . . . take good care of it."

"You don't have to read it," Patrick said. "It might upset you."

"I want to."

"Okay, but you don't have to. Thanks to you, I'm going to be okay."

"I know that, Patrick. I always knew that. I thought you knew that I knew that," she babbled.

"You're repeating yourself," he said, smiling. "I thought you said you went to college."

"Hey, you win some and you lose some. Want to go for a walk?"

"Yeah, I'd like that. Jake likes that Gucci collar and leash you got him."

"He deserves it. He'll be the only dog in Westfield with a Gucci collar and leash."

"Hell, I know that, but will anyone in Westfield even know who Gucci is? By the way, who is he?"

"Some guy who makes shoes and pocketbooks. I think he's in jail." Patrick let out a loud guffaw. "I'll be with you in a minute. I want to put your . . . gift in my room."

"If we're walking five miles, make sure you go to the bathroom. I get embarrassed when you pee in the bushes."

"Nag, nag, nag," Patrick said.

Kate finished reading Patrick's journal at quarter to five in the morning. She'd read straight through the night once the party was over and everyone had gone to bed. She closed the last one, her cheeks wet with tears, and carried the book to her desk. She took a three-minute shower, dressed in clean sweats, and marched out to the kitchen. She opened Della's door, tiptoed inside, and bent over to whisper in the older woman's ear.

In the kitchen she turned on the percolator and then raced back to her room. She could hear both showers running, which meant Patrick and the girls were up. She sat down at the desk, drew paper and pen from the drawer. She bit down on her lower lip, wrote steadily for five minutes.

"Guess it's time for me to be on my way," Patrick said with a catch in his voice. "I didn't think it was going to be so hard to say good-bye. Maybe I shouldn't say it."

"Maybe you shouldn't," Betsy said. "I'm going with you."

"Me too," Ellie said.

Patrick walked over to his wife, took the bag out of her hand, and handed it to Della. "No, Kate, you can't come. A month from now, maybe a year from now, you'd hate me. It wasn't meant to be. Look, I like you. I even love you. But . . . you don't fit into my life anymore. I can't fit into yours. It's nobody's fault. It's the way it is. It was your job to get me to this place in time. I can handle it now. If I falter, I'll give you a call and you can pep-talk me. Jake here will get me over the rough spots. Don't cry, Kate, you look ugly when you cry.

"I'm not taking the girls away from you. We're going to get really acquainted. I need to spend time with them, to get to know them. I promise to send them back."

"Oh, Patrick, this isn't right," Kate wailed. "I want to go with you. We're a family again. Why are you doing this?"

"Because *you* don't have the guts to do it. Yes, right now, this minute, you want to go with me, but it won't work. We're two different people. I'm not the old Patrick anymore. I'm Harry what's his name and you're Kate. You grew wings, Kate, and you need to fly. Call that guy and tell him you're on your way. Life's too short for this crap. Hey, I have things to do and places to go. I'm going to do it all. My way. Me and Jake here."

"Oh, Patrick . . . you're breaking my heart," Kate cried.

"Come on now, give us a send-off," Patrick said cheerfully.

"Go to hell, Patrick," Kate cried.

"If I were you, Kate, I'd shed ten pounds before you show up on that guy's doorstep." Patrick laughed as he settled himself on the driver's seat. He waved airily. Jake barked. The girls blew kisses as the Cherokee sailed down the driveway.

"Why did you lie to her like that?" Betsy demanded.

"She wanted to come. We would have been a family again," Ellie cried.

Patrick looked at his daughters. "Didn't either one of you learn anything in those fancy colleges you went to? Your mother loves someone else. She was willing to give that up. For me. I almost let her do that. Right up to the very last second I was going to. . . . I'm a taker. Your mother is a giver. You need to know that. If there's one thing I know, your mother is going to make all of this right. You see, we both made promises. We kept them, and now it's time for each of us to live our lives.

"Okay, troops, let's hear it! *Off we go, into the wild blue yonder . . .*"

EPILOGUE

Gus Stewart sat in his office, chair tilted back, feet propped on the desktop, his thoughts miles away in California. Work was piled up all around him, but he saw none of it. Very little mattered these days. Not his job, not his investments, not the white elephant in Connecticut he couldn't sell, not even the family shindig his siblings had invited him to for the upcoming weekend.

Kate was lost to him; he'd known that from the get-go, but he'd hung on, hoping something would work out in his favor. But when she'd called in July, crying and sobbing so hard he couldn't make sense of what she was saying, he'd known it was hopeless. Before she'd hung up, he'd heard her mutter something that sounded like "To have and to hold, for richer or poorer, in sickness and in health." He remembered how his stomach had heaved, how his eyes had burned.

343

That very night he'd swept everything on his desk onto the floor and taken off on a three-day drunk capped off with Chinese food that left him so sick it had taken two weeks to recover. He choked now, remembering. He hadn't been able to eat any Chinese food since.

"Yo, Gus," a copyboy shouted, "package for you. Plain brown wrapper. Only your name on the front. Bet it's spy stuff," the kid said as he sailed the hefty envelope toward Gus from the open doorway.

"Yeah, the Arabs are in the lobby and we're going to be held hostage," Gus muttered as he grabbed the package. The moment he recognized Kate's handwriting, his heart thumped in his chest, once, twice, three times, before it resumed its natural beat.

He weighed the package, trying to guess the contents. It must be the album she'd said she was going to make for him with all the pictures they'd taken in Hawaii and Costa Rica. There had to be at least six yards of see-through tape on the package. A nerve jangled and then another, until his feet hit the floor with a loud thump. He rummaged for scissors in his middle drawer, finally yanking them free of a wad of rubber bands and paper clips stuck to the bands. One of the bands snapped, snicking his finger. "Son of a bitch!" It took him a full two minutes to cut through the thick tape. Before he withdrew the contents, he swept his desk clear, everything flying in all directions. The wrapping sailed through the air and landed by the door. He thought it made a noise, but he wasn't sure. His breath exploded in a loud *swoosh*.

Four spiral-bound notebooks, one yellow, one blue, one red, and one a marbleized black and white. A letter with something paper-clipped underneath. His hands were trembling. It was a letter from Kate. He read it, his eyes burning.

My Dearest Gus,
    I'm sure I don't have to tell you what it is you're holding in your hands. With Patrick's permission I am giving you

your Pulitzer prize. All of us are placing our lives in your hands. If that sounds exaggerated, I apologize, but it's how we all feel. We're going back on our word, and that means you have to go back on yours, too.

I personally dropped off this package to ensure it wouldn't fall into other hands. Attached to this letter is all the proof you need. Betsy, in her rebellious period, when she thought she could single-handedly rescue her father, bought a fountain pen that doubled as a camera from one of the ads in *Soldier of Fortune* magazine. I didn't even know there was such a gadget, but she knew, and I guess that's all that's important. What you have are three photographs of the document Betsy, Ellie, and I signed at LAX a year ago. Betsy developed them herself. Real cloak-and-dagger stuff.

We're all going to try to get on with our lives. I'm asking you to help. I hope I'm not being melodramatic. On the other hand, I remember the look on Mr. Spindler's face that day.

I need you to do one last thing. When you lock this in your safe, take the elevator to the lobby. Someone will be waiting for you. I'm thanking you in advance because I know you'll do as I ask.

Love and affection,
Kate

His eyes blurred with tears, Gus unhooked the black pen attached to the red cover of the spiral notebook.

It was all here, but at what price? He flipped through the red notebook, took in the strange scrawl, the awful words. Kate was right. It was a Pulitzer prize.

Take the elevator to the lobby, the note said. He locked the books in his office safe. He blew his nose lustily.

He was blowing his nose a second time, not caring about the tears in his eyes, when the elevator slid open.

She was directly in his line of vision, a hot dog in each hand. "Hey, I promised you dinner, and I always keep my promises. What took you so long?"

Gus's fist shot in the air. "Hell, I always was a slow mover."

"Well, I'm not." Kate smiled. "Marry me, Gus Stewart. In my right-hand pocket I have a lab slip for our blood tests. Maybe we can rush it."

"Let's eat on the way. This is a hell of a prewedding supper."

Kate grinned. "It doesn't get any better than this."

"No, lady, it doesn't."